PREFACE

As an ancillary to Martha Gilleland's *Introduction to Chemistry*, this instructor's manual has several purposes. Within each chapter section, there is a Chapter Overview of the textbook chapter, the solutions to the end-of-chapter Study Questions and Problems, and a set of multiple-choice Sample Quiz Questions. The overviews of the chapter contents relieve some of the need to cross-reference the text. These overviews are not intended to be detailed listings of the topics and techniques covered in the chapters but, rather, to be brief descriptions of the major concepts and techniques presented and to alert users to special features within the chapter, such as the margin Math Tips and optional topic sections.

For each chapter, there are also the fully worked solutions to all of the end-of-chapter Study Questions and Problems. Rather than give short solutions in jargon only instructors could appreciate, I chose to write the solutions in a more detailed, comprehensive, and informal manner so that students can use the solutions as an instructional aid should instructors decide to share the solutions with them. I hope my explanations and the layout of the solutions serve this goal.

Also for each chapter, I have written a set of multiple-choice Sample Quiz Questions, numbering from 20 to 25 per chapter. Instructors should feel free to use them or to adapt them to suit their own particular needs.

At the end of this manual is a bibliography of audio-visual aids, arranged by chapter, which have been successfully used as classroom aids in the courses for which the text is intended. The materials may also be used in any course where they may be deemed appropriate.

If any mistakes are found or if there are any suggestions for improvement, please let us know.

For those interested in such things, the entire body of this manual was composed on a 128k Apple® Macintosh™ computer running Microsoft® Word™ for word processing and Apple® MacPaint™ for graphics. The camera-ready copy was printed on an Apple® LaserWriter™ printer.

For many reasons, this project has been an arduous one. I am deeply grateful for the understanding and assistance of the West Publishing Company editorial staff, particularly Theresa O'Dell. I must also thank Ms. Kathy Parkison, my colleague at the University of Nebraska at Omaha, who spent countless hours helping me work problems, proofreading the manuscript, and generally helping keep me motivated and the project going. Above all, though, this work is for my son, Robbie.

Dr. Robert C. Pfaff
Omaha, Nebraska
November, 1985

Instructor's Manual to Accompany

INTRODUCTION TO CHEMISTRY

MARTHA J. GILLELAND
California State College,
Bakersfield

Prepared by

DR. ROBERT C. PFAFF
Department of Chemistry
The University of Nebraska at Omaha

West Publishing Company
St. Paul   New York
Los Angeles   San Francisco

ISBN 0-314-96990-X

CONTENTS

CHEMISTRY: ORIGINS AND SCOPE

CHAPTER 1

Chapter Overview

Chapter 1 is primarily concerned with defining the study of chemistry within a historical context. This approach clearly shows the progression of thought which evolved into modern science. As further definition of the field of chemistry, many of the basic concepts and terms of chemistry are presented, such as matter, energy, conservation, physical states, physical and chemical properties, physical and chemical change, and reactions.

Also included in Chapter 1 is a series of helpful study tips for students. Although these tips are tailored to the study of chemistry, they are actually quite general and can be applied to all fields of study. New students, whether 18 year old freshmen or 35 year old returnees, will find them particularly useful.

Solutions to the Study Questions and Problems

1. **a.** A **fluid** is matter which has the ability to flow. Therefore, gases and liquids are fluids. **b.** The temperature at which a solid substance melts to give the liquid is its **melting point. c.** The temperature at which a liquid substance freezes to give the solid is its **freezing point. d.** The temperature at which a liquid substance boils to give the vapor is its **boiling point. e.** Any interconversion among the states (solid, liquid, and gas) which does not change the identity of the substance is a **change of state**. It is important to remember that, if the identity of the substance changes (*i.e.*, there is a chemical change), the chemical change has precedence over the physical change.

2. The three states of matter are solid, liquid, and gas. A **Solid** is characterized by having a fixed shape and a fixed volume. Examples would include any of the structural and coinage metals, rocks and minerals, and wood. A **Liquid** is characterized by taking on the shape of its container and having a fixed volume. Examples would include water (or anything you would drink), paints, and automobile and truck fuels. A **gas** is characterized by taking on the shape and the volume of its container. Examples would include air, the vapors of liquids, and the elements hydrogen, helium, nitrogen, oxygen, fluorine, neon, chlorine, argon, krypton, xenon, and radon.

3. **a.** Ice cream is a liquid at room temperature. **b.** Bread is a solid at room temperature. **c.** Water is a gas at 500 ° F since its normal boiling point is 212 ° F. **d.** Air is a gas at 200 ° F. Air can be liquified only at very low temperatures. **e.** Candle wax at -10 ° F is a solid. Elevated temperatures are required to liquify candle wax.

4. **a.** The conversion of gas to liquid is called condensation. **b.** The conversion of liquid to solid is called freezing. **c.** The conversion of liquid to gas is called vaporization. **d.** By lowering the temperature so as to cause hardening, this must be freezing. **e.** This bubbling action is the conversion of liquid to gas and therefore it is boiling. **f.** The liquid water in the clothes freezes on a cold day causing the hardening.

5. **a. Homogeneous matter** has the same properties and composition throughout the sample. For these conditions to be true, the sample must be a pure substance in one phase or a mixture of substances. **b. Heterogeneous matter** has different properties or composition in different parts of the sample. For this condition to be true, the sample must be a pure substance in more than one phase or a mixture of substances. **c.** A **phase** is a state of matter with clearly defined and distinguishable boundaries. For example, ice cubes in water forms two phases, one solid and one liquid, which are distinguishable. On the other hand, salt dissolved in water forms only one phase since the salt and the water are undistinguishably mixed. **d.** A **mixture** is matter which consists either of one substance in more than one phase or of more than one substance.

6. Examples of heterogeneous matter include ice water, fog, most foods (*e.g.*, casseroles), and a classroom desk. Examples of homogeneous matter include liquid water, gasoline, air, and metals and metal alloys.

7. **a.** Wood is heterogeneous. The wood's grain varies throughout the sample, leading to different properties and composition. **b.** Glass is homogeneous. There is no evidence of boundaries within the sample. **c.** Styrofoam is heterogeneous even though it seems superficially homogeneous. The bubbles formed in the styrofoam vary in size and shape and so the matter is not evenly distributed. **d.** A penny is homogeneous. Even if you assume it to be an alloy rather than pure copper, the matter is evenly distributed throughout. **e.** A section of grapefruit is heterogeneous. The juice, pulp, seeds, and peel are not evenly distributed. **f.** Gravel is heterogeneous. At the very least, the pieces vary in size and shape and, therefore, the way the pieces pack together is variable.

8. Fog consists of water in two phases. The fog particles are tiny droplets of liquid water but, due to evaporation, there is water vapor (gas) interspersed in it.

9. **a.** A **mixture** is matter which consists either of one substance in more than one phase or of more than one substance. **b.** A **pure substance** is matter which contains only one substance in only one phase.

10. The subclasses of heterogeneous matter are 1) a mixture of different substances in separate phases and 2) a pure substance in different phases.

11. The subclasses of homogeneous matter are 1) a mixture of different substances in one phase and 2) a pure substance (one substance in one phase).

12. In one type of heterogeneous matter, the differences observed in the sample arise from different phases of one substance, such as ice water and fog. In the other type of heterogeneous matter, the differences observed arise from having more than one substance existing in separate phases, such as oil or gasoline floating on water and any kind of metal plating, where one kind of metal is applied to the surface of another.

13. In one type of homogeneous matter, more than one substance is present, evenly mixed into one phase, such as sugar or salt dissolved in water and metal alloys like steel. In the other type of homogeneous matter, only one substance is present in one phase and is refered to as a pure substance.

14. **a.** Alcohol dissolved in water is a homogeneous mixture. **b.** Mist is a heterogeneous mixture due to the variance in particle size and spacing. **c.** Fruit cake is a heterogeneous mixture. **d.** The residue is a heterogeneous mixture due to the variety of minerals present. **e.** Partially frozen pop is a heterogeneous mixture due to the presence of two phases. **f.** Buttermilk is a heterogeneous mixture since several substances are suspended in it like in regular milk.

15. Vinegar is a homogeneous mixture. It has at least two substances in it, water and acetic acid. In addition, the components are evenly distributed in the vinegar and so there are no observable boundaries and the composition is the same throughout.

16. **a.** A **physical change** is one which does not alter the identity of a substance. **b.** A **chemical change** is one which does change the identity of a substance.

17. Examples of physical change include the state changes between gas, liquid, and solid. Examples of chemical change include the combustion of natural gas, food spoilage, and the formation of rust.

18. **a.** Burning is a chemical change. **b.** Crushing is a physical change. **c.** Sharpening a knife is a physical change since it only involves removing some of the substance. **d.** Tarnishing is a chemical change. **e.** The expansion of water is a physical change. **f.** The softening of lead is a physical change.

19. This is a physical change. The platinum is heated and cooled but its identity isn't changed. The return to its initial condition is a sign of physical change.

20. **a.** Simply placing the food in your mouth does not represent any change. Chewing, taken by itself, causes a physical change in the food. However, the saliva, in addition to mixing with the food, begins the digestion process and so causes a chemical change. Swallowing does not cause any change, it simply moves the food to the stomach. **b.** Mining causes a physical change in the ore as the rock is cut out of the mine. Crushing is also a physical change as it breaks the ore into still smaller pieces. Heating the ore with coal to give iron is a chemical change as the iron in the rock is converted to elemental iron.

21. **a.** **Properties** are those characteristics of matter which distinguish one type of matter from others. **b.** **Physical properties** are those which describe a substance without altering its identity. These properties include features of appearance, texture, taste, and odor. **c.** **Chemical properties** are those which describe a substance's ability to undergo chemical change. These properties include flammability and the ability of a substance to neutralize lye or acid.

22. **a.** The color of sugar is a physical property. **b.** The ability of copper to conduct electricity is a physical property. **c.** The ability of a metal to be corroded by acid is a chemical property. **d.** Flammability is a chemical property. **e.** The taste of baking soda is a physical property. **f.** The ability of a substance to burn is flammability and so it is a chemical property.

23. Simply, the law of conservation of mass says that mass cannot be created nor destroyed or that the total amount of mass must remain constant.

24. Although matter and mass are not strictly interchangeable terms, they can be interchanged in this context since mass is the measure of amount of matter.

25. In the combustion of coal, coal reacts with air to produce ash and some gases, predominantly carbon dioxide and water. No appreciable mass is lost in the process. The total mass of coal and air used in the reaction must essentially equal the total mass of ash and gases produced by the reaction.

26. a. Energy is the capacity to do work. **b. Work** generally is defined as moving an object over some distance. **c. Kinetic energy** is the energy associated with actually doing work or with motion. **d. Potential energy** is energy which is stored as a consequence of its position, condition, or composition and can be thought of as giving a substance the potential to do work.

27. Even though an object is moving, it also possesses potential energy. **a.** A speeding bullet is moving and so this is kinetic energy. **b.** Since no motion is mentioned, this must be potential energy. **c.** A dancing bear is moving and so this is kinetic energy. **d.** Since the hiker is standing and not moving, this is potential energy. **e.** A flashlight battery has stored energy to light the bulb. This is potential energy. **f.** Natural gas is flammable and its ability to burn refers to its potential energy.

28. The law of conservation of energy states that energy cannot be created nor destroyed, only redistributed. Hence, the total amount of kinetic and potential energy must remain constant.

29. a. Exothermic refers to the flow of energy out of a system and so is generally observed as generating heat. **b. Endothermic** refers to the flow of energy into a system and so is generally observed as cooling.

30. a. Boiling is an endothermic process since heat must be applied for it to occur. **b.** Burning is an exothermic process since it gives off heat. **c.** The formation of ice from liquid water is exothermic since heat must be removed for it to occur. **d.** Melting is an endothermic process since heat must be applied.

31. Einstein's equation is $E = mc^2$. It relates the energy of an object to its mass and suggests that mass and energy are interchangeable.

32. The disappearance of all mass is not possible although Einstein's equation shows that virtually all mass can disappear. Mass cannot completely disappear since that would require energy to rise to an infinite amount.

33. The conversion of mass to energy is not important in chemical reactions. This is due to the fact that the amount of energy involved in chemical reactions is vanishingly small compared to the amount of energy required to observe a mass change.

Sample Quiz Questions

1. The freezing point of a substance is
    a. the place in a liquid where solid first forms upon freezing.
    b. the temperature at which it changes from solid to liquid.
    c. the same for all pure substances.
    d. the temperature at which it changes from solid to gas.
    e. the temperature at which it changes from liquid to gas.

2. Boiling is
    a. the temperature at which a liquid changes to a gas.
    b. an exothermic process.
    c. dependent on the size of the sample.
    d. a physical change.
    e. a chemical change.

3. A liquid
    a. takes on the shape and volume of its container.
    b. is a fluid.
    c. must be an element.
    d. has the same properties as a gas.
    e. maintains its own shape.

4. Which of the following is (are) homogeneous?
    a. a chalkboard eraser.
    b. a silverplate spoon.
    c. bronze.
    d. the instructor's desk.
    e. a pencil.

5. Steel
    a. is a pure substance.
    b. is a homogeneous mixture.
    c. consists of two phases.
    d. is a heterogeneous mixture of one substance.
    e. is an element.

6. Which of the following is (are) heterogeneous?
    a. distilled water.
    b. window glass.
    c. a plastic trash bag.
    d. brass.
    e. the Mississippi River.

7. A pure substance
    a. refers only to the elements.
    b. has unique chemical properties.
    c. may have two phases together.
    d. has two or more components.
    e. has only one component.

8. Which of the following is (are) example(s) of chemical change?
    a. copper roofing turning green with age.
    b. the disappearance of snow on a cold day.
    c. the expansion of mercury in a thermometer when you have a fever.
    d. the cracking of a glass jar by a hot liquid.
    e. the condensation of water on a cold beverage container.

9. The conversion of aluminum ore to a beverage container is
    a. a physical change.
    b. a chemical change.
    c. a series of steps, some of which are chemical changes and some of which are physical changes.
    d. exothermic.
    e. a simple process.

10. Which of the following is (are) example(s) of physical properties?
    a. the ability of a substance to neutralize stomach acid.
    b. corrosiveness.
    c. flammability.
    d. hardness.
    e. toxicity.

11. Which of the following is (are) example(s) of chemical properties?
    a. odor.
    b. texture.
    c. corrosion resistance.
    d. ability of a diamond to shatter.
    e. ductility.

12. When wood is burned
    a. substantial mass is converted to energy.
    b. heat is absorbed.
    c. substantial mass is lost.
    d. substantial energy is converted to mass.
    e. gases are given off.

13. Potential energy
    a. is the energy of an object due to its motion.
    b. is the total energy of an object.
    c. is the energy of an object due to its position.
    d. is conserved.
    e. can be totally converted to kinetic energy.

14. Kinetic energy
    a. is the energy of an object due to its motion.
    b. is the total energy of an object.
    c. is the energy of an object due to its position.
    d. is conserved.
    e. is possessed by all objects.

15. Exothermic reactions
    a. consume heat.
    b. liberate heat.
    c. are explosive.
    d. convert energy to mass.
    e. cool their surroundings.

16. According to Einstein's equation
    a. the speed of light is variable.
    b. the universe will eventually disappear.
    c. chemical reactions should obey the law of conservation of mass.
    d. chemical reactions should obey the law of conservation of energy.
    e. mass and energy are related to the speed of light.

17. A phase is
    a. the same as a state of matter.
    b. a state of matter having clearly defined and distinguishable boundaries.
    c. a reference to the chemical properties of a substance.
    d. a boundary between two states of matter.
    e. a clearly defined state of matter.

18. A physical change
    a. may alter the identity of a substance.
    b. is always accompanied by a chemical change.
    c. does not alter the identity of a substance.
    d. cannot be reversed.
    e. must involve a state change.

19. A chemical change
    a. generally can be reversed.
    b. generally does not include physical change.
    c. does not alter the identity of the substance.
    d. generally cannot be reversed.
    e. is not generally accompanied by an energy change.

20. Nuclear reactions
    a. involve less energy than chemical reactions.
    b. obey the law of conservation of mass.
    c. always result in explosions.
    d. obey the law of conservation of energy.
    e. verify the Einstein equation.

Answers to the Sample Quiz Questions

1. (b), 2. (d), 3. (b), 4. (c), 5. (b), 6. (e), 7. (e), 8. (a), 9. (c), 10. (d), 11. (d), 12. (e), 13. (c), 14. (a), 15. (b), 16. (e), 17. (b), 18. (c), 19. (d), 20. (e)

SCIENTIFIC MEASUREMENTS

CHAPTER
2

Chapter Overview

Chapter 2 introduces students to the quantitative techniques required to succeed in chemistry. The topics covered include making measurements, units of measure, significant figures, and scientific notation. Conversions between unit systems are also discussed and used to introduce the factor-unit method for solving problems. The metric system and SI units are covered and used as examples of conversion factors.

The chapter also discusses the often confused concepts of precision, accuracy, mass, weight, density, and specific gravity.

Since the proper application of algebra is essential to success in the course, the chapter is filled with margin notes on mathematical techniques and with detailed solutions to examples. For additional guidance on algebraic principles, students are directed to Appendix A, Review of Basic Mathematics.

Solutions to the Study Questions and Problems

1. a. **Precision** refers of the reproducibility of measurements. When successive measurements yield values which are very close to one another, the measurement is precise. When successive measurements yield values which agree poorly, the measurement is not precise. b. **Accuracy** refers to how close to "truth" a measurement is. When a measurement yields a value which is close to the actual value, the measurement is accurate.

2. It is quite possible to make precise but not accurate measurements. If the experimenter makes the same mistake each time (a systematic error) the values from successive measurements may well be precise but will not be accurate.

3. It is also quite possible to make accurate but not precise measurements. If the experimenter makes a different mistake each time (a random error) the values from successive measurements will probably be accurate, on average, but precision will be poor.

4. Generally, accuracy is more dependent on human error, particularly systematic error. Precision is more often associated with the calibration and proper maintenance of the measuring device than with human error.

5. **a. Significant figures** are the number of digits in a value which properly reflect the precision of the value and, therefore, do not overstate nor understate its precision. If the value is a measured quantity, the digits given by the device are usually all significant. If the value is calculated from measured quantities, the number of significant figures is dependent on the measurement which was least precise. **b. Exact numbers** are those which are known with infinite precision. They either can be defined as exact, such as 2.54 cm = 1 inch, or they can be whole numbers, such as 12 eggs = 1 dozen eggs.

6. **a.** 370.5 feet has 4 significant figures. **b.** 4,020 square yards has 3 significant figures. The trailing zero serves only to hold the decimal point. **c.** 0.0010 grams has 2 significant figures. Leading zeros only hold the decimal point and, therefore, are never significant. **d.** 1.203 inches has 4 significant figures. **e.** 0.150 kilograms has 3 significant figures. Trailing zeros which do not hold the decimal point must be considered significant. **f.** 6,167 miles has 4 significant figures. **g.** 700 minutes has 1 significant figure. The trailing zeros only hold the decimal place. **h.** 300.0 milliliters has 4 significant figures. The last trailing zero is not needed to hold the decimal place and is, therefore, significant. Zeros between significant digits are always significant.

7. **a.** 1075 pounds has 4 significant figures. **b.** 650.2 hours has 4 significant figures. **c.** 0.0072 milliliters has 2 significant figures. Leading zeros are never significant. **d.** 87.3 years has 3 significant figures. **e.** 3040 meters has 3 significant figures. Trailing zeros which serve to hold the decimal place are not significant. **f.** 75.02 centimeters has 4 significant figures. **g.** 12.00 seconds has 4 significant figures. Trailing zeros to the right of the decimal point are significant. **h.** 1500.2 millimeters has 5 significant figures.

8. **a.** 4,735 becomes 4,700. Since the part of the number being dropped (35) is less than 50, it is removed (rounding down) and replaced by two zeros to hold the decimal place. **b.** 0.003651 becomes 0.0037. Since the part of the number being dropped (51) is greater than 50, the last significant figure is raised by 1 (rounding up). **c.** 2.550 becomes 2.6. Since the part of the number being dropped is 50, the number is rounded so that the last significant figure is an even number. **d.** 0.1693 becomes 0.17 (rounding up). **e.** 551.0 becomes 550 (rounding down). **f.** 35.50 becomes 36 (rounding to the even number).

9. **a.** 3.6275×10^5 becomes 3.63×10^5 (rounding up). **b.** 7,396 becomes 7400 (rounding up). The consequence of adding 1 to the last significant figure is to raise 39 to 40. The number of significant figures here is ambiguous, however. Scientific notation would make the number of significant figures clear (7.40×10^3). **c.** 200.5 becomes 200 or 2.00×10^2 (rounding to the even number). **d.** 4.8669×10^{-2} becomes 4.87×10^{-2} (rounding up). **e.** 0.0048732 becomes 0.00487 (rounding down). **f.** 1.975×10^{-7} becomes 1.98×10^{-7} (rounding to the even number).

10. **a.** $(102.5)(11.17) = 1145$

Since both factors in the multiplication have 4 significant figures, the answer is limited to 4 significant figures.

b. $(216.5)(0.018) = 3.9$

Since the second factor in the multiplication (0.018) has 2 significant figures, the answer is limited to 2 significant figures.

10. c. $(8.1)(1.23)(0.47) = 4.7$

Since two of the factors in the multiplication (8.1 and 0.47) have 2 significant figures, the answer is limited to 2 significant figures.

d. $75 - 0.76 - 1.49 = 73$

Since the first term of the subtraction (75) has no decimal places, the answer is limited to having no decimal places.

e. $\dfrac{(19)(1.059)(75)}{(6.2)(1.86)} = 130$

Since three of the terms have 2 significant figures, the answer is limited to 2 significant figures.

f. $\dfrac{(1.008)(32.6)}{149.1} = 0.220$

Since one factor (32.6) has 3 significant figures, the answer is limited to 3 significant figures.

11. a. $\dfrac{149 + 2.54}{376} = \dfrac{152}{376} = 0.404$

Significant figures should be addressed in the order of mathematical operations. The sum in the numerator is performed first and so its significant figures are dealt with first. Since 149 has no decimal places, the sum in the numerator is not allowed any, either. Then the division is performed. Since both values have 3 significant figures, the answer must be stated in 3 significant figures.

b. $39.0 + 42.6 + 1.39 = 83.0$

Since two of the terms of the addition have 1 decimal place, the answer is limited to 1 decimal place.

c. $55.841 - 4.10 = 51.74$

Since the second term of the subtraction has 2 decimal places, the answer is limited to 2 decimal places.

d. $\dfrac{67.9 - 12.73}{0.5152} = \dfrac{55.2}{0.5152} = 107$

The difference in the numerator is allowed only 1 decimal place. Then the 3 significant figure numerator is divided by the 4 significant figure denominator, limiting the answer to 3 significant figures.

e. $\dfrac{4.15}{2.077} = 2.00$

Since the numerator has 3 significant figures, the answer is limited to 3 significant figures.

11. f. $\dfrac{73.8}{65.21 - 47} = \dfrac{73.8}{18} = 4.1$

The difference in the denominator is allowed no decimal places. Then the division is by a 2 significant figure value so the answer is limited to 2 significant figures.

12. a. An **exponent** is the power to which a number is to be raised. For example, in 10^2, 10 is to raised to the second power (10 x 10) and 2 is the exponent. **b.** A **base** is the number which is to be raised to some power. In the preceding example, 10 is the base.

13. a. 732.6 becomes 7.326×10^2 **b.** 100.4 becomes 1.004×10^2 **c.** 7,000,000 becomes 7×10^6 Trailing zeros which serve to hold the decimal place are not significant. **d.** 0.0538 becomes 5.38 x 10^{-2} **e.** 0.0000000000437 becomes 4.37×10^{-11} **f.** 10,573 becomes 1.0573×10^4

14. a. 7,498,500 becomes 7.4985×10^6 **b.** 0.0003718 becomes 3.718×10^{-4} **c.** 458 becomes 4.58 x 10^2 **d.** 0.01269 becomes 1.269×10^{-2} **e.** 9,134,998,375 becomes 9.134998375×10^9 **f.** 0.00000000001 becomes 1×10^{-11}

15. a. 5.689×10^2 becomes 568.9 **b.** 2.367×10^4 becomes 23,670 **c.** 1.499×10^{-7} becomes 0.0000001499 **d.** 3.65×10^{-3} becomes 0.00365 **e.** 4.761×10^6 becomes 4,761,000 **f.** 7.2517 x 10^{-9} becomes 0.0000000072517

16. a. The **British system** is a system of measure traditionally used in the United States and British Commonwealth countries based on feet, pounds, and gallons. **b.** The **metric system** is a system measure used in science and trade in most countries which is based on meters, grams, and liters. **c.** SI stands for Systeme International. It is a uniform version of metric for international use.

17. Metric is considered easier to use than the British system since metric is based on powers of 10. The British system relates units by a variety of multiples.

18. a. Dimensional analysis is a computational technique which uses the dimensions (units) of the quantities involved as an aid to seeting up the solution. **b.** A **unit factor** is a fraction or ratio of measurements in different unit systems which equals 1. **c.** The **unit-factor method** is the use of unit factors in dimensional analysis to perform unit conversions.

19. a. $\dfrac{(67.3 \text{ nm})(1 \text{ m})}{(10^9 \text{ nm})} = 6.97 \times 10^{-8} \text{ m}$

b. $\dfrac{(84.92 \text{ g})(1 \text{ kg})}{(1000 \text{ g})} = 0.08492 \text{ kg}$

c. $\dfrac{(0.457 \text{ mL})(1 \text{ L})}{(1000 \text{ mL})} = 0.000457 \text{ L}$

d. $\dfrac{(52.3 \text{ mm})(1 \text{ m})(100 \text{ cm})}{(1000 \text{ mm})(1 \text{ m})} = 5.23 \text{ cm}$

e. $\dfrac{(0.059 \text{ g})(10^9 \text{ ng})}{(1 \text{ g})} = 5.9 \times 10^7 \text{ ng}$

f. $\dfrac{(0.394 \text{ m})(1000 \text{ mm})}{(1 \text{ m})} = 394 \text{ mm}$

20. a. $\dfrac{(1.759 \text{ L})(1000 \text{ mL})}{(1 \text{ L})} = 1759 \text{ mL}$

b. $\dfrac{(7.6 \text{ g})(1000 \text{ mg})}{(1 \text{ g})} = 7600 \text{ mg}$

c. $\dfrac{(20.6 \text{ mm})(1 \text{ m})}{(1000 \text{ mm})} = 0.0206 \text{ m}$

d. $\dfrac{(72 \text{ kg})(1000 \text{ g})}{(1 \text{ kg})} = 7.2 \times 10^4 \text{ g}$

e. $\dfrac{(143 \text{ g})(1000 \text{ mg})}{(1 \text{ g})} = 1.43 \times 10^5 \text{ mg}$

f. $\dfrac{(3.0 \text{ L})(1000 \text{ mL})(1 \text{ cm}^3)}{(1 \text{ L})(1 \text{ mL})} = 3000 \text{ cm}^3$

21. a. $\dfrac{(14.7 \text{ lb})(453.6 \text{ g})}{(1 \text{ lb})} = 6670 \text{ g}$

b. $\dfrac{(17.32 \text{ in})(2.54 \text{ cm})(1 \text{ m})}{(1 \text{ in})(100 \text{ cm})} = 0.4399 \text{ m}$

c. $\dfrac{(24.833 \text{ qt})(1 \text{ L})}{(1.057 \text{ qt})} = 23.49 \text{ L}$

d. $\dfrac{(13.0 \text{ yd})(36 \text{ in})(1 \text{ m})}{(1 \text{ yd})(39.37 \text{ in})} = 11.9 \text{ m}$

e. $\dfrac{(166 \text{ km})(1 \text{ mi})}{(1.61 \text{ km})} = 103 \text{ mi}$

f. $\dfrac{(39 \text{ cm})(1 \text{ in})}{(2.54 \text{ cm})} = 15 \text{ in}$

22. a. $\dfrac{(760 \text{ in})(2.54 \text{ cm})}{(1 \text{ in})} = 1.9 \times 10^3 \text{ cm}$

b. $\dfrac{(145 \text{ g})(1 \text{ lb})}{(453.6 \text{ g})} = 0.320 \text{ lb}$

c. $\dfrac{(250 \text{ mL})(1 \text{ L})(1.057 \text{ qt})}{(1000 \text{ mL})(1 \text{ L})} = 0.26 \text{ qt}$

d. $\dfrac{(2.63 \text{ m})(39.37 \text{ in})(1 \text{ ft})}{(1 \text{ m})(12 \text{ in})} = 8.63 \text{ ft}$

e. $\dfrac{(12.6 \text{ in})(2.54 \text{ cm})}{(1 \text{ in})} = 32.0 \text{ cm}$

f. $\dfrac{(1.65 \text{ qt})(1 \text{ L})}{(1.057 \text{ qt})} = 1.56 \text{ L}$

23. a. $\underline{(1,250\ ft)(30.48\ cm)(\ \ 1\ m\ \ )} = 381\ m$
$(\ \ 1\ ft\ \ )(100\ cm)$

b. $\underline{(1,250\ ft)(30.48\ cm)(\ \ 1\ m\ \ )(\ 1\ km\ )} = 0.381\ km$
$(\ \ 1\ ft\ \ )(100\ cm)(1000\ m)$

c. $\underline{(1,250\ ft)(30.48\ cm)} = 3.81\ x\ 10^4\ cm$
$(\ \ 1\ ft\ \ )$

d. $\underline{(1,250\ ft)(30.48\ cm)(10\ mm)} = 3.81\ x\ 10^5\ mm$
$(\ 1\ ft\ \ )(\ 1\ cm\ )$

24. $\underline{(0.1\ mm)(\ 1\ cm\ )(\ \ 1\ in\ \ )} = 4\ x\ 10^{-3}\ in$
$(10\ mm)(2.54\ cm)$

25. $\underline{(1.5\ in)(1.5\ in)(1.5\ in)(2.54\ cm)(2.54\ cm)(2.54\ cm)} = 55\ cm^3$
$(\ 1\ in\ )(\ 1\ in\ )(\ 1\ in\ )$

26. $\underline{(0.25\ oz)(\ 1\ lb\ )(453.6\ g)} = 7.1\ g$
$(16\ oz)(\ 1\ lb\ \ )$

27. $\underline{(238,857\ mi)(1.61\ km)} = 3.85\ x\ 10^5\ km$
$(\ 1\ mi\ \ )$

28. $\underline{(238,857\ mi)(5280\ ft)(30.48\ cm)(\ \ \ \ \ 1\ sec\ \ \ \ )} = 1.3\ sec$
$(\ 1\ mi\ )(\ \ 1\ ft\ \ \ )(3.0\ x\ 10^{10}\ cm)$

29. $\underline{(26.22\ mi)(1.61\ km)} = 14.2\ km/hr$
$(\ 1\ mi\ \ )(2\ hr + 58/60\ hr)$

30. $\underline{14.7\ gal)(\ 4\ qt\ )(\ \ 1\ L\ \ )} = 55.6\ L$
$(1\ gal)(1.057\ qt)$

31. a. Mass is the amount of matter in an object. For every object the mass is a constant value. **b. Weight** is the force applied on an object by the earth's gravitational field. As the object is moved to different places, the strength of the force varies.

32. The bowling ball weighs more in Death Valley. Since it is closer to the center of the earth in Death Valley, the attraction is stronger and the weight is greater.

33. Density is the mass of an object or substance which occupies a volume of one unit. Mathematically:

$$density = \frac{mass}{volume}$$

34. $\underline{(1.000\ kg)(1000\ g)(\ \ \ 1\ L\ \ \ )} = 0.9981\ g/mL$
$(\ 1\ kg\ \ )(1.00186\ L)(1000\ mL)$

35. $\underline{(\ 16.6\ g)} = 5.5\ g/mL$
$(3.0\ mL)$

36. $\underline{(\ 61.88\ g)} = 22.5\ g/mL$
$(2.75\ mL)$

37. $\dfrac{(0.25 \text{ lb})(453.6 \text{ g})(\underline{\quad 1 \text{ in} \quad})(\underline{\quad 1 \text{ in} \quad})(\underline{\quad 1 \text{ in} \quad})(1 \text{ cm}^3)}{(7.8 \text{ in}^3)(\quad 1 \text{ lb} \quad)(2.54 \text{ cm})(2.54 \text{ cm})(2.54 \text{ cm})(1 \text{ mL})} = 0.89$ g/mL

38. $\dfrac{(20.0 \text{ g})(\underline{\quad 1 \text{ mL} \quad})}{(13.5939 \text{ g})} = 1.47$ mL

39. $\dfrac{(736 \text{ g})(\underline{1 \text{ mL}})}{(1.00 \text{ g})} = 736$ mL

40. $\dfrac{(109 \text{ mL})(0.79 \text{ g})}{(1 \text{ mL})} = 86$ g

41. $\dfrac{(7.4 \text{ mL})(2.70 \text{ g})}{(1 \text{ mL})} = 2.0 \times 10^1$ g

42. Specific gravity is the ratio of the density of an object or substance to that of water at 4 °C. In metric, the density of water at 4 °C is 1.0000 g/mL and so in metric, the value of specific gravity is the same as the value of density. However, specific gravity has no units.

43. $\dfrac{(74.3 \text{ g})}{(8.96)}\dfrac{(\underline{\quad 1 \text{ mL} \quad})}{(1.0000 \text{ g})} = 8.29$ mL

44. $\dfrac{(6.000 \text{ mL})(1.1843 \times 10^{-3})(1.0000 \text{ g})}{(1 \text{ mL})} = 7$ g

45. For Aluminum: $\dfrac{(25 \text{ g})}{(2.70)}\dfrac{(\underline{\quad 1 \text{ mL} \quad})}{(1.0000 \text{ g})} = 9.3$ mL

For Molybdenum: $\dfrac{(75 \text{ g})}{(10.2)}\dfrac{(\underline{\quad 1 \text{ mL} \quad})}{(1.0000 \text{ g})} = 7.4$ mL

Therefore, the aluminum occupies the greater volume.

46. Heat is a form of energy which can be transferred between objects. **Temperature** is a measure of the warmth of an object.

47. a. (1200 - 32)(5/9) = 648.9 °C (This assumes temperature readings are precise to the whole degree.)

    b. (32 - 32)(5/9) = 0 °C

    c. (9/5)(37) + 32 = 99 °F

    d. (9/5)(45) + 32 = 110 °F

    e. (78 - 32)(5/9) = 26 °C

    f. (9/5)(590) + 32 = 1090 °F

48. a. (0 - 32)(5/9) = -18 °C

    b. (9/5)(-21) + 32 = -6 °F

48. c. (-150 - 32)(5/9) = -101 °C

   d. (220 - 32)(5/9) = 104 °C

   e. (9/5)(600) + 32 = 1110 °F

   f. (9/5)(14) + 32 = 57 °F

49. His temperature elevation is 102.3 °F - 98.6 °F = 3.7 °F. Therefore, the elevation in Celsius is (5/9)(3.7) = 2.1 °C.

50. Specific heat is the amount of heat required to raise the temperature of one gram of a substance 1 °C.

51. cal = (1.000 cal/g-°C)(100.0 g)(100.0 °C - 25.0 °C) = 7.50 x 10³ cal (assuming the density of water is 1 g/mL)

52. cal = (0.581 cal/g-°C)(93.7 g)(78 °C - 29 °C) = 2.7 x 10³ cal

53. cal = (0.1297 cal/g-°C)(472 g)(25 °C - 0 °C) = 1.5 x 10³ cal

54. The temperature change is: 200.0 °F - 78 °F = 122 °F or (122)(5/9) = 67.8 °C

   Therefore, cal = (1.000 cal/g-°C)(250.0 g)(67.8 °C) = 1.70 x 10⁴ cal

55. The temperature change is: 78 °F - 32 °F = 46 °F or (46)(5/9) = 26 °C

   Therefore, cal = (1.000 cal/g-°C)(52.7 g)(26 °C) = 1.4 x 10³ cal

Sample Quiz Questions

1. Precision refers to
    a. how close to the actual value a measurement is.
    b. how skillful the experimenter is.
    c. how careful the experimenter is.
    d. how well successive measurements of a quantity agree.
    e. how accurate successive measurements of a quantity are.

2. Accuracy refers to
    a. how close to the actual value a measurement is.
    b. how skillful the experimenter is.
    c. how many times the experiment is performed.
    d. how well successive measurements of a quantity agree.
    e. how precise successive measurements of a quantity are.

3. How many significant figures are there in 156,010?
    a. 2
    b. 3
    c. 4
    d. 5
    e. 6

4. How many significant figures are there in 0.01060?
    a. 2
    b. 3
    c. 4
    d. 5
    e. 6

5. Give the result of the following calculation with the proper number of significant figures.

$$\frac{(56.1 - 48.3)}{13.2}$$

    a. 0.6
    b. 0.59
    c. 0.591
    d. 0.5909
    e. 0.59091

6. Give the result of the following calculation with the proper number of significant figures.

$$(6.321)(7.11 + 3.27 + 9.9)$$

    a. 130
    b. 128
    c. 128.3
    d. 128.32
    e. 128.316

7. Express the number 56,110,000 in proper scientific notation.
    a. $5,611 \times 10^4$
    b. 5.6110000×10^7
    c. 5.6110×10^6
    d. 5.611×10^6
    e. 5.611×10^7

8. Express the number 3.7020×10^{-2} as an ordinary number without an exponent.
    a. 0.037020
    b. 370.20
    c. 3.7020
    d. 0.03702
    e. 370.2

9. Convert 33.1 mm to μm.
    a. 0.0331 μm
    b. 3.31×10^7 μm
    c. 3.31×10^{-5} μm
    d. 3.31 μm
    e. 3.31×10^4 μm

10. Convert 2.9979×10^8 m to cm.
     a. 2.9979×10^6 cm
     b. 3.00×10^{10} cm
     c. 2.9979×10^{10} cm
     d. 2.9979×10^{11} cm
     e. 3.00×10^6 cm

11. Convert 45.0 mL to qt.
     a. 0.0450 qt
     b. 0.0426 qt
     c. 42.6 qt
     d. 0.0476 qt
     e. 47.6 qt

12. Mass and weight
     a. are the same thing.
     b. are related but are distinctly different.
     c. differ only by the type of instrument used to measure them.
     d. can vary for an object.
     e. are similar enough that they can be used interchangeably.

13. An object has a mass of 56.32 g and occupies a volume of 8.75 mL. Calculate the density of the object.
     a. 6.44 g/mL
     b. 0.155 g/mL
     c. 493 g/mL
     d. 6.437 g/mL
     e. 0.1554 g/mL

14. An object has a mass of 192.77 g and a density of 7.953 g/mL. Calculate the volume which the object occupies.
     a. 0.04126 mL
     b. 1530 mL
     c. 24.24 mL
     d. 0.02424 mL
     e. 0.0413 mL

15. A liquid has a density of 0.8110 g/mL. Calculate the mass of a 156 L sample of the liquid.
     a. 156 g
     b. 127,000 g
     c. 192 g
     d. 127 g
     e. 192,000 g

16. The specific gravity of a gas is 0.001134 at 25 °C. At this temperature, what mass of the gas is needed to fill a 6.0 L balloon?
     a. 6.804 g
     b. 5.3×10^6 g
     c. 6.804×10^{-3} g
     d. 5.3×10^3 g
     e. 6.8 g

17. Copper melts at about 2300 °C. What is that temperature in °F?
     a. 1260 °F
     b. 4172 °F
     c. 2268 °F
     d. 4200 °F
     e. 4108 °F

18. A wax melts at 375 °F. What is that temperature in °C?
     a. 707 °C
     b. 343 °C
     c. 191 °C
     d. 643 °C
     e. 226 °C

19. How much heat, in calories, is needed to raise the temperature of 1.00 L of water from 37.1 °C to 55.1 °C?
     a. 1.00×10^3 cal
     b. 1.80×10^4 cal
     c. 37,100 cal
     d. 18.0 cal
     e. 18,000 cal

20. How much heat, in calories, is released when 90.00 g of a metal is cooled from 99.6 °C to 29.1 °C? The specific heat of the metal is 0.115 cal/g-°C.
     a. 7.30×10^2 cal
     b. 8.11 cal
     c. 729.68 cal
     d. 70.5 cal
     e. 6.34×10^3 cal

Answers to the Sample Quiz Questions

1. (d), 2. (a), 3. (d), 4. (c), 5. (b), 6. (b), 7. (e), 8. (a), 9. (e), 10. (c), 11. (d), 12. (b), 13. (a), 14. (c), 15. (b), 16. (e), 17. (d), 18. (c), 19. (b), 20. (a)

ELEMENTS, ATOMS, AND COMPOUNDS

CHAPTER

3

Chapter Overview

Chapter 3 introduces the elements and basic atomic theory. Many of the common elements are discussed in terms of their natural abundances and their characteristic behaviors. The periodic table is presented with an emphasis on its organization by the properties of the elements. The concept of the atom is developed with a historical perspective from the ancient Greeks through Dalton's atomic theory. From that point, the nuclear atom and subatomic particles are discussed as well as isotopes and atomic masses. To build on Dalton's theory, molecules, compounds, formulas and formula weights, the law of definite proportions, and percentage composition are also discussed.

As in previous chapters, margin notes are extensively used to give definitions and to reinforce math skills.

Solutions to the Study Questions and Problems

1. An **element** is a pure substance which cannot be broken down into simpler stable substances by ordinary chemical means.

2. The four elements of the ancient Greeks are not elements by our modern definition. Air is a mixture of gases. Earth is also a mixture which varies considerably with geography. Fire is a type of chemical reaction where the flames are mostly energy and glowing gases. Water is a compound; it can be broken down into simpler substances.

3. Hydrogen, being the lightest element, should be the one most abundantly formed in any theory of the creation of the universe. However, hydrogen is so light (and therefore has such a low density) that most of the elemental hydrogen that may have once been on earth has literally floated to the top of the atmosphere and escaped into space. What hydrogen that remains on earth is held in chemical compounds.

4. **a.** The **periodic table** is an organized representation of the elements in which elements are arranged by increasing atomic number so that elements with similar properties are placed in the same columns, called groups or families. **b. Period** is the name given to the rows in the periodic table. **c. Group** is the name given to the columns in the periodic table. A **family** is synonymous with a group. **d.** An **element symbol** is a one or two letter abbreviation for the name of an element (although perhaps not the element's name in English). As such, the symbols are a shorthand notation.

5. The basis of the periodic table is the recurring similarities of the properties of the elements. Properties vary in a fairly regular manner as you go across a period and tend to repeat the pattern as you go across the next period. Elements with similar properties belong to the same group. It is this cyclic nature of the elemental properties which gives the table its name.

6. **a.** He is helium. **b.** Au is gold. **c.** F is fluorine (note the spelling). **d.** Fe is iron. **e.** Ag is silver. **f.** Kr is krypton.

7. **a.** Polonium is Po (note that, for two letter symbols, the first letter is upper case and the second is lower case). **b.** Barium is Ba. **c.** Tungsten is W. **d.** Uranium is U. **e.** Fermium is Fm. **f.** Chromium is Cr.

8. The discontinuous theory of matter holds that it is possible to subdivide matter but that, eventually, small indivisible basic particles would be encountered making further subdivision impossible. The continuous theory of matter holds that matter is infinitely divisible and that there are no indivisible basic particles. Today, we believe the discontinuous theory of matter to be correct. It is certainly true that there is a limit to how much we can subdivide matter without changing its properties, the basic particles being atoms. At present, it is not clear to what extent we can subdivide atoms.

9. Dalton's atomic theory contained five main ideas. 1) The elements are composed of small, indivisible particles called atoms. 2) The atoms of each element are identical and the atoms of different elements are different. 3) Compounds are composed of atoms of two or more elements. 4) In compounds, the atoms of each element are present in small, whole number ratios. 5) If atoms of the same elements can combine in different ratios, then each ratio describes a different compound. In "ordinary" laboratory chemistry, Dalton's theory is still quite valid. However, we now know that the atom can be divided into subatomic particles. With the ability to subdivide atoms, we also have been able to change atoms of one element into atoms of another element. We also now know that all atoms of the same element are not necessarily the same; they can differ in the number of neutrons in the nucleus and, therefore, can have different masses. Although very uncommon, there are also examples of compounds which do not show whole number ratios of atoms.

10. An **atom** is now defined as the smallest unit of an element which has all the properties of that element. Inasmuch as the atom is known to be comprised of smaller particles, it should be possible to subdivide it. In fact, we have done it and subdivision of atoms is not a rare occurrence any more. Subdivision of the atom is the basis for many common applications such as in clinical diagnostics, X-rays, nuclear power plants, and nuclear weapons.

11. **a. Subatomic particles** are those particles which comprise the atom. **b. Nucleons** are the subatomic particles located in the nucleus of the atom. **c.** The **proton**, p, is a nucleon which has a positive electrical charge and a mass of 1.6726×10^{-24} gram. **d.** The **neutron**, n, is a nucleon which is electrically neutral and has a mass of 1.6748×10^{-24} gram. **e.** The **electron**, e^-, is a subatomic particle which moves around the nucleus and has a negative electrical charge and a mass of 9.1096×10^{-28} gram. **f.** An **ion** is an atom or group of atoms with a net electrical charge other than zero, achieved by either adding or removing one or more electrons. **g.** A **cation** is an ion with a net positive charge due to having more protons than electrons. **h.** An **anion** is an ion with a net negative charge due to having more electrons than protons.

12. ^{28}Si

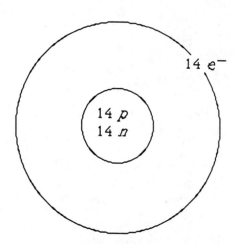

14 e^-

14 p
14 n

13. **a.** I$^-$ is an anion due to an excess of one electron. **b.** Ca^{2+} is a cation due to a deficiency of two electrons. **c.** S^{2-} is an anion due to an excess of two electrons. **d.** Al^{3+} is a cation due to a deficiency of three electrons.

14. An element's **atomic number** is the number of protons in the nuclei of its atoms.

15. **a.** Pb is atomic number 82. **b.** Np is atomic number 93. **c.** Ho is atomic number 67. **d.** Cs is atomic number 55. **e.** Tc is atomic number 43. **f.** Mo is atomic number 42.

16. **a.** Atomic number 74 is tungsten. **b.** Atomic number 96 is curium. **c.** Atomic number 12 is magnesium. **d.** Atomic number 15 is phosphorus. **e.** Atomic number 32 is germanium. **f.** Atomic number 49 is indium.

17. **Mass number** is the number of protons plus neutrons in an atom's nucleus. This is different from the atom's atomic number which is just the number of protons in the nucleus.

18. **a.** There are 56 - 30 = 26 protons. The element is iron. **b.** There are 201 - 121 = 80 protons. The element is mercury. **c.** There are 197 - 118 = 79 protons. The element is gold. **d.** There are 238 - 146 = 92 protons. The element is uranium. **e.** There are 84 - 48 = 36 protons. The element is krypton. **f.** There are 207 - 125 = 82 protons. The element is lead.

19. **a. Isotopes** are atoms of the same element which differ in the number of neutrons they contain (different mass numbers). **b. Protium** is the isotope of hydrogen with a mass number of 1 (^{1}H). It has no neutrons. **c. Deuterium** is the isotope of hydrogen with a mass number of 2 (^{2}H). It has one neutron. **d. Tritium** is the isotope of hydrogen with a mass number of 3 (^{3}H). It has two neutrons. **e. Isoelectronic ions** are ions which have the same number of electrons without regard for the number of protons or neutrons.

20.

	Protons	Neutrons	Electrons
a.	5	6	5
b.	20	21	20
c.	30	35	30
d.	73	108	73
e.	79	118	79
f.	54	77	54

21.

	Protons	Neutrons	Electrons
a.	56	81	54
b.	1	0	2
c.	13	14	10
d.	52	76	54
e.	50	69	48
f.	37	48	36

22. a and c are isoelectronic; b, e, and f are isoelectronic.

23. Isotopic mass is the actual mass of an atom expressed in grams. It is referred to as isotopic mass because each isotope of an element has its own isotopic mass just as it has its own mass number. The mass number is simply the sum of the number of protons and the number of neutrons in the atom. The atomic number is the number of protons in the atom.

24. An **atomic mass unit (amu)** is a relative mass unit corresponding to 1/12 the mass of a ^{12}C atom. The amu was devised as a way to get around the awkwardness of expressing atomic masses in grams. For example, the mass of a ^{12}C atom is 1.9925×10^{-23} gram or exactly 12 amu. However, the ratios of masses of the elements are the same in either system.

25. The three most important subatomic particles and their masses in amu are:

the proton - 1.007 amu
the neutron - 1.0087 amu
the electron - 5.4864×10^{-4} amu

26. The **atomic weight** of an element is the average of the masses of all the isotopes of the element found in nature. It differs from the isotopic masses in that isotopic masses are the masses of individual isotopes; the atomic weight is the average of the isotopic masses.

27. a. Y has an atomic weight of 88.9 amu. b. Tl has an atomic weight of 204.4 amu. c. Mn has an atomic weight of 54.9 amu. d. Ar has an atomic weight of 39.9 amu. e. Fr has an atomic weight of approximately 223 amu. f. Rh has an atomic weight of 102.9 amu.

28. The atomic weight of neon is:

^{20}Ne: (0.9092)(20.0 amu) = 18.2 amu
^{21}Ne: (0.00257)(21.0 amu) = 0.0540 amu
^{22}Ne: (0.0882)(22.0 amu) = <u>1.94 amu</u>
20.2 amu

29. The atomic weight of sulfur is:

$$^{32}S: (0.9502)(32.0 \text{ amu}) = 30.4 \text{ amu}$$
$$^{33}S: (0.0076)(33.0 \text{ amu}) = 0.251 \text{ amu}$$
$$^{34}S: (0.0422)(34.0 \text{ amu}) = \underline{1.43 \text{ amu}}$$
$$32.1 \text{ amu}$$

30. a. A **compound** is a pure substance composed of two or more elements combined in definite proportions by weight. **b.** A **molecule** is a group of two or more atoms, not necessarily of different elements, held together by the attraction of individual nuclei for the electrons of the other atoms in the molecule.

31. Ionic compounds are composed of two or more different ions (cations and anions) held together by the attraction of their opposite electrical charges. Molecular compounds are composed of two or more atoms of different elements held together by the attraction of individual nuclei for the electrons of the other atoms in the molecule.

32. Compounds and elements differ from each other in that compounds must be composed of atoms or ions of different elements. Many elements exist as isolated atoms but they do not occur as ions (unless combined with other ions, making an ionic compound). They are similar in that many elements and compounds exist as molecules.

33. No, the law of definite proportions applies only to pure compounds. The law simply states that a **compound** is composed of atoms of different elements combined in a definite proportion. A laboratory worker can choose to combine two or more pure compounds and the result is a **mixture** of variable proportion.

34. By saying sodium chloride is 39.3% sodium by weight, we are saying that 39.3/100 of the mass of the compound is attributed to sodium. Therefore:

$$\text{mass of sodium} = (0.393)(50.0 \text{ g}) = 19.6 \text{ g}$$

35. A **chemical formula** is a representation of a compound using the symbols of the elements to show what elements are present in the compound and numeric subscripts to show how many of each kind of atom or ion are present. A symbol refers to an element or to an atom of the element while a formula refers to a compound.

36. a. Ammonia contains nitrogen and hydrogen. **b.** Calcium carbonate contains calcium, carbon, and oxygen. **c.** Sulfuric acid contains hydrogen, sulfur, and oxygen. **d.** Sodium hydroxide contains sodium, oxygen, and hydrogen. **e.** Magnesium sulfate contains magnesium, sulfur, and oxygen. **f.** Potassium permanganate contains potassium, manganese, and oxygen.

37. a. Sodium carbonate contains 2 atoms Na, 1 atom C, and 3 atoms O. **b.** Magnesium phosphate contains 3 atoms Mg, 2 atoms phosphorus, and 8 atoms oxygen. **c.** Calcium hydrogen sulfate contains 1 atom Ca, 2 atoms H, 2 atoms S, and 8 atoms O. **d.** Barium acetate contains 1 atom Ba, 4 atoms C, 6 atoms H, and 4 atoms O. **e.** Aluminum bromide contains 1 atom Al and 3 atoms Br. **f.** Strontium nitrate contains 1 atom Sr, 2 atoms N, and 6 atoms O.

38. a. Sodium oxide is Na_2O. **b.** Nitric acid is HNO_3. **c.** Sodium acetate is $NaC_2H_3O_2$. **d.** Aluminum oxide is Al_2O_3. **e.** Carbon tetrachloride is CCl_4. **f.** Iron(III) sulfide is Fe_2S_3.

39. A **formula unit** is the simplest unit of a compound which shows the formula of a molecule for molecular compounds or the formula of the simplest ratio of ions for ionic compounds. **Formula weight** is the mass of the formula unit, expressed in amu.

40. a. FW of $Al(BrO_3)_3$ = (1 atom Al)$\underline{(27.0\ amu)}$ + (3 atoms Br)$\underline{(79.9\ amu)}$ + (9 atoms O)$\underline{(16.0\ amu)}$
                    (atom Al)   (atom Br)   (atom O)

= 27.0 amu + 239.7 amu + 144.0 amu

= 410.7 amu

b. FW of $Ba(CN)_2$ = (1 atom Ba)$\underline{(137.3\ amu)}$ + (2 atoms C)$\underline{(12.0\ amu)}$ + (2 atoms N)$\underline{(14.0\ amu)}$
                    (atom Ba)   (atom C)   (atom N)

= 137.3 amu + 24.0 amu + 28.0 amu

= 189.3 amu

c. FW of $CaCr_2O_4$ = (1 atom Ca)$\underline{(40.1\ amu)}$ + (2 atoms Cr)$\underline{(52.0\ amu)}$ + (4 atoms O)$\underline{(16.0\ amu)}$
                    (atom Ca)   (atom Cr)   (atom O)

= 40.1 amu + 104.0 amu + 64.0 amu

= 208.1 amu

d. FW of $Cr_2(SO_4)_3$ = (2 atoms Cr)$\underline{(52.0\ amu)}$ + (3 atoms S)$\underline{(32.1\ amu)}$
                    (atom Cr)   (atom S)

+ (12 atoms O)$\underline{(16.0\ amu)}$
                    (atom O)

= 104.0 amu + 96.3 amu + 192.0 amu

= 392.3 amu

41. a. FW of $Co(C_2H_3O_2)_3$ = (1 atom Co)$\underline{(58.9\ amu)}$ + (6 atoms C)$\underline{(12.0\ amu)}$
                    (atom Co)   (atom C)

+ (9 atoms H)$\underline{(1.0\ amu)}$ + (6 atoms O)$\underline{(16.0\ amu)}$
                    (atom H)   (atom O)

= 58.9 amu + 72.0 amu + 9.0 amu + 96.0 amu

= 235.9 amu

b. FW of $Cu(NO_3)_2$ = (1 atom Cu)$\underline{(63.5\ amu)}$ + (2 atoms N)$\underline{(14.0\ amu)}$ + (6 atoms O)$\underline{(16.0\ amu)}$
                    (atom Cu)   (atom N)   (atom O)

= 63.5 amu + 28.0 amu + 96.0 amu

= 187.5 amu

c. FW of $FeBr_3$ = (1 atom Fe)$\underline{(55.8\ amu)}$ + (3 atoms Br)$\underline{(79.9\ amu)}$
                    (atom Fe)   (atom Br)

= 55.8 amu + 239.7 amu

= 295.5 amu

41. d. FW of Li_2SO_4 = (2 atoms Li)$\underline{(6.9\ amu)}$ + (1 atom S)$\underline{(32.1\ amu)}$ + (4 atoms O)$\underline{(16.0\ amu)}$

                                 (atom Li)   (atom S)   (atom O)

                       = 13.8 amu + 32.1 amu + 64.0 amu

                       = 109.9 amu

42. FW of Fe_2O_3 is = (2 atoms Fe)$\underline{(55.8\ amu)}$ + (3 atoms O)$\underline{(16.0\ amu)}$

                         (atom Fe)   (atom O)

                    = 111.6 amu + 48.0 amu

                    = 159.6 amu

%Fe = $\dfrac{(111.6\ amu)}{(159.6\ amu)}$(100%)

     = 69.90%

%O = $\dfrac{(\ 48.0\ amu\ )}{(159.6\ amu)}$(100%)

     = 30.1%

43. FW of $C_3H_5(NO_3)_3$ = (3 atoms C)$\underline{(12.0\ amu)}$ + (5 atoms H)$\underline{(1.0\ amu)}$ + (3 atoms N)$\underline{(14.0\ amu)}$

                                (atom C)   (atom H)   (atom N)

                                                                 + (9 atoms O)$\underline{(16.0\ amu)}$

                                                                    (atom O)

                     = 36.0 amu + 5.0 amu + 42.0 amu + 144.0 amu

                     = 227.0 amu

%C = $\dfrac{(\ 36.0\ amu\ )}{(227.0\ amu)}$(100%)

     = 15.9%

%H = $\dfrac{(\ 5.0\ amu\ )}{(227.0\ amu)}$(100%)

     = 2.2%

%N = $\dfrac{(\ 42.0\ amu\ )}{(227.0\ amu)}$(100%)

     = 18.5%

%O = $\dfrac{(144.0\ amu)}{(227.0\ amu)}$(100%)

     = 63.4%

44. FW of $C_{12}H_{22}O_{11}$ = (12 atoms C)$\underline{(12.0\ amu)}$ + (22 atoms H)$\underline{(1.0\ amu)}$
$\qquad\qquad\qquad\qquad\qquad$ (atom C)$\qquad\qquad\qquad\qquad$ (atom H)

$\qquad\qquad\qquad\qquad\qquad\qquad\qquad\qquad\qquad\qquad\qquad\qquad$ + (11 atoms O)$\underline{(16.0\ amu)}$
$\qquad\qquad\qquad\qquad\qquad\qquad\qquad\qquad\qquad\qquad\qquad\qquad\qquad\qquad$ (atom O)

$\qquad\qquad\qquad$ = 144.0 amu + 22.0 amu + 176.0 amu

$\qquad\qquad\qquad$ = 342.0 amu

%C = $\dfrac{(144.0\ amu)}{(342.0\ amu)}$(100%)

$\qquad$ = 42.1%

%H = $\dfrac{(\ 22.0\ amu\ )}{(342.0\ amu)}$(100%)

$\qquad$ = 6.43%

%O = $\dfrac{(176.0\ amu)}{(342.0\ amu)}$(100%)

$\qquad$ = 51.5%

45. FW of Na_3AlF_6 = (3 atoms Na)$\underline{(23.0\ amu)}$ + (1 atom Al)$\underline{(27.0\ amu)}$ + (6 atoms F)$\underline{(19.0\ amu)}$
$\qquad\qquad\qquad\qquad\qquad$ (atom Na)$\qquad\qquad\qquad$ (atom Al)$\qquad\qquad\qquad$ (atom F)

$\qquad\qquad\qquad$ = 69.0 amu + 27.0 amu + 114.0 amu

$\qquad\qquad\qquad$ = 210.0 amu

%Na = $\dfrac{(\ 69.0\ amu\ )}{(210.0\ amu)}$(100%)

$\qquad$ = 32.9%

%Al = $\dfrac{(\ 27.0\ amu\ )}{(210.0\ amu)}$(100%)

$\qquad$ = 12.9%

%F = $\dfrac{(114.0\ amu)}{(210.0\ amu)}$(100%)

$\qquad$ = 54.3%

46. In 0.05 grams, there would be:

$$(0.05 \text{ g}) \left(\frac{\text{proton}}{1.6726 \times 10^{-24} \text{ g}} \right) = 3 \times 10^{22} \text{ protons}$$

$$(0.05 \text{ g}) \left(\frac{\text{neutron}}{1.6748 \times 10^{-24} \text{ g}} \right) = 3 \times 10^{22} \text{ neutrons}$$

$$(0.05 \text{ g}) \left(\frac{\text{electron}}{9.1096 \times 10^{-28} \text{ g}} \right) = 5 \times 10^{25} \text{ electrons}$$

47. The atomic weight of iron is:

^{54}Fe: (0.0584)(54.0 amu) =   3.15 amu
^{56}Fe: (0.9168)(56.0 amu) = 51.3 amu
^{57}Fe: (0.0217)(57.0 amu) =   1.24 amu
^{58}Fe: (0.0031)(58.0 amu) =   0.18 amu
$\qquad\qquad\qquad\qquad\qquad$ 55.9 amu

48. By saying water is 88.8% oxygen, we are saying there are 88.8 g of oxygen in every 100.0 g of water. Therefore:

$$(17.39 \text{ g O}) \frac{(100.0 \text{ g H}_2\text{O})}{(88.8 \text{ g O})} = 19.6 \text{ grams H}_2\text{O}$$

49. FW of FeCr$_2$O$_4$ = (1 atom Fe)$\frac{(55.8 \text{ amu})}{(\text{atom Fe})}$ + (2 atoms Cr)$\frac{(52.0 \text{ amu})}{(\text{atom Cr})}$ + (4 atoms O)$\frac{(16.0 \text{ amu})}{(\text{atom O})}$

$\qquad\qquad$ = 55.8 amu + 104.0 amu + 64.0 amu

$\qquad\qquad$ = 223.8 amu

%Cr = $\frac{(104.0 \text{ amu})}{(223.8 \text{ amu})}(100\%)$

$\qquad$ = 46.5%

To get 1.00 ton of chromium:

$$(1.00 \text{ ton Cr}) \frac{(100.0 \text{ ton chromite})}{(46.5 \text{ ton Cr})} = 2.15 \text{ ton chromite}$$

50. For hydrogen:

$$(1.1 \text{ g})\frac{(\text{ 1.00 amu }})(1 \text{ atom H})}{(1.6604 \times 10^{-24} \text{ g})(1.0 \text{ amu })} = 6.6 \times 10^{23} \text{ atoms H}$$

For chromium:

$$(14.7 \text{ g})\frac{(\text{ 1.00 amu }})(1 \text{ atom Cr})}{(1.6604 \times 10^{-24} \text{ g})(52.0 \text{ amu })} = 1.7 \times 10^{23} \text{ atoms Cr}$$

Therefore, there are more hydrogen atoms.

51. For P_4S_3: FW = (4 atoms P)$\frac{(31.0 \text{ amu})}{(\text{ atom P })}$ + (3 atoms S)$\frac{(32.1 \text{ amu})}{(\text{ atom S })}$

$$= 124.0 \text{ amu} + 96.3 \text{ amu}$$

$$= 220.3 \text{ amu}$$

%P = $\frac{(124.0 \text{ amu})(100\%)}{(220.3 \text{ amu})}$

$\quad$ = 56.3%

%S = $\frac{(96.3 \text{ amu })(100\%)}{(220.3 \text{ amu})}$

$\quad$ = 43.7%

For P_4S_5: FW = (4 atoms P)$\frac{(31.0 \text{ amu})}{(\text{ atom P })}$ + (5 atoms S)$\frac{(32.1 \text{ amu})}{(\text{ atom S })}$

$$= 124.0 \text{ amu} + 160.5 \text{ amu}$$

$$= 284.5 \text{ amu}$$

%P = $\frac{(124.0 \text{ amu})(100\%)}{(284.5 \text{ amu})}$

$\quad$ = 43.6%

%S = $\frac{(160.5 \text{ amu})(100\%)}{(284.5 \text{ amu})}$

$\quad$ = 56.4%

51. (continued)

For P_4S_7: FW = (4 atoms P)$\underline{(31.0\ amu)}$ + (7 atoms S)$\underline{(32.1\ amu)}$
(atom P)$$(atom S)

= 124.0 amu + 224.7 amu

= 348.7 amu

%P = $\dfrac{(124.0\ amu)}{(348.7\ amu)}$(100%)

= 35.6%

%S = $\dfrac{(224.7\ amu)}{(348.7\ amu)}$(100%)

= 64.4%

For P_4S_{10}: FW = (4 atoms P)$\underline{(31.0\ amu)}$ + (10 atoms S)$\underline{(32.1\ amu)}$
(atom P)$$(atom S)

= 124.0 amu + 321.0 amu

= 445.0 amu

%P = $\dfrac{(124.0\ amu)}{(445.0\ amu)}$(100%)

= 27.9%

%S = $\dfrac{(321.0\ amu)}{(445.0\ amu)}$(100%)

= 72.1%

Sample Quiz Questions

1. An element is
    a. a pure substance which cannot be separated into simpler substances by ordinary means.
    b. electrically charged, either positive or negative.
    c. a substance which has identical atoms.
    d. a molecule.
    e. part of a larger particle.

2. On the periodic table, a group
    a. is the term given to the elements on the right side of the table.
    b. is the term given to the two bottom rows which are separated from the other elements.
    c. is the same as a family.
    d. is the term given to any set of elements with similar properties.
    e. is the term given to the horizontal rows.

3. On the periodic table, a period
    a. is the term given to the elements on the right side of the table.
    b. is the term given to the two bottom rows which are separated from the other elements.
    c. is the same as a family.
    d. is the term given to any set of elements with similar properties.
    e. is the term given to the horizontal rows.

4. An atom
    a. is indivisible.
    b. is a homogeneous mixture of protons, neutrons, and electrons.
    c. is the smallest unit of matter.
    d. is the smallest unit of an element which has all the properties of the element.
    e. is easily divided by chemical means.

5. Ions
    a. are atoms with an excess of electrons.
    b. are atoms or groups of atoms with a net electrical charge other than zero.
    c. are formed by adding or removing neutrons to atoms.
    d. are atoms with a deficiency of electrons.
    e. are formed by adding or removing protons.

6. An atom's atomic number
    a. is the number of protons in the nucleus.
    b. is the sum of the number of protons and the number of neutrons in the nucleus.
    c. is the number of nucleons in the nucleus.
    d. is the number of electrons circulating around the nucleus.
    e. is the number of neutrons in the nucleus.

7. An atom's mass number
    a. is the number of protons in the nucleus.
    b. is the sum of the number of protons and the number of neutrons in the nucleus.
    c. is the number of nucleons circulating around the nucleus.
    d. is the number of electrons circulating around the nucleus.
    e. is the number of neutrons in the nucleus.

8. Isotopes are
    a. atoms with different numbers of protons and neutrons.
    b. atoms with the same numbers of neutrons and electrons.
    c. atoms with the same atomic number and different mass numbers.
    d. atoms with the same numbers of protons and electrons.
    e. atoms with different atomic numbers and the same mass number.

9. Which of the following pairs of ions are isoelectronic?
    a. O^{2-} and S^{2-}
    b. Na^+ and K^+
    c. Al^{3+} and Cl^-
    d. Mg^{2+} and O^{2-}
    e. Li^+ and Cl^-

10. Isotopic mass
    a. is the mass number of an atom.
    b. is the average of the masses of the isotopes of an element.
    c. is the atomic number times the mass of each nucleon.
    d. is expressed in the units of grams per amu.
    e. is the mass of an isotope of an element.

11. Protons, electrons, and neutrons
    a. are the nucleons.
    b. are the three principal subatomic particles.
    c. are charged particles.
    d. have approximately the same mass.
    e. are parts of the nucleus of the atrom.

12. Atomic weight
    a. is the average of the masses of the isotopes of an element.
    b. is the mass number of an atom.
    c. is the atomic number times the mass of each nucleon.
    d. is expressed in units of grams per amu.
    e. is the mass of an isotope of an element.

13. Bromine is composed of 50.54% ^{79}Br and 49.46% ^{81}Br. Calculate the atomic weight of bromine. (Assume a mass of 1.0 amu for each proton and neutron.)
    a. 8.00×10^4 amu
    b. 35.0 amu
    c. 320.0 amu
    d. 80.0 amu
    e. 45.0 amu

14. A molecule
    a. involves the attraction between oppositely charged ions.
    b. contains two atoms.
    c. involves the attraction of each nucleus for the electrons of the other atoms.
    d. involves the attraction among the nuclei of the atoms.
    e. is a gas.

15. If lithium nitrate is 20.3% nitrogen by weight, how many grams of nitrogen are in 750.0 grams of lithium nitrate?
    a. 140 g
    b. 55.8 g
    c. 7.38 g
    d. 34.0 g
    e. 55.82 g

16. The law of definite proportions
    a. applies only to molecules.
    b. says that elements can combine in one ratio to form compounds.
    c. is one of the parts of Dalton's theory which is no longer believed valid.
    d. says that compounds with different ratios of the same elements are different compounds.
    e. applies to mixtures as well as compounds.

17. For $(NH_4)_3PO_4$, give the number of atoms of each element in the simplest unit of the compound.
    a. 12 H; 3 N; 4 O; 1 P
    b. 43 H; 3 N; 4 O; 1 P
    c. 3 H; 3 N; 1 O; 4 P
    d. 12 H; 1 N; 4 O; 4 P
    e. 4 H; 1 N; 4 O; 1 P

18. A chemical formula
    a. is a representation of a compound which indicates the proportions in which atoms or ions are combined.
    b. applies to mixtures.
    c. is a representation of an element.
    d. shows which elements are contained in the compound.
    e. is an arbitrary group of symbols of elements.

19. Calculate the formula weight of $Mg(ClO_4)_2$.
    a. 123.8 amu
    b. 159.3 amu
    c. 223.3 amu
    d. 75.8 amu
    e. 187.8 amu

20. Calculate the formula weight of $Ba_3(PO_4)_2$.
    a. 232.3 amu
    b. 327.3 amu
    c. 184.3 amu
    d. 464.6 amu
    e. 601.9 amu

21. Calculate the percentage composition of Na_2SO_4.
    a. 19.3% Na; 27.0% S; 53.7% O
    b. 32.4% Na; 22.6% S; 45.0% O
    c. 48.9% Na; 34.1% S; 17.0% O
    d. 32.3% Na; 45.1% S; 22.5% O
    e. 19.3% Na; 53.9% S; 26.8% O

22. Calculate the percentage composition of NH_4CN.
    a. 44.4% C; 3.7% H; 51.9% N
    b. 27.3% C; 9.1% H; 63.6% N
    c. 29.3% C; 2.4% H; 68.3% N
    d. 40.0% C; 13.3% H; 46.7% N
    e. 20.7% C; 6.9% H; 72.4% N

Answers to the Sample Quiz Questions

1. (a), 2. (c), 3. (e), 4. (d), 5. (b), 6. (a), 7. (e), 8. (c), 9. (d), 10. (e), 11. (b), 12. (a), 13. (d), 14. (c), 15. (b), 16. (d), 17. (a), 18. (a), 19. (c), 20. (e), 21. (b), 22. (b)

ELECTRON ARRANGEMENTS IN ATOMS

CHAPTER
4

Chapter Overview

Chapter 4 describes the development of models of the atom from Lord Kelvin's model of a homogeneous atom through the modern quantum mechanical model. In order to explain the modern concepts of the atom, particularly quantized energy, a complete discussion of light and emission line spectra is included. Without delving into the mathematics, the modern picture of the atom is developed, beginning with the Bohr atom. A brief description of the Heisenberg Uncertainty Principle emphasizes orbitals as probability volumes rather than paths taken by electrons. The modern atom is then discussed in terms of energy levels, sublevels, shapes of the orbitals, and electron configurations.

The chapter concludes with an optional section which presents quantum numbers. The relationships between the quantum numbers and the orbitals and electron configurations are developed in this section for those instructors wishing to give students a more detailed introduction to atomic structure.

Solutions to the Study Questions and Problems

1. **A scientific model** is a way of expressing an abstract scientific concept, such as the atom, in more easily and clearly visualized terms.

2. The **Thomson plum pudding model** of the atom described the atom as a sphere of uniformly distributed positive charge with the electrons randomly scattered throughout, like the raisins in plum pudding. The atom overall was electrically neutral. The model did not acknowledge the existence of the proton; the proton had not yet been discovered. The positive charge was assumed to be uniformly distributed throughout the atom without an attempt to describe the nature of that charge.

3. The **Rutherford model** of the atom improved on the Thomson model by predicting that all of the positive charge and virtually all of the mass of the atom were contained in an extremely small, rigid **nucleus,** located at the center of the atom. The electrons therefore had very little mass but occupied most of the volume of the atom as they orbited around the nucleus.

35

4. The major shortcoming of the Rutherford model was that it failed to explain the atomic emission spectra observed when atoms are heated to high temperatures. By relating the atom to a solar system, the electrons should spiral into the nucleus as natural and manmade satellites do; this clearly does not happen.

5. **a. Radiant energy** is a continuous wave of energy emitted by an object at a speed of 3.0×10^8 meter/second. Radiant energy ranges from very low energy radio waves, through visible light, up to very high energy gamma (γ) radiation. **b. Light** is radiant energy in the wavelength range from 10^{-8} to 10^{-6} meter or from 10 to 1000 nm. This encompasses not only visible light but also ultraviolet light and infrared radiation. **c.** A **wavelength** (λ) is the distance from one point on a wave (usually a crest or a trough) to the equivalent point on the next wave. **d.** The **visible spectrum** is the small range of radiant energy ($\lambda = 380$ nm to 780 nm) that stimulates the receptors in our eyes and is perceived as colored or white light. Each specific color of visible light corresponds to a specific wavelength with red having the longest wavelength and violet having the shortest. **e.** Light having a longer wavelength than red but shorter than the wavelength associated with microwaves is referred to as **infrared light** (beneath red). **f.** Light having a shorter wavelength than violet but longer than about 1 nm is referred to as **ultraviolet light** (beyond violet). **g. Planck's constant**, given the symbol h, relates energy to wavelength by the equation $E = hc/\lambda$. Thus, the shorter the wavelength, the higher the energy the light possesses and visa versa.

6. Rainbows occur when droplets of water in the air act as prisms to separate sunlight into its component colors.

7. Energy is related to wavelength by the formula:

$$E = \frac{hc}{\lambda}$$

The longer the wavelength, the less energy the light possesses. Thus, infrared light, with a longer wavelength than ultraviolet light, has less energy.

8. Ultraviolet light, X-rays, and γ radiation have shorter wavelengths than visible light and therefore possess more energy than visible light. Living organisms have adapted to visible light. When exposed to the higher energy radiation to which they have not adapted, these organisms can be damaged. The higher the energy of the radiation, the more easily the tissues of the organisms are damaged.

9. **a.** When white light is passed through a prism, it spreads into a wide band of all possible colors. The uninterrupted band of colors is called a **continuous spectrum**. **b.** When an element is heated to high temperatures and vaporized, light is given off but not as a contiunuous spectrum. Only a few colors (wavelengths) are produced and are characteristic of the element emitting the light. This discontinuous spectrum of colors is called the element's **atomic emission spectrum**. **c.** Atomic emission spectra contain only the specific wavelengths characteristic of the element heated. The wavelengths emitted appear as lines rather than bands and so the phenomenon is also known as a **line spectrum**.

10. In incandescent light bulbs, the tungsten filament is heated up enough to glow. Since tungsten is a heavy element, many lines are expected in its emission spectrum and the overall effect is perceived as white light. The number of lines approximate a continuous spectrum. The tungsten also remains a solid so that individual atoms are not glowing, the sample as a whole is.

11. A continuous spectrum contains all the wavelengths of visible light. A line spectrum contains only a few wavelengths or lines. Neon lights emit the line spectrum of neon which has a bronze glow. The various colors of neon signs are produced by painting the glass tubes.

12. If you heat copper to an extremely high temperature (hot enough to vaporize some of the copper atoms), it will emit the line spectrum which is characteristic of copper. This can be demonstrated by heating copper wire in a flame and noting the blue colored flame produced.

13. **a.** The **Bohr atomic model** proposed that the atom consisted of a nucleus at the center and the electrons in definite, discrete orbits or shells with no other electron locations being possible. The electrons, therefore, could only have certain discrete, well defined energies. **b.** In the Bohr model, the electrons orbit on the surfaces of spherical **electron shells** which are concentric and at increasing distances from the nucleus. **c.** The **ground state of an atom** occurs when all electrons are in the lowest available energy levels and, therefore, the atom contains the minimum amount of energy. This occurs in the absence of radiant energy or other form of high energy input. **d.** When an atom absorbs energy, an electron can move to a higher energy level (an orbit farther away from the nucleus) and the atom is said to be in an **excited state**. **e.** When an electron falls from an excited state back to the ground state, it emits the same amount of energy previously absorbed. This definite amount of energy is referred to as a **quantum of energy**.

14. Rutherford's model failed to account for the definite quantum of energy released and, therefore, for the atomic emission spectra of elements. According to Rutherford's model, electrons could have any energy; they were not confined to a few discrete energies. Consequently, Rutherford's model would have predicted a continuous spectrum, not a line spectrum.

15. The Bohr model proposed a nucleus at the center of the atom and the electrons in definite, discrete orbits. The electrons orbit on the surfaces of spheres or shells of increasing radius with each shell being a specific distance from the nucleus. When an electron is confined to a discrete orbit, it has a fixed amount of energy because of its fixed distance from the nucleus. Therefore, electrons can only possess certain, well defined energies. This feature represented a vast improvement over the Rutherford model.

16. In the Bohr model, atomic emission spectra are due to the electrons falling from higher orbits (excited states) to lower orbits. In the process, energy in the form of light with specific energies and, therefore, specific wavelengths is released, producing the atomic emission spectrum. The number of lines and the wavelengths observed depend on the atom involved.

17. Electrons go from the ground state to an excited state by absorbing radiant energy. While the atom is in an excited state, it is unstable. To achieve stability, the electrons will emit the excess energy and return to the ground state.

18. The letters K, L, M, N, ... are the electron shells in the Bohr model of the atom with K being the shell closest to the nucleus.

19. **a.** The **de Broglie hypothesis** stated that matter may have some of the properties of waves. **b.** The **Heisenberg uncertainty principle** states that it is impossible to accurately determine both the position and the energy of an electron simultaneously. **c.** The region in space near the nucleus where there is a good probability of finding an electron is called an **atomic orbital. d. Cloud density maps** are used to illustrate atomic orbitals by plotting the most likely locations for an electron. **e.** A **boundary surface diagram** is an outline of the area defined by a cloud density map, usually at the 90% or 95% likelihood level.

20. The Bohr atomic model worked very well for hydrogen and some ions which contained only a single electron but could not account for repulsion between electrons in other atoms and ions.

21. De Broglie made the radical suggestion that matter may be able to exhibit both particle and wave properties under the right circumstances.

22. According to the Heisenberg uncertainty principle, you cannot determine the exact position and energy of an electron at the same time.

23. An orbital is an electron probability cloud with a specific shape; it is a statistical result. Bohr described electrons as traveling in specific paths which he called orbits.

24. In the modern atomic theory, the electrons are distributed into shells of varying electron capacities. Each shell is called a principal energy level, symbolized as n.

25. The electron capacity of each shell is given by $2n^2$. **a.** For $n = 1$, the total electron capacity is 2. **b.** For $n = 2$, the total electron capacity is 8. **c.** For $n = 3$, the total electron capacity is 18. **d.** For $n = 4$, the total electron capacity is 32.

26. Each shell contains one or more subshells or sublevels. The number of subshells in a given shell is the same as the shell number, n. Each subshell contains one or more orbitals.

27. The number of subshells in a shell is equal to n.

28. The letter designations of the orbitals are s, p, d, and f, where the s is lowest in energy and the f is the highest in energy.

29. An s orbital has the shape:

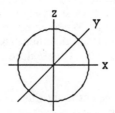

The $2s$ orbital is the same shape (spherical) as the $1s$ orbital but the $2s$ orbital is larger since it occurs at a high principal energy level.

30. The 1st principal energy level does not have any p orbitals. All other principal energy levels contain three p orbitals.

31. A set of p orbitals have the shapes:

p_z: p_x: p_y:

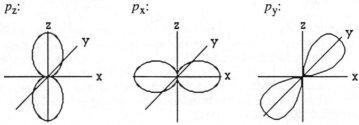

The p_x, p_y, and p_z orbitals differ only in the directions they point in space.

32. A $3p$ orbital differs from a $2p$ orbital only in that the $3p$ orbital is larger and has a higher energy.

33. All three of the $4p$ orbitals are identical except that they each point along a different axis. This includes having equal energies.

34. There can only be two electrons in each orbital. Electrons have negative charges and repel each other, especially if they are spinning in the same direction. Two electrons can occupy one orbital only if they have opposite spins.

35. There can only be 2 s electrons in any principal energy level since there is only one s orbital. When allowed, there can be 6 p electrons in any principal energy level since there are three orbitals in a p subshell. When allowed, there can be 10 d electrons in any principal energy level since there are five orbitals in a d subshell. When allowed, there can be 14 f electrons in any principal energy level since there are seven orbitals in an f subshell.

36. The arrangement of the electrons of an atom in the atomic orbitals is called the **electron configuration**.

37. a. $_5$B: $1s^22s^22p^1$

    b. $_{16}$S: $1s^22s^22p^63s^23p^4$

    c. $_{18}$Ar: $1s^22s^22p^63s^23p^6$

    d. $_{23}$V: $1s^22s^22p^63s^23p^64s^23d^3$

    e. $_{48}$Cd: $1s^22s^22p^63s^23p^64s^23d^{10}4p^65s^24d^{10}$

    f. $_{75}$Re: $1s^22s^22p^63s^23p^64s^23d^{10}4p^65s^24d^{10}5p^66s^24f^{14}5d^5$

38. a. $_{53}$I$^-$: $1s^22s^22p^63s^23p^64s^23d^{10}4p^65s^24d^{10}5p^6$

    b. $_{88}$Ra^{2+}: $1s^22s^22p^63s^23p^64s^23d^{10}4p^65s^24d^{10}5p^66s^24f^{14}5d^{10}6p^6$

    c. $_{34}$Se^{2-}: $1s^22s^22p^63s^23p^64s^23d^{10}4p^6$

    d. $_{13}$Al^{3+}: $1s^22s^22p^6$

39. In Group IA, the common electron configuration is ns^1 for the valence shell. In Group VIIIA or Group 0, the common electron configuration is ns^2np^6, except for helium which is $1s^2$.

40. a. n represents the principal number. **b.** l represents the orbital type quantum number. **c.** m_l represents the magnetic orbital quantum number. **d.** m_s represents the spin quantum number.

41. a. n signifies size. **b.** l signifies shape. **c.** m_l signifies orientation in space. **d.** m_s signifies the spin of the electron.

42. The allowed values of m_l for d orbitals ($l = 2$) are -2, -1, 0, +1, +2. Since there are five allowed values, there are five orbitals in a d subshell.

43. For $l = 3$, there are seven values of m_l: -3, -2, -1, 0, +1, +2, +3. There are seven orbitals in the subshell (the f subshell).

44. When $n = 4$, there are 16 orbitals, one s, three p, five d, and seven f.

45. a. 3, 2, 1, -1/2: This is a $3d$ orbital.

    b. 4, 2, 2, +1/2: This is a $4d$ orbital.

    c. 5, 1, -1, +1/2: This is a $5p$ orbital.

    d. 4, 2, -1, -1/2: This is a $4d$ orbital.

46. In the 2nd principal energy level, $n = 2$. The only allowed values of l are 0 and +1. For d orbitals, the value of l is +2. Since $l = 2$ is not allowed there can be no d orbitals in the 2nd principal energy level.

Sample Quiz Questions

1. The Thomson plum pudding model of the atom
   a. adequately explained the stability of atoms.
   b. described electrons as being distributed in a sea of positive charge.
   c. led to the discovery of electrons.
   d. resembled a solar system.
   e. remains a suitable explanation of the atom for most purposes.

2. The Rutherford model of the atom
   a. adequately explained the stability of atoms.
   b. described electrons as being distributed in a sea of positive charge.
   c. led to the discovery of electrons.
   d. resembled a solar system.
   e. remains a suitable explanation of the atom for most purposes.

3. The wavelength (λ) of light
   a. is directly proportional to energy.
   b. is shorter in the infrared region of the spectrum than in the visible.
   c. applies to white light.
   d. determines its speed.
   e. is inversely proportional to energy.

4. Which of the following relationships is correct?
   a. $E = \lambda c/h$
   b. $E = \lambda h/c$
   c. $E = hc/\lambda$
   d. $E = \lambda/hc$
   e. $E = h/\lambda c$

5. An atomic emission spectrum
   a. cannot be used to identify an element.
   b. contains only a few, discrete wavelengths.
   c. contains a continuous series of wavelengths.
   d. contains fewer lines for heavier elements.
   e. usually consists of white light.

6. In the Bohr model of the atom,
   a. electrons move around the nucleus in spherical orbits.
   b. electrons can occupy positions at any distance from the nucleus.
   c. an electron's energy depends on the speed at which it travels.
   d. an electron cannot move to another orbit.
   e. electrons move around the nucleus in elliptical orbits like planets around the sun.

7. In the Bohr model of the atom, when an electron moves from a lower shell to a higher shell
    a. the atom enters the ground state.
    b. one quantum of energy is emitted.
    c. the atomic line spectrum is produced.
    d. one quantum of energy is absorbed.
    e. another electron moves from a higher shell to a lower shell.

8. In the Bohr model of the atom,
    a. the excited state is stable.
    b. energy absorbed is $\Delta E = E_{higher\ shell} - E_{lower\ shell}$.
    c. the lowest energy shell is called "L".
    d. the electron may fall into the nucleus under the right circumstances.
    e. energy absorbed is $\Delta E = E_{lower\ shell} - E_{higher\ shell}$.

9. The Bohr model of the atom
    a. worked well for all but the heaviest elements.
    b. accounted for interactions between atoms.
    c. worked well for hydrogen but did not satisfactorily work for other elements.
    d. remains the most useful model of the atom.
    e. addressed the repulsion between electrons in an atom.

10. De Broglie's hypothesis
    a. stated that particles should exhibit some of the properties of waves.
    b. stated that waves should exhibit some of the properties of particles.
    c. defined the quantum.
    d. disproved the Bohr model of the atom.
    e. was considered interesting but did little to change atomic theory.

11. Heisenberg
    a. suggested that electrons have some of the properties of waves.
    b. showed how to determine the location and the energy of an electron.
    c. proved the existence of defined electron orbits in atoms.
    d. was able to determine the location of an electron in an atom given its energy.
    e. stated that it is impossible to know both the location and the energy of an electron.

12. An atomic orbital
    a. illustrates well defined paths for electrons in an atom.
    b. is a statistically determined volume in which an electron should be found.
    c. is of little use in describing an atom.
    d. is no longer considered a valid concept.
    e. is the same as an orbit in the Bohr model of the atom.

13. In modern atomic theory,
    a. each electron shell has a capacity of the same number of electrons.
    b. zero is an allowed value of n.
    c. the first principal energy level, $n = 1$, has a capacity of eight electrons.
    d. the concept of electron shells is a central idea.
    e. heavy atoms still are difficult to describe.

14. *p* orbitals
    a. occur in sets of five.
    b. occur in all principal energy levels.
        c. look like: d. look like: e. look like:

 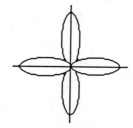

15. Principal energy levels have electron capacities given by
    a. $2n^2$
    b. $2n^3$
    c. $4n^2$
    d. $2n+1$
    e. n^2

16. The orbitals which exist at $n = 3$ are
    a. $2s2p_x2p_y2p_z3s3p_x3p_y3p_z3d_{xy}3d_{yz}3d_{xz}3d_z^23d_{x^2-y^2}$.
    b. $1s2s2p_x2p_y2p_z3d_{xy}3d_{yz}3d_{xz}3d_z^23d_{x^2-y^2}$.
    c. $1s2s2p_x2p_y2p_z3s3p_x3p_y3p_z3d_{xy}3d_{yz}3d_{xz}3d_z^23d_{x^2-y^2}$.
    d. $3s3p_x3p_y3p_z3d_{xy}3d_{yz}3d_{xz}3d_z^23d_{x^2-y^2}$.
    e. $1s2s2p_x2p_y2p_z3s3p_x3p_y3p_z$.

17. The electron configuration for $_{24}Cr$ is
    a. $1s^22s^22p^63s^23p^64s^23d^4$.
    b. $[Ne]4s^13d^5$.
    c. $[Ar]4s^13d^5$.
    d. $1s^22s^22p^63s^23p^63d^6$.
    e. $[Ar]4s^23d^4$.

18. The electron configuration for $_{13}Al^{3+}$ is
    a. $1s^22s^22p^6$.
    b. $1s^22s^22p^63s^23p^6$.
    c. $1s^22s^22p^63s^23p^1$.
    d. $[Ar]$
    e. $1s^22s^22p^63s^23p^4$.

19. In the quantum mechanical model of the atom, the orbital type quantum number, *l*,
    a. describes the size of the orbital.
    b. describes the spacial orientation of the orbital.
    c. describes the spin of the electron in the orbital.
    d. describes the shape of the orbital.
    e. is allowed the values 0, 1,..., *n*.

20. The allowed values of the magnetic orbital quantum number, m_l, are
    a. 1, 2, 3,...
    b. 0, 1,..., +(l-1).
    c. 0, 1, 2,..., n-1.
    d. +n, +(n-1),..., 0,..., -(n-1), -n.
    e. +l, +(l-1),..., 0,..., -(l-1), -l.

Answers to the Sample Quiz Questions

1. (b), 2. (d), 3. (e), 4. (c), 5. (b), 6. (a), 7. (d), 8. (b), 9. (c), 10. (a), 11. (e), 12. (b), 13. (d), 14. (c), 15. (a), 16. (d), 17. (c), 18. (a), 19. (d), 20. (e)

CHEMICAL PERIODICITY

CHAPTER
5

Chapter Overview

Chapter 5 continues the development of the periodic table by focusing on the trends in elemental behavior usually referred to as periodic trends or, simply, as periodicity. By examining periodicity, the empirical basis of the periodic table, introduced in Chapter 3, is then reinforced.

As in previous chapters, the approach to the development of the periodic table is historical. Beginning with Dobereiner's "triad" scheme and proceeding through Newlands' "law of octaves", the periodic law is used to show the logic used by Meyer and Mendeleev to independently devise the basis of our modern periodic table. The discussion of the periodic table includes the common terminology used, such as groups (families), periods, actinides, lanthanides, representative elements, and transition elements.

A survey of the representative elements by group follows to reinforce the similarities in family properties and the periodic law. The general properties of the transition elements are also discussed.

The chapter then turns to periodicity, discussing the major periodic trends of atomic size, ionization energy, and electron affinity within the context of the elements' positions on the periodic table. The chapter concludes with a section which ties the various properties together into a unified description of elemental properties and the periodic table.

Solutions to the Study Questions and Problems

1. Chemical periodicity is the observed recurrence of similar chemical properties with increasing atomic number (and therefore, roughly, with increasing atomic weight).

2. Mendeleev arranged his periodic table in increasing atomic weight order such that elements with similar properties were placed in the same group. He left gaps in his table when the group properties called for an element with properties other than those possessed by the next element in atomic weight order. His rationale was that there was an element, as yet undiscovered, which had the right properties to fill each gap. Subsequent research has found elements which do fill all of the gaps left by Mendeleev. Therefore, he was quite right in leaving the gaps and his rationale for doing so was correct.

3. Mendeleev's statement of the periodic law was very close to the modern version. However, Mendeleev (and others of his time) incorrectly associated periodicity with increasing atomic weight. This is not surprising since the subatomic particles were not yet known and so the concept of atomic number had not yet been conceived. Now, we could state the periodic law as "the elements, arranged in increasing atomic number order, show recurring (periodic) chemical and physical properties".

4. **a. A period of elements** is the set of elements which occur in the same row of the periodic table. **b. A group or family of elements** is a set of elements which occur in the same column of the periodic table. **c. Valence electrons** are electrons which are in the outermost occupied shell of an atom. Alternatively, the valence electrons are those which have the highest value of n in an atom. **d.** The **valence shell** is the outermost occupied electron shell. Alternatively, it is the shell which contains the valence electrons. **e. A metal** is an element which possesses properties such as shininess, electrical and thermal conductivity, malleability, and ductility. The metals occupy roughly the left 2/3 of the periodic table. **f. A nonmetal** is an element which possesses properties such as dull appearance (not shiny), brittleness, and nonconductivity. The nonmetals roughly occupy the right 1/3 of the periodic table. **g. Metalloids** are those elements which possess some properties of metals and some properties of nonmetals. The metalloids occupy the positions adjacent to the zigzag line from boron to astatine which is traditionally drawn on the periodic table.

5. The modern periodic table differs from Mendeleev's in two major ways. First, Mendeleev devised a scheme using eight numbered columns and subdividing each column into "A" and "B". We now recognize the "A" and "B" subdivisions as separate groups. Second, with the discovery of the lanthanide and actinide elements, the current periodic table also includes these 28 elements, either separated from the rest of the table for convenience or included as parts of the 6th and 7th periods, respectively. The modern periodic table also has elements where Mendeleev left gaps.

6. **a.** The 5th period contains 18 elements. **b.** The 7th period can contain 32 elements. However, the last of the currently known elements are in this period. At this time, 21 elements in the 7th period are known. **c.** The 3rd period contains 8 elements. **d.** The 1st period contains only 2 elements.

7. **a.** Group 0 has 6 elements. **b.** Group IIIA has 5 elements. **c.** Group IA has 7 elements. **d.** Group VIA has 5 elements.

8. **a.** Sn has 4 valence electrons. **b.** Mg has 2 valence electrons. **c.** In has 3 valence electrons. **d.** Ba has 2 valence electrons. **e.** K has 1 valence electron. **f.** Sb has 5 valence electrons.

9. The boiling points of the elements vary with increasing atomic number across each period in a complex way. The trend is for boiling points to decrease from Group IA to Group 0 but the highest boiling point is seen for the member of the period from Group IVA. The vertical trend in boiling points is even more complex (it is not discussed in the text). In Groups IA through IVA, boiling points tend to decrease down each group. In Groups VIA through 0, boiling points tend to increase down each group.

10. The period numbers are the same as the numbers of the principal energy levels. Therefore, the principal energy level increases going down the periodic table.

11. **a.** For C: $2s^2 2p^2$ **b.** For Ba: $6s^2$ **c.** For Ar: $3s^2 3p^6$ **d.** For As: $4s^2 4p^3$ **e.** For Cs: $6s^1$ **f.** For S: $3s^2 3p^4$

12. The electron capacities of the periods is determined by which subshells are in use and their capacities. Therefore, the 1st period has a capacity of 2 electrons since there is only a $1s$ subshell, the 4th period has a capacity of 18 electrons since there are the $4s$, $3d$, and $4p$ subshells.

13. The principal energy levels begin to overlap in the 4th period. The period begins by filling the $4s$ subshell, then fills the $3d$ subshell, and finally fills the $4p$ subshell. Since the order of use of the subshells is the order of increasing subshell energy, this means that the $4s$ subshell is lower in energy than the $3d$ subshell. The overlap introduces the transition elements. The 10 groups (Sc to Zn) represent the filling of d subshells. Therefore, the transition metals are those which are effected by the overlap.

14. The 7th period is incomplete simply because the elements which would complete it have not been discovered. There is considerable debate as to whether the remaining elements of the 7th period can exist and will ever be discovered.

15. Hydrogen and helium are similar in that both are gases and both use only the $1s$ subshell. They differ in that hydrogen is a reactive diatomic element with one valence electron ($1s^1$) while helium is a monatomic element which is a noble gas. It is therefore nonreactive and its valence shell is filled ($1s^2$).

16.

	First Element	Last Element
1st period	H	He
2nd period	Li	Ne
3rd period	Na	Ar
4th period	K	Kr
5th period	Rb	Xe
6th period	Cs	Rn
7th period	Fr	Number 109

17. There are several element properties which vary going across a period. Within a given period, going from left to right, atomic size decreases, ionization energy increases, electron affinity increases, and metallic character decreases (or nonmetallic character increases).

18. The transition elements of the 4th period are filling the $3d$ subshell. The transition elements of the 5th period are filling the $4d$ subshell. The transition elements of the 6th period are filling the $5d$ subshell.

19. The lanthanides and actinides are the two rows of the periodic table usually separated from the body of the table and written at the bottom. The lanthanides are those 14 elements of the 6th period which represent the filling of the $4f$ subshell and properly follow the element lanthanum on the periodic table. The actinides are those 14 elements of the 7th period which represent the filling of the $5f$ subshell and properly follow actinium on the periodic table.

20. The groups designated as "A" groups are the representative elements. Those groups designated as "B" groups are the transition elements.

21. The representative elements are those in which the s and p subshells are being filled. The transition elements are those in which the d and f subshells are being filled. The representative elements are filling valence shell orbitals. The transition elements are filling orbitals "beneath" the valence shell; the d orbitals are in the $n - 1$ principal level and the f orbitals are in the $n - 2$ principal level.

22. a. Br is representative. **b.** W is transition. **c.** Ra is representative. **d.** Ti is transition. **e.** Pb is representative. **f.** F is representative. **g.** Si is representative. **h.** In is representative. **i.** Os is transition. **j.** Sr is representative. **k.** Te is representative. **l.** Ar is representative.

23. For the representative elements, the group numbers give the number of valence electrons possessed by the group members. The only exception is group 0 (the noble gases). Those elements have 8 valence electrons (helium has 2 valence electrons).

24. Group 0 elements have 8 valence electrons with the exception of helium. Helium has only 2 valence electrons since it is in the 1st period which has a capacity of only 2 electrons ($1s^2$).

25. a. The **alkali metals** are the members of Group IA. **b.** A **diatomic molecule** is a molecule composed of two atoms. **c.** The **alkaline earth metals** are the members of Group IIA. **d.** When an element occurs in more than one natural form, for example oxygen occurs as O_2 and as O_3, the forms are called **allotropes. e. Ozone** is the allotrope of oxygen with the formula O_3. **f.** The **halogens** are the members of Group VIIA. **g.** The **noble gases** are the members of Group 0. **h.** The **octet rule** states that an atom or ion is least reactive when it has 8 electrons in its valence shell.

26. group   valence shell electron configuration

group	valence shell electron configuration
Group IA	ns^1
Group IIA	ns^2
Group IIIA	ns^2np^1
Group IVA	ns^2np^2
Group VA	ns^2np^3
Group VIA	ns^2np^4
Group VIIA	ns^2np^5
Group 0	ns^2np^6

27. The most reactive metals are those in Group IA, the alkali metals. The most reactive nonmetals are those in Group VIIA, the halogens.

28. The diatomic elements are hydrogen, nitrogen, oxygen, fluorine, chlorine, bromine, and iodine which have the formulas H_2, N_2, O_2, F_2, Cl_2, Br_2, and I_2, respectively.

29. Hydrogen is often classified as a Group IA element due to its electron configuration, $1s^1$, which matches the other members of the group. Other than that, hydrogen bears little resemblance to the other members of Group IA.

30. Groups IA, IIA, and 0 are the only representative groups which contain no metalloids. Group VIIA is the only group which contains one metalloid (At). The other representative groups contain two metalloids.

31. The only group which contains only gases is Group 0.

32. Ozone (an allotrope of oxygen, O_3) absorbs ultraviolet radiation from sunlight, filtering much of it so that only a small amount of ultraviolet light reaches earth. Without that filtering, sunlight would be potentially lethal to most forms of life on earth. Ozone differs from the normal element oxygen in its formula (normal oxygen is O_2) and in that ozone is considerably more reactive.

33. The transition elements are all metals and so are often referred to as the transition metals. Most of them are shiny solids; mercury is the only liquid, although it is shiny. All conduct heat and electricity, are malleable and are ductile. All of the transition elements have 1 or 2 valence electrons (ns^1 or ns^2) and are filling either a d or f subshell. All of them exhibit at least two cations of different charge and do not, without extreme effort, make anions. In addition, most of the transition elements make highly colored compounds.

34. The cations of the transition elements differ from those of the representative metals mostly in that the transition elements will form more than one cation. Transition elements form one cation through the removal of one or two ns electrons but higher charged cations are then formed by the subsequent removal of $(n-1)d$ or $(n-2)f$ electrons. Representative elements form only one cation through the removal of all of the valence electrons. The cations of transition elements also tend to be colored while those of the representative elements tend to be colorless.

35. Atomic size tends to decrease going left to right across a period. This is caused by the addition of protons to the nucleus while adding electrons to the same principal energy level and therefore at about the same distance from the nucleus. The effect of it is to strengthen the nucleus' hold on the electrons, shrinking the atom.

36. Atomic size increases going down a group. This is caused by the addition of electrons to succeedingly higher principal energy levels and therefore at increasing distances from the nucleus. This expansion overrrides any shrinkage which may be predicted due to the increase in the number of protons in the nucleus.

37. Excluding Group 0, the smallest atom should be hydrogen. This is, in fact, true; the noble gases do not adhere to most of the periodic trends due to their electron configurations and innate stabilities. The largest atom should be francium .

38. **Ionization energy** is the energy <u>required</u> to remove an electron from an atom in the gaseous state. The first ionization energy is the energy to remove the first electron; the second ionization energy is the energy required to remove a second electron (it is not the energy required to remove two electrons).

39. The first ionization energies increase going left to right across a period. This can be explained in much the same way as the accompanying decrease in size. As you proceed to the right, the atoms shrink due to an increase in attraction between the nucleus and the valence electrons. This increase in attraction also requires that more energy be used to remove a valence electron. Therefore, as you proceed to the right, ionization energy increases.

40. The first ionization energies decrease going down a group. Since going down a group represents the addition of principal energy levels and each succeeding level is larger, the attraction between the nucleus and the valence electrons decreases. Therefore, less energy is required to remove an electron as you proceed down a group and the ionization energy decreases.

41. **a.** Cl has the higher first ionization energy since it lies to the right of Al. **b.** As has the higher first ionization energy since it lies above and to the right of Rb. **c.** B has the higher first ionization energy since it lies to the right of Li. **d.** F has the higher first ionization energy since it lies above and to the right of Cs. In fact, fluorine has the highest first ionization energy of all the elements.

42. Metals form cations much more readily than nonmetals. This tendency can be explained in terms of the octet rule. It is easier (less energy involved) for a metal to lose electrons to achieve the electron configuration of the preceding noble gas (the octet) than to gain electrons to achieve the electron configuration of the succeeding noble gas.

43. In order to remove a second electron from lithium, a $1s$ electron would have to be taken. Since that involves taking an electron from a deeper principal energy level, the energy required is much greater than if the second electron came from the valence shell.

44. The third ionization energy of strontium is very high since the first two ionization energies involve removing the $5s$ electrons and the third involves removing a $4p$ electron. Any time ionization requires taking an electron from beneath the valence shell, the ionization energy is very high.

45. The stability of the octet is shown in the large increases in the ionization energies when ionization involves taking an electron from a shell beneath the valence shell. By comparison, removing electrons until an octet is achieved involves relatively small amounts of energy.

46. Electron affinity is the amount of energy <u>liberated</u> by the addition of an electron to an atom in the gaseous state. By this definition, if energy is required to add an electron, the value of the electron affinity will be negative.

47. Electron affinity increases going left to right across a period. This is due to the decrease in atomic size across a period. Atoms on the right are smaller so the attraction for electrons is greater. Therefore, atoms on the right will release more energy when an electron is added.

48. Electron affinity decreases going down a group. The atoms get larger going down a group and so atoms lower in a group will not have as strong an attraction for electrons. Therefore, addition of an electron will not release as much energy.

49. a. F has the higher electron affinity since it is above and to the right of K. **b.** Se has the higher electron affinity since it lies to the right of Ca. **c.** N has the higher electron affinity since it lies above As. **d.** Cl has the higher electron affinity since it lies above and to the right of Po.

50. Nonmetals form anions more readily. This tendency can be explained in terms of the octet rule. It is easier (less energy involved) for a nonmetal to gain electrons to achieve the electron configuration of the succeeding noble gas (the octet) than to lose electrons to achieve the electron configuration of the preceding noble gas.

51. The most metallic elements are in the lower left corner of the periodic table. These elements have the lowest ionization energies, the lowest electron affinities, the largest atomic sizes, and the greatest tendency to form cations. Therefore, they are the most metallic.

52. The most nonmetallic elements are in the upper right corner of the periodic table. These elements have the highest ionization energies, the highest electron affinities, the smallest atomic sizes, and the greatest tendency to form anions. Therefore, they are the most nonmetallic.

53. a. Ca is more metallic in nature since it lies below and to the left of B. **b.** Ba is more metallic in nature since it lies below and to the left of N. **c.** Fr is more metallic in nature since it lies below Li. **d.** Al is more metallic in nature since it lies to the left of S.

54. The noble gases are so unreactive since their first ionization energies are very high, their electron affinities are extremely low, and their atomic sizes are slightly larger than the halogens. Since the noble gases already have an octet of electrons, there is no driving force to gain or lose electrons.

55. a. Cl is a nonmetal. **b.** Am is a metal. **c.** Mo is a metal. **d.** Ce is a metal. **e.** Rb is a metal. **f.** P is a nonmetal. **g.** Ge is a metalloid. **h.** Be is a metal. **i.** Na is a metal. **j.** Rn is a nonmetal. **k.** B is a metalloid. **l.** Cd is a metal.

56. The 4th through 6th periods are longer than the 1st through 3rd periods because they have more orbitals. The 1st period has only the $1s$ subshell. The 2nd and 3rd periods have ns and np subshells. The 4th and 5th periods have ns, $(n-1)d$, and np subshells. The 6th period has ns, $(n-2)f$, $(n-1)d$, and np subshells.

57. "Silicon Valley" is a fairly appropriate name for the area slightly south of San Francisco. The semiconductor technology on which most modern electronics is based utilizes silicon, particularly in the form of solid mixtures with other metalloids, in the fabrication of integrated circuits. These integrated circuits are the heart (or brain, if you prefer) of modern computers.

58. Helium is preferred over hydrogen in balloons because helium is virtually as buoyant as hydrogen but is nonflammable. Hydrogen is dangerously flammable, as was tragically demonstrated in the crash of the German dirigible Hindenburg on May 6, 1937, which took 36 lives.

59. **a.** Al^{4+} should not exist since the removal of the 4th electron would break into the 2nd principal energy level. **b.** Mg^{3+} should not exist since the removal of the 3rd electron would break into the 2nd principal energy level. **c.** Rb^+ should and does exist. Removal of one electron leads to an octet. **d.** F^+ should not exist since removal of an electron takes fluorine farther away from an octet. The ionization energy of fluorine supports the conclusion. **e.** Sr^+ should not exist since removal of one electron still leaves strontium with one electron more than an octet ($5s^1$). **f.** K^{2+} should not exist since the removal of the second electron would break into the 3rd principal energy level.

60. The observation of compounds of krypton, xenon, and radon can be rationalized based on their sizes. The electron affinities of all the noble gases are very low and the ionization energies are very high. In compound formation, it will be somewhat easier for the noble gases to gain electrons than to lose them. Atomic size then becomes a controlling factor. The larger atoms (the lower ones) will be more able to accommodate additional electrons.

Sample Quiz Questions

1. The periodic law
    a. was first stated by Johann Dobereiner.
    b. relates chemical and physical properties to atomic number.
    c. is no longer considered valid.
    d. initially accounted for the 108 known elements.
    e. relates chemical and physical properties to atomic weight.

2. A period of elements
    a. begins with a noble gas.
    b. contains 18 elements.
    c. refers to the columns on the periodic table.
    d. refers to the rows on the periodic table.
    e. contains five or six elements.

3. A group of elements
    a. begins with a noble gas.
    b. contains 18 elements.
    c. refers to the columns on the periodic table.
    d. refers to the rows on the periodic table.
    e. contains five or six elements.

4.   The valence shell
  a. for 4th period elements consists of 4s, 3d, and 4p electrons.
  b. is the outermost occupied electron shell in an atom.
  c. consists of only s and p electrons.
  d. contains eight electrons.
  e. is the lowest energy shell in an atom.

5.   The metals
  a. tend to be brittle.
  b. are all solids.
  c. tend to be malleable.
  d. all make cations with 1+ charges.
  e. make cations by losing electrons from shells below the valence shell.

6.   The metalloids
  a. are members of the p block.
  b. have primarily metallic properties.
  c. tend to conduct electricity well.
  d. include the element radon.
  e. are relatively inert elements.

7.   The 1st period
  a. has eight elements in it.
  b. contains a metal and a nonmetal.
  c. fills the 1s and 1p subshells.
  d. contains the most reactive elements.
  e. has two elements in it.

8.   The 3rd period
  a. is a short period.
  b. is a long period.
  c. contains all nonmetals.
  d. fills the 2s and 2p subshells.
  e. is unique in that its members all occur as diatomic molecules.

9.   The lanthanides
  a. fill the 5f subshell.
  b. are members of the 6th period.
  c. fill the 5d subshell.
  d. are metalloids.
  e. are sometimes referred to as outer transition elements.

10. The 7th period
  a. includes the elements with atomic numbers 87 through 118.
  b. includes the lanthanides.
  c. contains metals and nonmetals.
  d. has a capacity of 32 electrons.
  e. fills the 7s, 6f, 5d, and 7p subshells.

11. The representative elements
    a. are labelled as the "B" groups on the periodic table.
    b. are the nonmetals.
    c. are those which are members of the *s* and *p* blocks.
    d. are generally nonreactive.
    e. are those which best illustrate the properties of the elements.

12. The alkali metals
    a. include hydrogen.
    b. have a common valence shell electron configuration of ns^2.
    c. are dense, hard metals.
    d. are highly reactive.
    e. are relatively inert.

13. Group IVA
    a. contains the metalloid tin.
    b. contains carbon, which is the only important member of the group.
    c. exhibits allotropes for all its members.
    d. elements have the common valence shell electron configuration of ns^2np^4.
    e. contains metals, nonmetals, and metalloids.

14. Group 0 elements
    a. are fairly reactive.
    b. tend to form anions like all nonmetals.
    c. are also known as the inert gases.
    d. are not known to make compounds.
    e. all make compounds.

15. The transition elements
    a. tend to make more than one cation.
    b. consist of the "A" groups on the periodic table.
    c. tend to make more than one anion.
    d. lose one or more *d* electrons to form an ion.
    e. tend to make colorless or pale compounds.

16. Atomic size tends to
    a. increase across a period from the left due to an increase in the number of protons.
    b. decrease across a period from the left due to an increase in the number of neutrons.
    c. remain almost constant across a period from the left since the principal energy level stays constant.
    d. decrease across a period from the left due to an increase in the number of protons.
    e. decrease down a group due to the increase in the number of protons.

17. Which of the following is larger than gallium?
    a. germanium.
    b. calcium.
    c. silicon.
    d. selenium.
    e. aluminum.

18. Ionization energy tends to
    a. increase across a period from the right.
    b. decrease going up a group.
    c. increase going up a group.
    d. decrease from the lower left corner of the periodic table to the upper right corner.
    e. remain fairly constant across a period.

19. The 2nd ionization energy of an element
    a. is greater than the 1st ionization energy of the element.
    b. is less than the 1st ionization energy of the element.
    c. is the energy required to remove two electrons from an atom of the element.
    d. is the energy released when a second electron is removed from an atom of the element.
    e. is lower for sodium than for magnesium.

20. Which of the following has a 1st ionization energy less than Rh?
    a. Zn.
    b. Pd.
    c. I.
    d. Co.
    e. Ba.

21. Electron affinity tends to
    a. increase across a period from the right.
    b. decrease going down a group.
    c. increase going down a group.
    d. decrease from the lower left corner of the periodic table to the upper right corner.
    e. remain fairly constant across a period.

22. Which of the following has an electron affinity greater than In?
    a. Ge.
    b. Hg.
    c. Cd.
    d. Au.
    e. Sr.

23. Metallic character tends to
    a. include brittleness.
    b. increase to the upper left corner of the periodic table.
    c. parallel nonmetallic character.
    d. require diatomic molecules.
    e. increase to the lower left corner of the periodic table.

24. The trends in ionization energy and electron affinity tend to
    a. run opposite each other on the periodic table.
    b. show that the greatest metallic character is in the upper right corner of the periodic table.
    c. contradict the trend in atomic size.
    d. parallel each other on the periodic table.
    e. show little change across a period.

Answers to the Sample Quiz Questions

1. (b), 2. (d), 3. (c), 4. (b), 5. (c), 6. (a), 7. (e), 8. (a), 9. (b), 10. (d), 11. (c), 12. (d), 13. (e), 14. (c), 15. (a), 16. (d), 17. (b), 18. (c), 19. (a), 20. (e), 21. (b), 22. (a), 23. (e), 24. (d)

CHEMICAL BONDS

CHAPTER 6

Chapter Overview

Chapter 6 takes the material on atomic structure from Chapter 4 and the material on chemical periodicity from Chapter 5 and applies it to the phenomena of chemical bonding. Electron dot formulas are used extensively to illustrate the stability of octets in both ionic and covalent bonding. Ionic bonding is presented as an electrostatic attraction between ions and emphasizes the predictability of representative monatomic ions using the octet rule. This treatment also includes an introduction to oxidation and reduction which reinforces the charge balance required of compounds.

Molecular compounds are also discussed within the context of the octet rule. Multiple bonds are completely covered as are polyatomic molecular ions. Following the descriptions of covalent bonding are a discussion of molecular geometry as predicted by the valence shell electron pair repulsion theory (VSEPR) and a discussion of electronegativity. The concept of electronegativity is then applied to bond polarity and molecular polarity.

No attempt is made in this chapter to cover the nomenclature of inorganic compounds; this is the focus of Chapter 7. Chapter 6 concentrates on helping the student construct valid compounds given the properties of the elements, adequately describe the nature of the bonding in compounds, and understand some of the ramifications of molecular structure.

Solutions to the Study Questions and Problems

1. **Chemical bonds** are the forces of attraction that hold the atoms or ions of a compound together.

2. The two major types of chemical bonds are ionic bonds and covalent bonds.

3. The two main types of chemical compounds are ionic compounds and molecular compounds. The ionic compounds are held together by ionic bonds between the two kinds of ions (anions and cations) and are usually composed of a metal with one or more nonmetals. Molecular compounds are held together by covalent bonds between nonmetal atoms in which the atoms share electrons.

4. **a.** MnO_2 is ionic. **b.** SiH_4 is molecular. **c.** $SOCl_2$ is molecular. **d.** KI is ionic. **e.** $BaCl_2$ is ionic. **f.** $PbBr_2$ is ionic. **g.** Ag_2S is ionic. **h.** $AlPO_4$ is ionic. **i.** HCl is molecular. **j.** $GaCl_3$ is ionic. **k.** $Mg(C_2H_3O_2)_2$ is ionic. **l.** $Fe_2(SO_4)_3$ is ionic.

5. Cations are smaller than their parent atoms because they have lost their valence electrons and the remaining electrons will be more strongly attracted to the nucleus.

6. Anions are larger than their parent atoms because the increase in electrons lessens the attraction between the electrons and the nucleus.

7. **Ionic bonds** are the forces of attraction between oppositely charged ions which hold ionic compounds together.

8.

 a. Ba^{2+} **b.** $\cdot \ddot{I} :$ **c.** $:\ddot{S}:^{2-}$ **d.** $\cdot \dot{P}:$

 e. $:\ddot{Xe}:$ **f.** Al^{3+} **g.** $:\ddot{N}:^{3-}$ **h.** $:\ddot{Br}:^{-}$

 i. Rb^{+} **j.** $\cdot Be \cdot$ **k.** $\cdot \dot{Pb} \cdot$ **l.** $:\dot{O}:^{2-}$

9.

 a. $:\ddot{Se}:^{2-}$ **b.** Cs^{+} **c.** $:\ddot{Br}:^{-}$ **d.** Sr^{2+}

 e. $:\ddot{S}:^{2-}$ **f.** In^{3+}

10.

 a. $Ba^{2+} :\ddot{O}:^{2-}$ **b.** $Be^{2+}(:\ddot{I}:^{-})_2$

 c. $(Tl^{3+})_2(:\ddot{O}:^{2-})_3$ **d.** $Mg^{2+}(:\ddot{F}:^{-})_2$

 e. $(K^{+})_2:\ddot{S}:^{2-}$ **f.** $(Ra^{2+})_3(:\ddot{N}:^{3-})_2$

11. **a.** Cs_2O **b.** Al_2S_3 **c.** $CaAt_2$ **d.** BaSe **e.** Na_3N **f.** K_2Se

12. **a.** An **ionic compound** is a compound composed of cations and anions in which the overall charge is always zero. **b.** Ionic compounds such as NaCl don't consist of just one Na^+ and one Cl^-. Each Na^+ is surrounded by eight Cl^- and visa versa. This arrangement of the Na^+ and Cl^- ions is known as the **crystal lattice. c. Binary ionic compounds** are ionic compounds which are composed of the monatomic ions of just two elements.

13. Ionic compounds are composed of oppositely charged ions in a crystal lattice that are strongly attracted to each other. These strong forces of attraction must be overcome in melting or boiling an ionic compound. This requires more energy or higher temperatures.

14. **a.** K has an oxidation number of 0. **b.** Fe^{3+} has an oxidation number of 3. **c.** He has an oxidation number of 0. **d.** Pt^{2+} has an oxidation number of 2. **e.** I^- has an oxidation number of -1. **f.** P^{3-} has an oxidation number of -3.

15. A reaction in which electrons are gained is a **reduction**. A reaction in which electrons are lost is an **oxidation**. Inasmuch as matter cannot be created nor destroyed (conservation), any oxidation reaction must occur simultaneously with a reduction reaction which involves the same number of electrons.

16. a. $Fe + 2H^+ \rightarrow Fe^{2+} + 2H$ Fe is oxidized; H^+ is reduced
   b. $Ni + Cu^{2+} \rightarrow Ni^{2+} + Cu$ Ni is oxidized; Cu^{2+} is reduced
   c. $Pb + Zn^{2+} \rightarrow Pb^{2+} + Zn$ Pb is oxidized; Zn^{2+} is reduced
   d. $Cu + 2Ag^+ \rightarrow Cu^{2+} + 2Ag$ Cu is oxidized; Ag^+ is reduced
   e. $Sn^{2+} + Pb \rightarrow Sn + Pb^{2+}$ Pb is oxidized; Sn^{2+} is reduced
   f. $Zn + 2AgCl \rightarrow ZnCl_2 + 2Ag$ Zn is oxidized; AgCl (or Ag^+) is reduced

17. A **covalent bond** is a bond in which two atoms are held together through the mutual attraction of one or more pairs of valence electrons by the nuclei of both atoms; the electrons are shared. In ionic bonds, the electrons are not shared; the anion has an excess number of electrons (making it negative) and the cation has a deficiency of electrons (making it positive). The attractive force in ionic bonding is then the attraction between the oppositely charged ions.

18. The valence electrons not involved in a covalent bond (*i.e.*, those not shared) are called **nonbonding electrons**.

19. Assuming the bond utilizes a p orbital from each of the two chlorine atoms, the diagram would be:

20. In the hydrogen molecule (H_2), each nucleus attracts two electrons and each electron is attracted to two nuclei. As a result, each nucleus has "control" over two electrons which approximates a noble gas electron configuration for each nucleus ($1s^2$). This gives the diatomic molecule its stability.

21. The noble gases contain the full octet of electrons (except helium with a duet) and so there is no need to share any electrons to fill the valence shell; there is no additional stability in forming molecules.

22. The nonmetals have similar tendencies to gain and lose electrons and so are more likely to share. Metals have very low electron affinities and electronegativities; they are not likely to attract electrons in a covalent bond.

23. Molecules, rather than ions, occupy positions in the crystal lattice in solid molecular compounds.

24. The attractive forces between molecules are relatively weak in comparison to the attraction between ions in ionic compounds. Therefore, less energy or lower temperatures are required to break the crystal of a molecular compound.

25. A **double bond** consists of two pairs of electrons shared between two atoms. A **triple bond** consists of three pairs of electrons shared between two atoms.

26. Atoms will form multiple bonds if doing so will give them an octet of valence electrons.

27. The electron dot fomula of molecular nitrogen (N_2) is :N≡N:

28. Polyatomic ions are ions (*i.e.*, they have a net charge other than zero) which contain two or more atoms covalently bonded together so as to act as a single unit.

29. Covalent bonds hold the atoms together in a polyatomic ion.

30. In a **coordinate covalent bond,** both of the electrons in the covalent bond are contributed by one of the atoms. In "normal" covalent bonds, each of the atoms involved contributes an electron to each shared pair.

31. Valence is defined as the number of covalent bonds an atom can form. Carbon has a valence of 4 because it has 4 valence electrons and can accept 4 more from other atoms (making an octet) to form 4 bonds. Nitrogen has 5 valence electrons, one pair and 3 single or unpaired electrons. The 3 unpaired electrons give nitrogen its valence of 3. Oxygen has 6 valence electrons, 2 pairs and 2 unpaired electrons. The two unpaired electrons give oxygen a valence of 2.

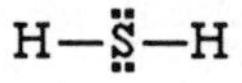

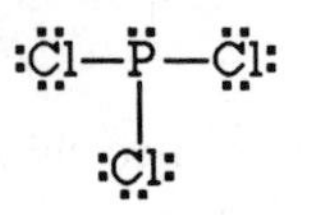

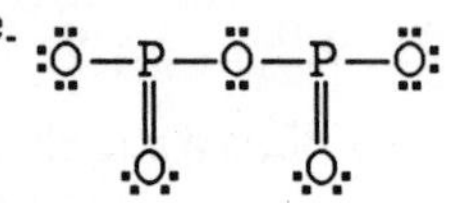

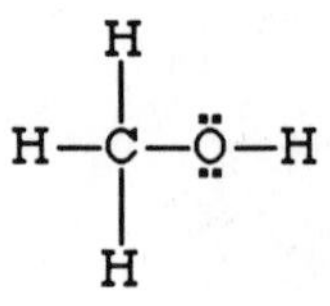

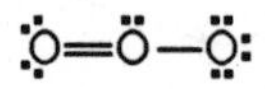

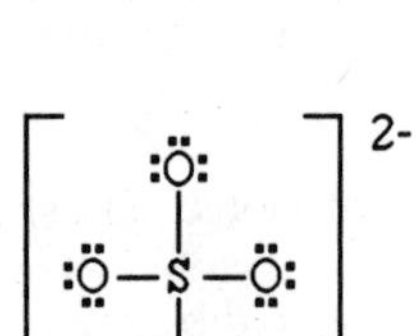

32.

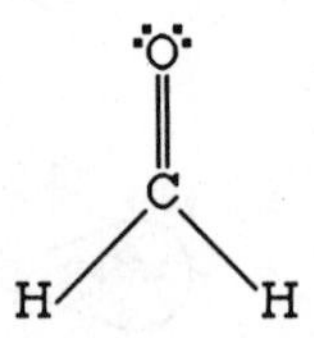

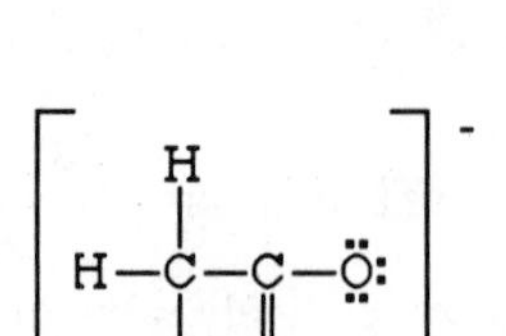

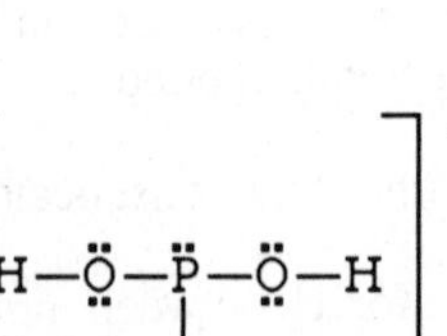

33.

34.

a. Ca^{2+} $\left[\ :\!\ddot{O}\!-\!\overset{\displaystyle :\ddot{O}:}{\underset{\displaystyle :\ddot{O}:}{S}}\!-\!\ddot{O}:\ \right]^{2-}$

b. Na^{+} $\left[\ \ddot{O}\!=\!\underset{\displaystyle :\ddot{O}:}{N}\!-\!\ddot{O}:\ \right]^{-}$

c. K^{+}_{3} $\left[\ :\!\ddot{O}\!-\!\overset{\displaystyle :\ddot{O}:}{\underset{\displaystyle :\ddot{O}:}{P}}\!-\!\ddot{O}:\ \right]^{3-}$

d. Na^{+}_{2} $\left[\ :\!\ddot{O}\!-\!\overset{\displaystyle :\ddot{O}:}{\underset{\displaystyle :\ddot{O}:}{S}}\!-\!\ddot{O}:\ \right]^{2-}$

e. Mg^{2+} $\left[\ H\!-\!\overset{\displaystyle H}{\underset{\displaystyle H}{C}}\!-\!\overset{}{\underset{\displaystyle \cdot\ddot{O}\cdot}{C}}\!-\!\ddot{O}:\ \right]^{-}_{2}$

f. Sr^{2+} $\left[\ :\!\ddot{O}\!-\!\overset{\displaystyle :\ddot{O}:}{\underset{\displaystyle :\ddot{O}:}{Cl}}\!-\!\ddot{O}:\ \right]^{-}_{2}$

35. The **VSEPR theory** stands for Valence Shell Electron Pair Rupulsion theory. It predicts the shapes of molecules based on the geometry of the maximum separation of valence electron pairs around the atom.

36. a. CH_4 is a tetrahedron with bond angles of 109.5°. **b.** NH_3 is a pyramid with bond angles of 107.3° (slightly less than the tetrahedral 109.5°). **c.** H_2O is bent with a bond angle of 104.5° (slightly less than the tetrahedral 109.5°). **d.** BF_3 is trigonal with bond angles of 120°.

37.

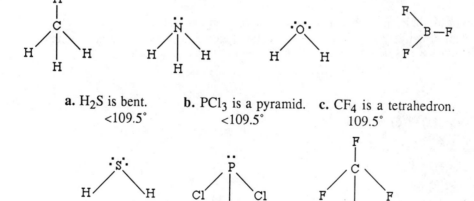

38.   **a.** H_2S is bent.   **b.** PCl_3 is a pyramid.   **c.** CF_4 is a tetrahedron.
<109.5°   <109.5°   109.5°

39. Electronegativity is a measure of an atom's relative ability to attract or compete for electrons in a covalent bond.

40. Electronegativity values increase from left to right across a period and from bottom to top in a group.

41. The most electronegative element is fluorine. The least electronegative element is francium.

42. A **polar covalent bond** is a covalent bond in which the electrons are not shared equally. The atom with the higher electronegativity will have the greater share of the electrons.

43. a. H_2 is nonpolar covalent. **b.** MgO is ionic. **c.** H_2O is polar covalent with $H^{\delta+}$—$O^{\delta-}$. **d.** NaI is polar covalent with $Na^{\delta+}$—$I^{\delta-}$. **e.** CF_4 is polar covalent with $C^{\delta+}$—$F^{\delta-}$. **f.** HBr is polar covalent with $H^{\delta+}$—$Br^{\delta-}$. **g.** N_2 is nonpolar covalent. **h.** AlF_3 is ionic. **i.** $CaCl_2$ is ionic. **j.** CCl_4 is polar covalent with $C^{\delta+}$—$Cl^{\delta-}$. **k.** SO_2 is polar covalent with $S^{\delta+}$—$O^{\delta-}$. **l.** NH_3 is polar covalent with $H^{\delta+}$—$N^{\delta-}$.

44. The polarity is in the order N—Cl (nonpolar) $< S^{\delta+}$—$O^{\delta-} < H^{\delta+}$—$O^{\delta-} < P^{\delta+}$—$F^{\delta-}$.

45. The molecule H—C≡N: is polar because of the fact that the electronegativities of the elements increase left to right in the molecule (N > C > H) and due to the unbonded electron pair on the nitrogen.

46. The molecular polarity increases in the order $CCl_4 < CHCl_3 < CH_2Cl_2 < CH_3Cl$. CCl_4 is a nonpolar molecule due to its tetrahedral symmetry. The remaining ones can be ranked in terms of increasing loss of symmetry and the fact that the C—Cl bond is more polar than the C—H bond. In $CHCl_3$ and CH_2Cl_2, however, much of the C—Cl bond polarity is cancelled out by opposing directions.

47. a. CBr_4 is nonpolar since it has the symmetry of a tetrahedron. **b.** H_2S is polar due to its bent geometry and the fact that the S—H bonds are polar. **c.** Br_2 is nonpolar since it is linear and the bond is nonpolar.

48. a. In $CoCl_2$, cobalt is Co^{2+}. **b.** In FeO, iron is Fe^{2+}. **c.** In MnO_2, manganese is Mn^{4+}. **d.** In Cu_2O, copper is Cu^+. **e.** In VCl_3, vanadium is V^{3+}. **f.** In Ag_2S, silver is Ag^+.

49. As shown by their electron dot formulas, both I_2 and Br_2 share one pair of electrons between atoms. This effectively gives each atom an octet of electrons, which is stable. The individual atoms of each have seven valence electrons, which is not as stable as an octet.

:B̈r̈—B̈r̈:   :Ï—Ï:

50. a. 5+3(6)+1 = 24 **b.** 6+4(6)+2 = 32 **c.** 1+6+4(6)+1 = 32 **d.** 5+4(6)+3 = 32 **e.** 2(1)+5+4(6)+1 = 32 **f.** 2(4)+3(1)+2(6)+1 = 24

51.

a.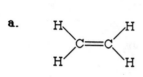

b. Ca^{2+} $\left[\begin{array}{c} :\ddot{O}\!-\!\ddot{Br}\!-\!\ddot{O}: \\ | \\ :\ddot{O}: \end{array} \right]^{-}_{2}$

c. $K^{+}\left[:C\!\equiv\!N: \right]^{-}$

d. $:\ddot{Cl}\!-\!\ddot{O}\!-\!\ddot{Cl}:$

e. $Mg^{2+}\left[:\ddot{O}\!-\!\ddot{N}\!=\!\ddot{O}: \right]^{-}_{2}$

f. $:\ddot{Br}\!-\!\ddot{P}\!-\!\ddot{Br}:$
   $\quad\quad |$
   $\quad\quad:\ddot{Br}:$

52.

	Electron Dot Formula	Structural Formula	Shape	Bond Angles
a.	$:N\!\equiv\!N:$	$N\!\equiv\!N$	linear	—
b.	$H\!-\!C\!\equiv\!N:$	$H\!-\!C\!\equiv\!N$	linear	180°
c.	$H\!-\!\overset{\displaystyle\cdot\ddot{O}\cdot}{\underset{\displaystyle\parallel}{C}}\!-\!H$	$\overset{\displaystyle O}{\underset{\displaystyle H^{\diagup}\,{}^{\diagdown}H}{C\!=\!}}$	trigonal	120°
d.	$H\!-\!C\!\equiv\!C\!-\!H$	$H\!-\!C\!\equiv\!C\!-\!H$	linear	180°
e.	$:\ddot{O}\!-\!\ddot{S}\!=\!\ddot{O}:$	$\overset{\displaystyle\cdot\cdot S}{\underset{\displaystyle O^{\diagup}\,{}^{\diagdown}O}{}}$	bent	120°
f.	$:\!S\!=\!C\!=\!S\!:$	$S\!=\!C\!=\!S$	linear	180°

53. a. $H^{\delta+}\!-\!Cl^{\delta-}$ **b.** $H^{\delta+}\!-\!N^{\delta-}$ (all three bonds are equivalent) **c.** $Cl^{\delta-}\!-\!Br^{\delta+}$ **d.** $H^{\delta+}\!-\!S^{\delta-}$ (both bonds are equivalent) **e.** $P^{\delta+}\!-\!Cl^{\delta-}$ (all three bonds are equivalent) **f.** $C^{\delta-}\!-\!H^{\delta+}$, $O^{\delta-}\!-\!H^{\delta+}$, $C^{\delta+}\!-\!O^{\delta-}$

54. a. PH_3 is polar. There is a nonbonding pair of electrons on the phosphorus. **b.** SO_3 is nonpolar. The trigonal geometry cancels the polarity of the individual bonds. **c.** CS_2 is nonpolar. The linear geometry cancels the polarity of the individual bonds.

Sample Quiz Questions

1. Ionic compounds
    a. may have a net charge other than zero.
    b. are held together by the attraction of oppositely charged ions in a random arrangement.
    c. often are composed of molecules.
    d. are held together by the attraction of electrons to two nuclei.
    e. are held together by the attraction of oppositely charged ions arranged in a regular pattern.

2. Molecular compounds
    a. may have a net charge other than zero.
    b. are held together by the attraction of oppositely charged ions in a random arrangement.
    c. often are composed of molecules.
    d. are held together by the attraction of electrons to two nuclei.
    e. are held together by the attraction of oppositely charged ions arranged in a regular pattern.

3. Na^+
    a. is smaller than Na.
    b. is larger than Na.
    c. has the same electron configuration as Ar.
    d. is an anion.
    e. behaves like a noble gas.

4. In LiF,
    a. Li^+ is larger than F^-.
    b. both atoms achieve an octet by converting to ions.
    c. Li becomes an anion while F becomes a cation.
    d. the bonding is covalent.
    e. LiF exists as isolated molecules.

5. The electron dot formula of Bi^{3+} is

    a. $\cdot \overset{\cdot\cdot}{\underset{\cdot}{B}i}\;^{3+}$

    b. $:\overset{\cdot\cdot}{\underset{\cdot\cdot}{B}i}\;^{3+}$

    c. $\cdot Bi\cdot^{3+}$

    d. Bi^{3+}

    e. $:\overset{\cdot}{\underset{\cdot}{B}i}\cdot^{3+}$

6. The electron dot formula of As^{3-} is

    a. $\cdot\overset{\cdot\cdot}{\underset{\cdot}{A}s}\cdot^{3-}$

    b. As^{3-}

    c. $\cdot As\cdot^{3-}$

    d. $\cdot\overset{\cdot\cdot}{\underset{\cdot}{A}s}\;^{3-}$

    e. $:\overset{\cdot\cdot}{\underset{\cdot\cdot}{A}s}:^{3-}$

7. Ionic compounds
    a. are held together by the attraction of electrons by both nuclei.
    b. tend to have fairly low melting points.
    c. are composed of isolated molecules.
    d. are composed of orderly arrays of ions.
    e. are generally composed of nonmetals.

8. A crystal lattice
    a. is a three-dimensional pattern of particles in solids.
    b. is irregular in its geometry.
    c. makes a solid compound easy to boil.
    d. ensures that ionic compounds have net charges other than zero.
    e. exists only for ionic compounds.

9. Which of the following equations represents an oxidation?
    a. $H + e^- \rightarrow H^-$
    b. $H \rightarrow H^+ + e^-$
    c. $F + e^- \rightarrow F^-$
    d. $Cl_2 \rightarrow 2Cl$
    e. $H^+ + I^- \rightarrow HI$

10. Given the reaction: $3Cu + 2Fe^{3+} \rightarrow 3Cu^{2+} + 2Fe$,
    a. iron(III) is oxidized and copper is reduced.
    b. copper(II) is oxidized and iron is reduced.
    c. copper is oxidized and iron(III) is reduced.
    d. iron is oxidized and copper(II) is reduced.
    e. three electrons are transferred.

11. Covalent bonds
    a. are not stable.
    b. always involve two electrons.
    c. must contain one electron from each atom.
    d. are formed by sharing electrons between two nuclei.
    e. are usually found in bonds between two metals.

12. In this picture of the orbitals of Cl combining to form Cl_2,

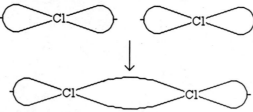

the orbitals being used by the chlorine atoms are the
    a. $1s$ orbitals.
    b. $2p$ orbitals.
    c. $3p$ orbitals.
    d. $3d$ orbitals.
    e. $4p$ orbitals.

13. Which of the following electron dot formulas is correct?

a.
$$Cl-C-Cl$$
$$|$$
$$Cl$$

b.
$$:\ddot{I}=\ddot{I}:$$

c.
$$:\ddot{O}-\ddot{O}-\ddot{O}:$$

d.
$$H-F$$

e.
$$:\ddot{C}l:$$
$$|$$
$$:\ddot{C}l-C-\ddot{C}l:$$
$$|$$
$$:\ddot{C}l:$$

14. Which of the following electron dot formulas is not correct?

a.
$$:\ddot{I}-\ddot{C}l:$$

b.
$$:\ddot{C}l:$$
$$|$$
$$H-C-\ddot{C}l:$$
$$|$$
$$:\ddot{C}l:$$

c.
$$:\ddot{F}-\ddot{S}-\ddot{F}:$$

d.
$$:\ddot{O}=\ddot{O}:$$

e.
$$:\ddot{H}-\ddot{O}-\ddot{H}:$$

15. Which of the following is a correct electron dot formula for SiBr$_4$?

a.
$$:\ddot{B}r:$$
$$|$$
$$:\ddot{B}r-Si-\ddot{B}r:$$
$$|$$
$$:\ddot{B}r:$$

b.
$$Br$$
$$|$$
$$Br-Si-Br$$
$$|$$
$$Br$$

c.
$$:\ddot{B}r:$$
$$|$$
$$\ddot{B}r-Si-\ddot{B}r$$
$$|$$
$$:\ddot{B}r:$$

d.
$$:\ddot{B}r-Si-\ddot{B}r:$$
$$|$$
$$:\ddot{B}r:$$

e.
$$:\ddot{B}r:$$
$$|$$
$$\ddot{B}r=Si=\ddot{B}r$$
$$|$$
$$:\ddot{B}r:$$

16. Which of the following electron dot formulas is correct?

a. 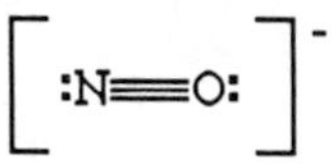 $\left[:N≡≡O:\right]^-$

b. 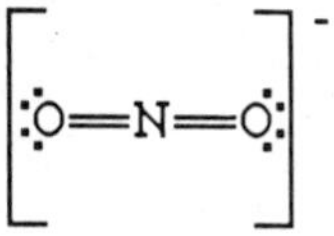 $\left[:O=N=O:\right]^-$

c. 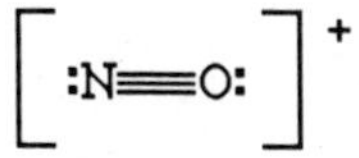 $\left[:N≡≡O:\right]^+$

d. 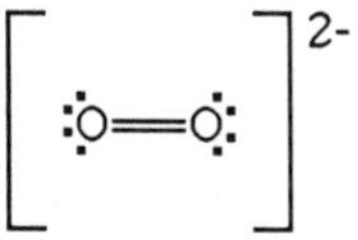 $\left[:O=O:\right]^{2-}$

e. 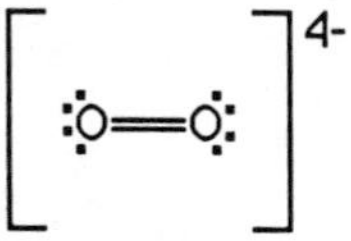 $\left[:O=O:\right]^{4-}$

17. Which of the following electron dot formulas is not correct?

a. 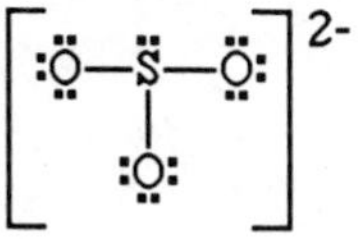 $\left[:\overset{..}{\underset{..}{O}}-\overset{..}{\underset{\overset{|}{:\underset{..}{O}:}}{S}}-\overset{..}{\underset{..}{O}}:\right]^{2-}$

b. 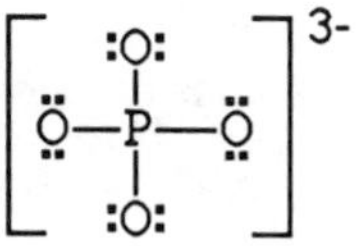 $\left[\overset{:\underset{..}{O}:}{\underset{:\underset{..}{O}:}{\overset{..}{O}-P-\overset{..}{O}}}\right]^{3-}$

c. 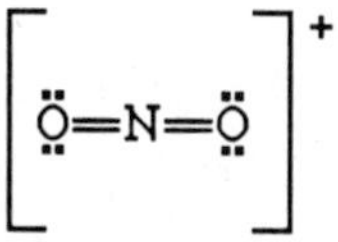 $\left[\overset{..}{\underset{..}{O}}=N=\overset{..}{\underset{..}{O}}\right]^+$

d. 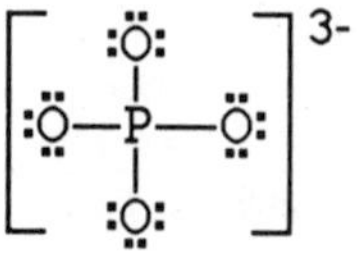 $\left[\overset{:\ddot{O}:}{\underset{:\underset{..}{O}:}{:\overset{..}{\underset{..}{O}}-P-\overset{..}{\underset{..}{O}}:}}\right]^{3-}$

e. 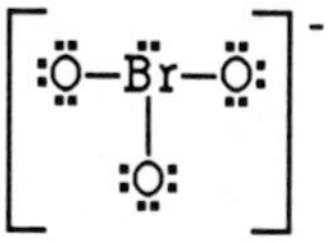 $\left[:\overset{..}{\underset{..}{O}}-\overset{|}{\underset{:\underset{..}{O}:}{Br}}-\overset{..}{\underset{..}{O}}:\right]^-$

18. Which of the following is a correct electron dot formula for $PO_2{}^{3-}$?

a. 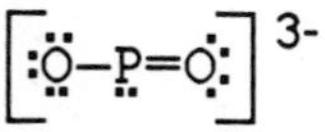 $\left[:\overset{..}{\underset{..}{O}}-\underset{..}{P}=\overset{..}{\underset{..}{O}}:\right]^{3-}$

b. 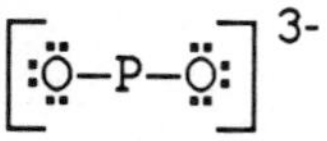 $\left[:\overset{..}{\underset{..}{O}}-P-\overset{..}{\underset{..}{O}}:\right]^{3-}$

c. 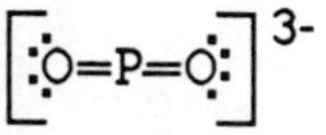 $\left[:\overset{..}{\underset{..}{O}}=P=\overset{..}{\underset{..}{O}}:\right]^{3-}$

d. 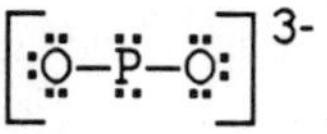 $\left[:\overset{..}{\underset{..}{O}}-\underset{..}{P}-\overset{..}{\underset{..}{O}}:\right]^{3-}$

e. 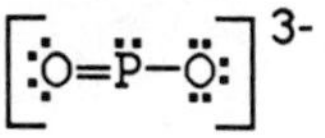 $\left[:\overset{..}{O}=\underset{..}{P}-\overset{..}{\underset{..}{O}}:\right]^{3-}$

19. The shape of PCl_3 is
    a. trigonal.
    b. a tetrahedron.
    c. bent.
    d. linear.
    e. a pyramid.

20. The shape of ClO_4^- is
    a. bent.
    b. linear.
    c. a tetrahedron.
    d. trigonal.
    e. a pyramid.

21. The shape of H_2Se is
    a. bent.
    b. linear.
    c. a tetrahedron.
    d. trigonal.
    e. a pyramid.

22. Which of the following bonds is the most polar?
    a. Be—B
    b. P—N
    c. Te—I
    d. Y—O
    e. H—C

23. Which of the following bonds is the least polar?
    a. S—F
    b. In—P
    c. B—C
    d. Na—Cl
    e. Cs—Br

24. Which of the following compounds is polar?
    a. BF_3
    b. H_2Te
    c. CBr_4
    d. CO_2
    e. N_2

25. Which of the following compounds is not polar?
    a. O_3
    b. SiO_2
    c. NCl_3
    d. OF_2
    e. KClO

Answers to the Sample Quiz Questions

1. (e), 2. (d), 3. (a), 4. (b), 5. (c), 6. (e), 7. (d), 8. (a), 9. (b), 10. (c), 11. (d), 12. (a), 13. (e), 14. (e), 15. (a), 16. (c), 17. (b), 18. (d), 19. (e), 20. (c), 21. (a), 22. (d), 23. (c), 24. (b), 25. (b)

NAMING INORGANIC COMPOUNDS

CHAPTER 7

Chapter Overview

As the title indicates, Chapter 7 is devoted to naming inorganic compounds. Oxidation numbers are covered early in the chapter to set the framework for naming these compounds. The compound types discussed are binary and polyatomic ionic compounds, binary molecular compounds, acids, and hydrates.

The chapter stresses the need to understand the historically developed common naming system since it is still encountered routinely in chemistry. It also fully discusses the modern systematic method of naming compounds and emphasizes its utility in yielding less ambiguous names.

Solutions to the Study Questions and Problems

1. **a. Oxidation numbers** are numbers assigned to an atom, whether uncombined, combined in a molecule, or in an ion that help keep track of bond formation and electron transfers between atoms.
    b. Peroxides are compounds in which oxygen has an oxidation number of -1 instead of the normal -2. In peroxides, an oxygen atom is bonded to another oxygen atom, forming the unit O_2^{2-}.

2. **a.** $AlBr_3$ **b.** BaO_2 **c.** $NiCl_2$ **d.** CaH_2 **e.** Co_2S_3
    +3 -1   +2 -1   +2 -1   +2 -1   +3 -2

3. **a.** HCO_3^- **b.** $S_2O_3^{2-}$ **c.** $C_2O_4^{2-}$ **d.** OH^- **e.** NH_4^+
    +1+4-2   +2 -2   +3 -2   -2 +1   -3 +1

4. **a.** $Rh_2(SO_4)_3$ **b.** $H_4P_2O_5$ **c.** $C_{12}H_{22}O_{11}$ **d.** $Po(IO_3)_4$ **e.** Cl_2O_7
    +3 +6 -2   +1 +3 -2   0 +1 -2   +4 +5-2   +7 -2

5. **a.** gallium iodide **b.** iron(II) sulfide **c.** mercury(I) oxide **d.** platinum(II) chloride

6. **a.** FeI_2 **b.** NaH **c.** ZrO_2 **d.** $BaTe$ **e.** HgF_2

7. **a.** ferrous fluoride **b.** cuprous sulfide **c.** plumbic chloride **d.** mercurous iodide **e.** stannic oxide

8. **a.** FeI_3 **b.** Cu_2O **c.** PbS_2 **d.** Hg_2S **e.** $SnBr_4$

9. **Oxyanions** are polyatomic ions that contain oxygen and one other element, usually a nonmetal. They are named according to the oxidation state of that element in the anion.

10. **a.** aluminum bisulfate **b.** calcium cyanide **c.** iron(III) hydrogen phosphate **d.** strontium iodate

11. **a.** $Ba(OH)_2$ **b.** $KHSO_3$ **c.** $In(ClO_4)_3$ **d.** $Pb(IO_3)_2$ **e.** $Cu(CN)_2$

12. **a.** diboron tetrabromide **b.** bromine trifluoride **c.** calcium diselenide **d.** hydrogen fluoride

13. **a.** XeO_4 **b.** S_4N_2 **c.** H_2S **d.** Si_2I_6 **e.** P_2Cl_4

14. **a.** hydrocyanic acid **b.** sulfuric acid **c.** acetic acid **d.** nitric acid **e.** hydrofluoric acid

15. **a.** H_2SO_3 **b.** H_2S **c.** HIO_4 **d.** oxalic acid **e.** H_2CrO_4

16. **a.** **Inorganic hydrates** are ionic compounds that contain a definite number of water molecules, relative to the number of ions, in their crystals. **b.** **Water of hydration** is the term applied to the water molecules contained in an inorganic hydrate. The waters of hydration can be removed from the crystal by heating.

17. **a.** magnesium chlorate hexahydrate **b.** iron(II) sulfate tetrahydrate **c.** bismuth(III) nitrate pentahydrate **d.** ammonium sulfite monohydrate

18. **a.** $Cd(NO_3)_2 \cdot 4H_2O$ **b.** $Au(CN)_3 \cdot 3H_2O$ **c.** $Pb(ClO_4)_4 \cdot 3H_2O$ **d.** $K_2CO_3 \cdot 2H_2O$ **e.** $Na_2HPO_4 \cdot 7H_2O$

19. **a.** $CaSO_4$ **b.** $Mg(OH)_2$ **c.** K_2SO_3 **d.** $Na_2S_2O_3$ **e.** $RbBrO_3$
       +2 +6-2   +2 -2 +1   +1+4-2   +1 +2 -2   +1 +5 -2

20. **a.** MnF_3 **b.** $Cr_2(SO_4)_3$ **c.** $KClO$ **d.** VBr_4 **e.** $Sr(BrO_3)_2$

21. **a.** potassium selenide **b.** zinc oxalate **c.** dinitrogen pentasulfide **d.** hydrogen chlorate (or, if assumed to be dissolved in water, chloric acid) **e.** gallium oxalate tetrahydrate

22. **a.** dichlorine heptoxide **b.** chromium(III) acetate monohydrate or chromic acetate monohydrate **c.** mercury(I) carbonate or mercurous carbonate **d.** hydrogen phosphate (or, if assumed to be dissolved in water, phosphoric acid) **e.** ammonium hydrogen sulfite or ammonium bisulfite

23. **a.** $PtBr_2$ **b.** $ReO_2 \cdot 2H_2O$ **c.** P_2Se_5 **d.** $HC_2H_3O_2$ **e.** $KHCO_3$ **f.** $Na_2S_2O_3 \cdot 5H_2O$

Sample Quiz Questions

1. Which set of oxidation numbers is correct?
    a. $HClO_4$
       +1 +5 -2
    b. H_2Te
       +1 -1
    c. SO_4^{2-}
       +3 -2
    d. NO_2
       +5 -2
    e. OF_2
       +2 -1

2. Which set of oxidation numbers is correct?
    a. $Co(CN)_3$
       +3 +2 -3
    b. $KMnO_4$
       +1 +7 -3
    c. MgS_2O_3
       +1 +3 -2
    d. $PbCr_2O_7$
       +4 +7 -2
    e. Cs_3PO_4
       +1 +3 -2

3. Name the compound AsI_3.
    a. arsenic iodate
    b. arsenous iodide
    c. arsenic iodide
    d. arsenic triiodide
    e. arsenic(V) iodide

4. Name the compound P_4O_{10}.
    a. phosphorus oxide
    b. decaoxygen tetraphosphide
    c. tetraphosphorus decaoxide
    d. phosphorus tetroxide
    e. potassium oxide

5. Which compound is dinitrogen pentoxide?
    a. NO_5
    b. N_2O
    c. N_5O_2
    d. NO
    e. N_2O_5

6. Which compound is boron trihydride?
    a. B_3H
    b. BH
    c. BH_3
    d. BeH_3
    e. BHe_3

7. Name the compound $Mg_3(PO_4)_2$.
    a. manganese phosphate
    b. magnesium(III) phosphate
    c. magnesium phosphite
    d. magnesium phosphate
    e. manganese phosphide

8. Name the compound $FeSO_3$.
    a. ferric sulfate
    b. ferrous sulfite
    c. ferric sulfite
    d. iron(II) sulfate
    e. iron(III) sulfide

9. Which of the following compounds is vanadium(V) nitrite?
    a. V_5NO_3
    b. V_3N_5
    c. VNO_2
    d. $V(NO_4)_5$
    e. $V(NO_2)_5$

10. Which of the following compounds is sodium perchlorate?
    a. $NaClO_4$
    b. $SClO_3$
    c. $NaClO_2$
    d. $NaClO$
    e. SCl_2

11. Name the compound $CuCl_2$.
    a. copper(I) chlorate
    b. cuprous chloride
    c. copper chloride
    d. cobalt(II) chlorite
    e. cupric chloride

12. Name the compound Al_2S_3.
    a. aluminum(II) sulfide
    b. aluminum sulfite
    c. aluminum sulfate
    d. aluminum sulfide
    e. aluminum sulfurate

13. Which of the following compounds is chromic oxide?
  a. CrO_3
  b. Cr_2O_3
  c. CrO_2
  d. Cr_3O_2
  e. CrO_4

14. Which of the following compounds is calcium nitride?
  a. Ca_2N_3
  b. CaN
  c. Ca_3N_2
  d. CaN_2
  e. $Ca(NO_3)_2$

15. Name the compound HIO_4.
  a. iodic acid
  b. hydrogen iodite
  c. iodous acid
  d. hydrogen iodate
  e. periodic acid

16. Name the compound NaH_2PO_4.
  a. sodium hydrogen phosphate
  b. sodium biphosphate
  c. sodium phosphite
  d. sodium dihydrogen phosphate
  e. sodium phosphoric acid

17. Name the compound H_2Se
  a. hydroselenic acid
  b. hydrogen selenate
  c. hydrogen hyposelenite
  d. hydrogen diselenide
  e. dihydrogen selenite

18. Which of the following compounds is hydroarsenic acid?
  a. HAs_3
  b. HAs
  c. H_3As
  d. ArH_2
  e. HA_2

19. Name the compound $Ba(NO_3)_2 \cdot 4H_2O$
  a. barium nitrite hydrate
  b. barium nitride trihydrate
  c. boron nitrate tetrahydrate
  d. barium nitrate tetrahydrate
  e. barium nitrate

20. Name the compound $CoCl_2 \cdot 5H_2O$.
 a. copper(II) chlorate pentahydrate
 b. cobalt(II) chloride pentahydrate
 c. cuprous chloride hydrate
 d. cobalt(II) chloride heptahydrate
 e. cobaltic chloride pentahydrate

21. Which of the following compounds is scandium oxide octahydrate?
 a. $ScO_2 \cdot 6H_2O$
 b. $SO_3 \cdot H_2O$
 c. $Sc_3O_2 \cdot 8H_2O$
 d. $Sc_2O \cdot 9H_2O$
 e. $Sc_2O_3 \cdot 8H_2O$

22. Which of the following compounds is ferric cyanide dihydrate?
 a. $Fe(CN)_3 \cdot 2H_2O$
 b. $Fe_2CN \cdot H_2O$
 c. $Fe(CN)_2 \cdot 2H_2O$
 d. $Fe_2(CN)_3 \cdot 3H_2O$
 e. $FeCN_3 \cdot 2H_2O$

Answers to the Sample Quiz Questions

1. (e), 2. (a), 3. (d), 4. (c), 5. (e), 6. (c), 7. (d), 8. (b), 9. (e), 10. (a), 11. (b), 12. (d), 13. (b), 14. (c), 15. (e), 16. (d), 17. (a), 18. (c), 19. (d), 20. (b), 21. (e), 22. (a)

CALCULATIONS BASED ON CHEMICAL FORMULAS

CHAPTER

8

Chapter Overview

Chapter 8 concentrates on the quantitative relationships <u>within</u> chemical formulas. The discussion begins with the concept of the chemical mole and the interrelationships of the number of moles, mass, and the numbers of molecules and atoms in a formula. This is followed by the definition of molar mass and its differentiation from formula weight.

After this expansion of chemical formulas from individual species to numbers of moles of species, the concept of the percentage composition of compounds is developed and is used to describe the experimental determination of chemical formulas, the empirical formula. The chapter closes with a discussion of calculating the true formula of a compound from the empirical formula and the actual molar mass of the compound.

As in other chapters, there are several margin notes giving mathematical tips on manipulating relevent variables and a section on working with ratios.

Solutions to the Study Questions and Problems

1. There are 6.02×10^{23} particles per mole. This value is called Avogadro's number, named for the Italian chemist Amedeo Avogadro.

2. Avogadro's number is not exact; it is expressed in the text to a precision of 3 significant figures and is rarely seen stated to more than 4 significant figures. The precision is limited because Avogadro's number is a measured quantity. Since it does represent a finite number of particles, much like a dozen or a gross, it should be a whole number (and, therefore, infinitely precise) but we lack the equipment to make measurements with sufficient precision to learn all the digits.

3. **a.** 9.62 moles • 6.02×10^{23} particles/mole = 5.79×10^{24} particles
   b. 4.07×10^{-4} moles • 6.02×10^{23} particles/mole = 2.45×10^{20} particles
   c. 1.93 moles • 6.02×10^{23} particles/mole = 1.16×10^{24} particles
   d. 25 moles • 6.02×10^{23} particles/mole = 1.5×10^{25} particles

4. **a.** $\dfrac{7.49 \times 10^{11} \text{ particles}}{6.02 \times 10^{23} \text{ particles/mole}}$ = 1.24×10^{-12} mole

  b. $\dfrac{9.21 \times 10^{32} \text{ particles}}{6.02 \times 10^{23} \text{ particles/mole}}$ = 1.53×10^{9} moles

  c. $\dfrac{1.05 \times 10^{6} \text{ particles}}{6.02 \times 10^{23} \text{ particles/mole}}$ = 1.74×10^{-18} mole

  d. $\dfrac{1 \text{ particle}}{6.02 \times 10^{23} \text{ particles/mole}}$ = 1.66×10^{-24} mole

5. The **molar mass** of a substance is the mass of one mole or 6.02×10^{23} particles of that substance. The value of the molar mass corresponds to the formula weight of the substance but has units of grams/mole rather than amu.

6. While one mole of an element has the same number of particles as one mole of any other element, they have different masses since the elements have different atomic weights, originating from the different number of nucleons.

7.

	Element	Weight (g)	Number of Moles	Number of Atoms
a.	Rb	14.9	0.174	1.05×10^{23}
b.	Kr	1.80×10^{-2}	2.14×10^{-4}	1.29×10^{20}
c.	N	17.2	1.23	7.40×10^{23}
d.	Cr	3.53×10^{17}	6.78×10^{15}	4.08×10^{39}
e.	S	40.5	1.26	7.59×10^{23}
f.	Mo	754.	7.86	4.73×10^{24}

8.

	Compound	Number of Molecules	Number of Atoms		
a.	NO_2	1.20×10^{24}	N: 1.20×10^{24}	O: 2.40×10^{24}	
b.	PCl_3	1.20×10^{24}	P: 1.20×10^{24}	Cl: 3.60×10^{24}	
c.	$HC_2H_3O_2$	1.20×10^{24}	H: 4.80×10^{24}	C: 2.40×10^{24}	O: 2.40×10^{24}

9.

	Compound	Number of Cations	Number of Anions
a.	$Na_2Cr_2O_7$	4.21×10^{24}	2.11×10^{24}
b.	HgC_2O_4	2.11×10^{24}	2.11×10^{24}
c.	K_2SO_4	4.21×10^{24}	2.11×10^{24}

10. a. For NO_2: 1(14.0 g/mole) + 2(16.0 g/mole) = 46.0 g/mole
   b. For PCl_3: 1(31.0 g/mole) + 3(35.5 g/mole) = 137.5 g/mole
   c. For $HC_2H_3O_2$: 4(1.0 g/mole) + 2(12.0 g/mole) + 2(16.0 g/mole) = 60.0 g/mole

11. a. For $Na_2Cr_2O_7$: 2(23.0 g/mole) + 2(52.0 g/mole) + 7(16.0 g/mole) = 262.0 g/mole
   b. For HgC_2O_4: 1(200.6 g/mole) + 2(12.0 g/mole) + 4(16.0 g/mole) = 288.6 g/mole
   c. For K_2SO_4: 2(39.1 g/mole) + 1(32.1 g/mole) + 4(16.0 g/mole) = 174.3 g/mole

12. The molar mass of $MgSO_4 \cdot 7H_2O$ is: $1(24.3 \text{ g/mole}) + 1(32.1 \text{ g/mole}) + 11(16.0 \text{ g/mole}$
$$+ 14(1.0 \text{ g/mole}) = 246.4 \text{ g/mole}$$

In 32.6 grams of epsom salts, there is $\dfrac{32.6 \text{ g}}{246.4 \text{ g/mole}} = 0.132$ mole of $MgSO_4 \cdot 7H_2O$.

Therefore:

1 cation/formula unit $\cdot$ 6.02 x 10^{23} formula units/mole $\cdot$ 0.132 mole = 7.95 x 10^{22} cations

1 anion/formula unit $\cdot$ 6.02 x 10^{23} formula units/mole $\cdot$ 0.132 mole = 7.95 x 10^{22} anions

7 waters/formula unit $\cdot$ 6.02 x 10^{23} formula units/mole $\cdot$ 0.132 mole = 5.56 x 10^{23} waters

13. The molar mass of NaOH is: $1(23.0 \text{ g/mole}) + 1(16.0 \text{ g/mole}) + 1(1.0 \text{ g/mole}) = 40.0 \text{ g/mole}$

In 1.93 x 10^{-3} grams of lye, there is $\dfrac{1.93 \text{ x } 10^{-3} \text{ g}}{40.0 \text{ g/mole}} = 4.82$ x 10^{-5} mole of NaOH.

Therefore:

1 cation/formula unit $\cdot$ 6.02 x 10^{23} formula units/mole $\cdot$ 4.82 x 10^{-5} mole =
$$2.90 \text{ x } 10^{19} \text{ cations}$$

1 anion/formula unit $\cdot$ 6.02 x 10^{23} formula units/mole $\cdot$ 4.82 x 10^{-5} mole =
$$2.90 \text{ x } 10^{19} \text{ anions}$$

14. The molar mass of O_3 is: $3(16.0 \text{ g/mole}) = 48.0 \text{ g/mole}$

Therefore:

$\dfrac{(\ 9.42 \text{ g}\ )(6.02 \text{ x } 10^{23} \text{ molecules/mole})}{(48.0 \text{ g/mole})} = 1.18$ x 10^{23} molecules

15. The molar mass of NaClO is $1(23.0 \text{ g/mole}) + 1(35.5 \text{ g/mole}) + 1(16.0 \text{ g/mole}) = 74.5 \text{ g/mole}$

Therefore:

$\dfrac{(\ 6.57 \text{ x } 10^{17} \text{ formula units}\ )(74.5 \text{ g/mole})}{(6.02 \text{ x } 10^{23} \text{ formula units/mole})} = 8.13$ x 10^{-5} grams NaClO

16.

Compound	Weight (g)	Number of Moles	Number of Molecules or Formula Units
a. $SbBr_3$	8.97 x 10^{24}	2.48 x 10^{22}	1.49 x 10^{46}
b. $Cd(C_2H_3O_2)_2$	24.7	0.107	6.45 x 10^{22}
c. ISO_3F	3209.2	14.9	8.55 x 10^{24}
d. $LiMnO_4$	2.66 x 10^{-5}	2.11 x 10^{-7}	1.27 x 10^{17}
e. $MgCO_3 \cdot 5H_2O$	0.753	4.32 x 10^{-3}	2.60 x 10^{21}
f. $Rb_2Cr_2O_7$	6.42 x 10^{-5}	1.66 x 10^{-7}	9.98 x 10^{16}

17. a. Elemental analysis involves decomposing a compound and finding the percentage of each element in the compound. **b.** An **empirical formula** is the simplest whole number ratio of ions or atoms in a compound. **c.** The **apparent molar mass** is the molar mass calculated from the empirical formula. **d.** The **actual molar mass** is the molar mass of a compound determined experimentally for the actual molecule. **e.** The **true formula** is the formula of a compound which gives the actual number of ions or atoms present in a formula unit of the compound.

18. Several different compounds can have the same empirical formula because the empirical formula only gives the relative numbers of each element present in the compound, not the actual numbers of each. For example, the compounds C_2H_2, C_4H_4, and C_6H_6 all have the same empirical formula, CH, since all contain carbon and hydrogen in a 1:1 ratio.

19. Yes, the actual molar mass can be the same as the apparent molar mass. This will occur if the true formula is the same as the empirical formula.

20. No. The true formula can have more atoms or ions than the empirical formula but never less since, by its definition, the empirical formula is the smallest ratio of of atoms or ions in a compound.

21. For isooctane:

% By Weight	Mass in 100. g	Moles	Relative Moles
C 84.2	84.2	84.2/12.0 = 7.02	7.02/7.02 = 1.00
H 15.8	15.8	15.8/1.0 = 15.8	15.8/7.02 = 2.25

To remove the decimal, it is apparent that $\dfrac{1.00}{2.25} = \dfrac{4}{9}$

Therefore, the empirical formula is C_4H_9.

22. For Lindane:

% By Weight	Mass in 100. g	Moles	Relative Moles
C 24.7	24.7	24.7/12.0 = 2.06	7.02/2.06 = 1.00
H 2.06	2.06	2.06/1.0 = 2.06	2.06/2.06 = 1.00
Cl 73.2	73.2	73.2/35.5 = 2.06	2.06/2.06 = 1.00

Therefore, the empirical formula is CHCl.

23. For this compound, masses are given so there is no need to assume a 100 gram sample:

Mass (g)	Moles	Relative Moles
Bi 2.81	2.81/209.0 = 0.0134	0.0134/0.0134 = 1.00
P 0.417	0.417/31.0 = 0.0135	0.0135/0.0134 = 1.01
O 0.863	0.863/16.0 = 0.0539	0.0539/0.0134 = 4.02

Therefore, the empirical formula is $BiPO_4$.

24. For this compound:

% By Weight	Mass in 100. g	Moles	Relative Moles
N 14.9	14.9	14.9/14.0 = 1.06	1.06/1.06 = 1.00
S 85.1	85.1	85.1/32.1 = 2.65	2.65/1.06 = 2.50

To remove the decimal, it is apparent that $\dfrac{1.00}{2.50} = \dfrac{2}{5}$

Therefore, the empirical formula is N_2S_5.

25. For this compound, the fact that 3.04 g of magnesium combined with 2.00 g of oxygen gives the relative masses of the two elements directly:

Mass (g)	Moles	Relative Moles
Mg 3.04	3.04/24.3 = 0.125	0.125/0.125 = 1.00
O 2.00	2.00/16.0 = 0.125	0.125/0.125 = 1.00

Therefore, the empirical formula is MgO.

26. For cyclopropane:

% By Weight	Mass in 100. g	Moles	Relative Moles
C 85.7	85.7	85.7/12.0 = 7.14	7.14/7.14 = 1.00
H 14.3	14.3	14.3/1.0 = 14.3	14.3/7.14 = 2.00

Therefore, the empirical formula is CH_2 and the apparent molar mass is:

1(12.0 g/mole) + 2(1.0 g/mole) = 14.0 g/mole.

Since the actual molar mass is 42.0 g/mole, the true formula of the compound contains:

42.0/14.0 = 3.00 empirical formula units.

Therefore, the true formula of cyclopropane is C_3H_6.

27. For hydrazine:

% By Weight	Mass in 100. g	Moles	Relative Moles
N 87.5	87.5	87.5/14.0 = 6.25	6.25/6.25 = 1.00
H 12.5	12.5	12.5/1.0 = 12.5	12.5/6.25 = 2.00

Therefore, the empirical formula is NH_2 and the apparent molar mass is:

1(14.0 g/mole) + 2(1.0 g/mole) = 16.0 g/mole.

Since the actual molar mass is 32.0 g/mole, the true formula of the compound contains:

32.0/16.0 = 2.00 empirical formula units.

Therefore, the true formula of hydrazine is N_2H_4.

28. For butyric acid:

% By Weight	Mass in 100. g	Moles	Relative Moles
C 54.5	54.5	54.5/12.0 = 4.54	4.54/2.28 = 1.99
H 9.09	9.09	9.09/1.0 = 9.09	9.09/2.28 = 3.99
O 36.4	36.4	36.4/16.0 = 2.28	2.28/2.28 = 1.00

Therefore, the empirical formula is C_2H_4O and the apparent molar mass is:

$$2(12.0 \text{ g/mole}) + 4(1.0 \text{ g/mole}) + 1(16.0 \text{ g/mole}) = 44.0 \text{ g/mole.}$$

Since the actual molar mass is 88.0 g/mole, the true formula of the compound contains:

$$88.0/44.0 = 2.00 \text{ empirical formula units.}$$

Therefore, the true formula of butyric acid is $C_4H_8O_2$.

29.

	Compound	Number of Molecules		Number of Atoms		
a.	$XeOF_4$	2.56×10^{24}	Xe: 2.56×10^{24}	O: 2.56×10^{24}	F: 1.02×10^{25}	
b.	C_2H_6	2.56×10^{24}	C: 5.12×10^{24}	H: 1.54×10^{25}		
c.	$PSBr_2Cl$	2.56×10^{24}	P: 2.56×10^{24}	S: 2.56×10^{24}	Br: 5.12×10^{24}	
				Cl: 2.56×10^{24}		

30.

	Compound	Number of Cations	Number of Anions
a.	$AlCl_3$	3.37×10^{24}	1.01×10^{25}
b.	$Mg(HSO_3)_2$	3.37×10^{24}	6.74×10^{24}
c.	$Ba_3(PO_4)_2$	1.01×10^{25}	6.74×10^{24}

31. The molar mass of N_2O is: $2(14.0 \text{ g/mole}) + 1(16.0 \text{ g/mole}) = 44.0 \text{ g/mole}$

$$\frac{(4.92 \times 10^{52} \text{ molecules})(44.0 \text{ g/mole})}{(6.02 \times 10^{23} \text{ molecules/mole})} = 3.60 \times 10^{30} \text{ grams}$$

32. For freon:

% By Weight	Mass in 100. g	Moles	Relative Moles
C 8.73	8.73	8.73/12.0 = 0.728	0.728/0.726 = 1.00
Cl 77.5	77.5	77.5/35.5 = 2.18	2.18/0.726 = 3.00
F 13.8	13.8	13.8/19.0 = 0.726	0.726/0.726 = 1.00

Therefore, the empirical formula of freon is CCl_3F.

33. For the compound, the products show that the numbers of moles of carbon and hydrogen in the compound sample are:

Carbon: The molar mass of CO_2 is $1(12.0 \text{ g/mole}) + 2(16.0 \text{ g/mole}) = 44.0 \text{ g/mole}$

$$\frac{(\quad 13.2 \text{ g } CO_2 \quad)}{(44.0 \text{ g } CO_2/\text{mole } CO_2)}\frac{(1 \text{ mole C })}{(1 \text{ mole } CO_2)} = 0.300 \text{ mole C}$$

Hydrogen: The molar mass of H_2O is $2(1.0 \text{ g/mole}) + 1(16.0 \text{ g/mole}) = 18.0 \text{ g/mole}$

$$\frac{(\quad 10.8 \text{ g } H_2O \quad)}{(18.0 \text{ g } H_2O/\text{mole } H_2O)}\frac{(2 \text{ mole H })}{(1 \text{ mole } H_2O)} = 1.20 \text{ mole H}$$

Then: $\dfrac{1.20 \text{ mole H}}{0.300 \text{ mole C}} = \dfrac{4 \text{ mole H}}{1 \text{ mole C}}$

Therefore, the empirical formula is CH_4.

34. Of the 17.77 grams of oxide formed, $17.77 - 10.00 = 7.77$ grams of it is oxygen.

Then:

Mass (g)	Moles	Relative Moles
P 10.00	$10.00/31.0 = 0.323$	$0.323/0.323 = 1.00$
O 7.77	$7.77/16.0 = 0.486$	$0.486/0.323 = 1.50$

Since $\dfrac{1.50 \text{ mole O}}{1.00 \text{ mole P}} = \dfrac{3 \text{ mole O}}{2 \text{ mole P}}$

the empirical formula is P_2O_3 and the apparent molar mass is

$$2(31.0 \text{ g/mole}) + 3(16.0 \text{ g/mole}) = 110 \text{ g.}$$

The actual molar mass is 220 g/mole, so there are $220/110 = 2$ empirical formula units in the actual formula.

Therefore, the actual formula is P_4O_6.

Sample Quiz Questions

1.   A chemical mole
       a. is the number of ions in one formula unit of an ionic compound.
       b. is a fundamental chemical property.
       c. has the same mass as a molecule.
       d. applies only to molecular compounds.
       e. is a specific number of particles.

2. Give the number of moles represented by the quantity 7.73×10^{15} particles.
    a. 7.79×10^7 moles.
    b. 4.65×10^{39} moles.
    c. 1.28×10^{-8} mole.
    d. 1.28×10^{15} moles.
    e. 2.15×10^{-40} mole.

3. The molar mass of a substance
    a. is the mass of one mole of the substance expressed in amu.
    b. is the mass of one mole of the substance expressed in grams.
    c. is an exact quantity.
    d. is the mass of a sample of the substance expressed in moles.
    e. is the same as its formula weight.

4. The molar mass of $K_3Fe(CN)_6$ is
    a. 120.9 g/mole.
    b. 199.1 g/mole.
    c. 259.1 g/mole.
    d. 329.1 g/mole.
    e. 250.9 g/mole.

5. How many atoms are there in 1.82 moles of H_2SO_4?
    a. 3.31×10^{23} atoms.
    b. 2.31×10^{24} atoms.
    c. 1.10×10^{24} atoms.
    d. 4.71×10^{22} atoms.
    e. 7.70×10^{24} atoms.

6. How many moles of N and O are represented by 9.06×10^{21} molecules of N_2O_4?
    a. 3.00×10^{-2} mole N; 6.00×10^{-2} mole O.
    b. 1.50×10^{-2} mole N; 3.00×10^{-2} mole O.
    c. 3.00×10^{-2} mole N; 3.00×10^{-2} mole O.
    d. 1.50×10^{-2} mole N; 1.50×10^{-2} mole O.
    e. 6.00×10^{-2} mole N; 3.00×10^{-2} mole O.

7. How many grams are there in 1.38 moles of ICl_5?
    a. 304 grams
    b. 162 grams.
    c. 4.20×10^2 grams.
    d. 224 grams.
    e. 221 grams.

8. What is the mass of 9.85×10^{27} formula units of $KClO_4$?
    a. 2.28×10^6 grams.
    b. 6.10×10^{-5} gram.
    c. 1.64×10^4 grams.
    d. 8.48×10^{-3} gram.
    e. 139 grams.

9. What is the mass of 6.77 moles of Rb_3PO_4?
    a. 352 grams.
    b. 52.0 grams.
    c. 2380 grams.
    d. 181 grams.
    e. 1230 grams.

10. How many moles of Na_2O_2 are there in 155 grams of the substance?
    a. 78.0 moles.
    b. 3.97 moles.
    c. 12100 moles.
    d. 1.99 moles.
    e. 0.503 mole.

11. Give the number of cations and the number of anions present in 5.00 moles of H_2CrO_4.
    a. 6.02×10^{24} H^+; 3.01×10^{24} Cr^{6+}; 1.20×10^{25} O^{2-}.
    b. 6.02×10^{24} H^+; 3.01×10^{24} CrO_4^{2-}.
    c. 3.01×10^{24} H^+; 6.02×10^{24} CrO_4^{2-}.
    d. 6.02×10^{24} H^+; 6.02×10^{24} CrO_4^{2-}.
    e. 3.01×10^{24} H^+; 3.01×10^{24} CrO_4^{2-}.

12. How many molecules are there in 98.5 grams of $CoCl_2$?
    a. 6.28×10^{23} molecules.
    b. 5.93×10^{25} molecules.
    c. 0.758 molecules.
    d. 4.56×10^{23} molecules.
    e. 6.02×10^{23} molecules.

13. A compound is found to be 39.8% copper, 20.1% sulfur, and 40.1% oxygen. What is the compound's empirical formula?
    a. $CuSO_3$.
    b. $CuSO_4$.
    c. CuS_2O_3.
    d. Cu_2SO_2.
    e. Cu_2SO_4.

14. A sugar is found to be 40.2% carbon, 6.15% hydrogen, and 53.6% oxygen. What is the empirical formula of the sugar?
    a. $C_3H_5O_3$.
    b. C_7HO_9.
    c. CH_2O.
    d. CH_2O_2.
    e. $C_6H_{11}O_6$.

15. A compound has the composition 80.4% silver, 7.70% phosphorus, and 11.9% oxygen. What is the empirical formula of the compound?
     a. Ag_3PO_3.
     b. Ag_3PO_4.
     c. $Ag_{20}P_2O_3$.
     d. $AgPO$.
     e. Ag_8PO.

16. A compound is found to be 16.2% K, 39.8% Ir, and 44.1% Cl. What is the empirical formula of this compound?
     a. KIr_2Cl_3.
     b. $KIrCl_3$.
     c. $KIrCl_6$.
     d. K_2IrCl_6.
     e. KIr_2Cl_2.

17. A compound is found to be 9.86% Mg, 13.0% S, 5.68% H, and 71.4% O. What is the empirical formula of this compound?
     a. $MgSH_{14}O_{11}$.
     b. $MgSH_6O_5$.
     c. $Mg_{10}S_{13}H_6O_{71}$.
     d. $Mg_2S_2HO_{12}$.
     e. $MgSH_{10}O_5$.

18. A compound is found to be 69.6% sulfur and 30.4% nitrogen. The actual molar mass is known to be 184.4 g/mole. What is the true formula of the compound?
     a. SN.
     b. S_2N.
     c. S_2N_2.
     d. S_4N_2.
     e. S_4N_4.

19. A compound is found to be 47.1% carbon, 6.54% hydrogen, and 46.4% chlorine. The actual molar mass is 153.0 g/mole. What is the true formula of the compound?
     a. C_4H_6Cl.
     b. $C_6H_{10}Cl_2$.
     c. $C_4H_{10}Cl_3$.
     d. C_4H_7Cl.
     e. C_3H_5Cl.

20. A compound is found to be 30.7% carbon, 1.28% hydrogen, and 68.1% bromine. The actual molar mass is 469.6 g/mole. What is the true formula of the compound?
     a. $C_6H_3Br_2$.
     b. $C_{12}H_5Br_5$.
     c. $C_{12}H_6Br_4$.
     d. $C_{18}H_6Br_3$.
     e. $C_6H_6Br_5$.

Answers to the Sample Quiz Questions

1. (e), 2. (c), 3. (b), 4. (d), 5. (e), 6. (a), 7. (c), 8. (a), 9. (c), 10. (d), 11. (b), 12. (d), 13. (b), 14. (e), 15. (a), 16. (d), 17. (a), 18. (e), 19. (b), 20. (c)

CHEMICAL EQUATIONS

CHAPTER
9

Chapter Overview

Chapter 9 covers the qualitative and quantitative features of chemical equations. The use of equations to describe chemical reactions is discussed as a shorthand notation which can remove much of the ambiguity which can plague word descriptions of reactions. The Law of Conservation of Mass is used to introduce balancing chemical equations. Several types of common chemical reactions are presented next with an emphasis on predicting the products of these reactions and as further practice on balancing them.

The chapter then turns to the area of stoichiometry where the idea of conservation finds its application. The various stoichiometric relationships are discussed: mole-mole, mole-weight, and weight-weight. This is followed by discussions of the more general situations of percentage yield and limiting reactants.

Given the calculation intensive nature of the material, there are several margin notes which present math tips and a section which discusses the methods used in combining sequential steps into a single computation.

Solutions to the Study Questions and Problems

1. **a. Chemical equations** are concise, unambiguous descriptions of chemical reactions using symbols for elements and formulas for compounds rather than words. **b. A reactant** is a chemical substance which is consumed in a reaction. Reactants are usually placed on the left side of an equation. **c. A product** is a chemical substance which is produced in a reaction. Products are usually placed on the right side of an equation. **d. A coefficient** is a number placed in front of the formula of a chemical specie in a balanced chemical equation which shows the smallest number of formula units of the substance that can participate in the reaction.

2. **a.** The notation (s) or ↓ means that the substance it follows is a solid. **b.** The notation (l) means that the substance it follows is a liquid. **c.** The notation (g) or ↑ means that the substance it follows is a gas. **d.** The notation Δ means that heat is applied to the reaction. **e.** The notation (aq) means that the substance it follows is dissolved in water.

89

3. **a.** An atom of solid magnesium reacts with two molecules of gaseous hydrogen chloride to yield one formula unit of solid magnesium chloride and one molecule of gaseous hydrogen. **b.** One molecule of gaseous hydrogen chloride reacts with one molecule of gaseous ammonia to yield one formula unit of solid ammonium chloride. **c.** Two formula units of aqueous potassium bromide react with one molecule of gaseous chlorine to yield two formula units of aqueous potassium chloride and one molecule of liquid bromine. **d.** One formula unit of aqueous sulfuric acid reacts with two formula units of solid sodium cyanide to yield two molecules of gaseous hydrogen cyanide and one formula unit of aqueous sodium sulfate.

4. The term **combustion** refers to a type of reaction which is defined to be the reaction of a compound of carbon and hydrogen with gaseous oxygen to yield gaseous carbon dioxide and gaseous water.

5. To conserve mass:

$$\text{mass of } S_8 + \text{mass of } O_2 = \text{mass of } SO_2$$
$$\text{mass of } O_2 = \text{mass of } SO_2 - \text{mass of } S_8$$
$$\text{mass of } O_2 = 17.0 \text{ g} - 8.50 \text{ g}$$
$$\text{mass of } O_2 = 8.5 \text{ g}$$

6. To conserve mass:

$$\text{mass of } KNO_3 = \text{mass of } KNO_2 + \text{mass of } O_2$$
$$\text{mass of } O_2 = \text{mass of } KNO_3 - \text{mass of } KNO_2$$
$$\text{mass of } O_2 = 15.2 \text{ g} - 12.8 \text{ g}$$
$$\text{mass of } O_2 = 2.4 \text{ g}$$

7. To conserve mass:

$$\text{mass of } MgSO_4 \cdot 7H_2O = \text{mass of } MgSO_4 + \text{mass of } H_2O$$
$$\text{mass of } MgSO_4 \cdot 7H_2O = 12.0 \text{ g} + 12.6 \text{ g}$$
$$\text{mass of } MgSO_4 \cdot 7H_2O = 24.6 \text{ g}$$

8. **a.** $2 \, CH_4O_{(l)} + 3 \, O_{2(g)} \rightarrow 2 \, CO_{2(g)} + 4 \, H_2O_{(g)}$

    b. $2 \, Ag_2O_{(s)} \rightarrow 4 \, Ag_{(s)} + O_{2(g)}$

    c. $2 \, NH_4OH_{(aq)} + H_2SO_{4(aq)} \rightarrow (NH_4)_2SO_{4(aq)} + 2 \, H_2O_{(l)}$

    d. $VO_{(s)} + Fe_2O_{3(s)} \rightarrow FeO_{(s)} + V_2O_{5(s)}$

    e. $2 \, C_4H_{10(g)} + 13 \, O_{2(g)} \rightarrow 8 \, CO_{2(g)} + 10 \, H_2O_{(g)}$

    f. $CaBr_{2(aq)} + H_2SO_{4(aq)} \rightarrow CaSO_{4(s)} + 2 \, HBr_{(g)}$

9. **a.** $2 \, B_2O_{3(s)} + 7 \, C_{(s)} \rightarrow B_4C_{(s)} + 6 \, CO_{(g)}$

    b. $CaC_{2(s)} + 2 \, H_2O_{(l)} \rightarrow Ca(OH)_{2(s)} + C_2H_{2(g)}$

    c. $Ba(NO_3)_{2(aq)} + H_2SO_{4(aq)} \rightarrow BaSO_{4(s)} + 2 \, HNO_{3(aq)}$

    d. $4 \, Bi_{(s)} + 3 \, O_{2(g)} \rightarrow 2 \, Bi_2O_{3(s)}$

    e. $(NH_4)_2Cr_2O_{7(s)} \rightarrow N_{2(g)} + 4 \, H_2O_{(g)} + Cr_2O_{3(s)}$

10. From Question 8: **a.** This is a double replacement reaction since hydrogen is passed from carbon to oxygen and additional oxygen is passed to carbon. **b.** This is a decomposition reaction since a molecule is broken into the elements. **c.** This is a double replacement reaction since the ions change partners. **f.** This is a double replacement reaction since the ions change partners.

11. From Question 9: **b.** This is a double replacement reaction since calcium passes carbide to hydrogen and hydrogen passes hydroxide to calcium. **c.** This is a double replacement reaction since the ions change partners. **d.** This is a combination reaction since a molecule is made from the elements. **e.** This is a decomposition reaction since a large molecule is broken into smaller ones.

12. a. $Ni(NO_3)_2 + 2\,NaOH \rightarrow \underline{Ni(OH)_2 + 2\,NaNO_3}$

b. $3\,KOH + H_3PO_4 \rightarrow \underline{K_3PO_4 + 3\,H_2O}$

c. $Ba(OH)_2 + 2\,HCl \rightarrow \underline{BaCl_2 + 2\,H_2O}$

d. $KCN + HCl \rightarrow \underline{HCN + KCl}$

13. a. $2\,PbO_{2(s)} \rightarrow 2\,\underline{Pb}_{(l)} + 2\,O_{2(g)}$

b. $Cl_{2(g)} + 2\,\underline{KI}_{(aq)} \rightarrow I_{2(s)} + 2\,KCl_{(s)}$

c. $\underline{CuO}_{(s)} + 2\,HNO_{3(aq)} \rightarrow Cu(NO_3)_{2(aq)} + H_2O_{(l)}$

d. $\underline{SO}_{3(g)} + H_2O_{(l)} \rightarrow H_2SO_{4(l)}$

e. $Fe_{(s)} + \underline{CuSO}_{4(aq)} \rightarrow Cu_{(s)} + FeSO_{4(aq)}$

f. $2\,\underline{HCl}_{(aq)} + Zn_{(s)} \rightarrow ZnCl_{2(aq)} + H_{2(g)}$

14. For: $CdSO_{4(aq)} + 2\,NaOH_{(aq)} \rightarrow Cd(OH)_{2(s)} + Na_2SO_{4(aq)}$

a. 1 mole Na_2SO_4/1 mole $CdSO_4$ **b.** 1 mole $CdSO_4$/2 moles NaOH **c.** 1 mole $Cd(OH)_2$/2 moles NaOH **d.** 1 mole Na_2SO_4/2 moles NaOH **e.** 2 moles NaOH/1 mole $CdSO_4$ **f.** 1 mole $Cd(OH)_2$/1 mole $CdSO_4$

15. For: $3\,Fe(s) + 4\,H_2O_{(l)} \rightarrow Fe_3O_{4(s)} + 4\,H_{2(g)}$

a. 1 mole Fe_3O_4/3 moles Fe **b.** 4 moles H_2O/3 moles Fe **c.** 4 moles H_2/1 mole Fe_3O_4 **d.** 1 mole Fe_3O_4/4 moles H_2O **e.** 1 mole Fe_3O_4/4 moles H_2 **f.** 4 moles H_2/3 moles Fe

16. For: $3\,KOH_{(aq)} + H_3PO_{4(aq)} \rightarrow K_3PO_{4(aq)} + 3\,H_2O_{(l)}$

a. $\dfrac{(2.15 \text{ moles KOH})(1 \text{ mole } H_3PO_4)}{(3 \text{ moles KOH})} = 0.717$ moles H_3PO_4

b. $\dfrac{(17.8 \text{ g } H_3PO_4)(1 \text{ mole } H_3PO_4)(1 \text{ mole } K_3PO_4)(212.3 \text{ g } K_3PO_4)}{(98.0 \text{ g } H_3PO_4)(1 \text{ mole } H_3PO_4)(1 \text{ mole } K_3PO_4)} = 38.6$ g K_3PO_4

c. $\dfrac{(24.6 \text{ g } H_3PO_4)(1 \text{ mole } H_3PO_4)(3 \text{ moles KOH})}{(98.0 \text{ g } H_3PO_4)(1 \text{ mole } H_3PO_4)} = 0.753$ mole KOH

d. $\dfrac{(34.7 \text{ g } K_3PO_4)(1 \text{ mole } K_3PO_4)(3 \text{ moles } H_2O)(18.0 \text{ g } H_2O)}{(212.3 \text{ g } K_3PO_4)(1 \text{ mole } K_3PO_4)(1 \text{ mole } H_2O)} = 8.83$ g H_2O

17. For: $P_{4(s)} + 5\,O_{2(g)} \rightarrow 2\,P_2O_{5(s)}$

$$\frac{(3.10\text{ g P}_4)(1\text{ mole P}_4)(5\text{ moles O}_2)(32.0\text{ g O}_2)}{(124.0\text{ g P}_4)(1\text{ mole P}_4)(1\text{ mole O}_2)} = 4.00\text{ g O}_2$$

18. For: $2\,KClO_{3(s)} \rightarrow 2\,KCl_{(s)} + 3\,O_{2(g)}$

$$\frac{(0.96\text{ g O}_2)(1\text{ mole O}_2)(2\text{ moles KClO}_3)(122.6\text{ g KClO}_3)}{(32.0\text{ g O}_2)(3\text{ moles O}_2)(1\text{ mole KClO}_3)} = 2.5\text{ g KClO}_3$$

19. For: $2\,NaCl_{(s)} + H_2SO_{4(aq)} \rightarrow Na_2SO_{4(aq)} + 2\,HCl_{(g)}$

$$\frac{(234\text{ g NaCl})(1\text{ mole NaCl})(2\text{ mole HCl})(36.5\text{ g HCl})}{(58.5\text{ g NaCl})(2\text{ mole NaCl})(1\text{ mole HCl})} = 146\text{ g HCl}$$

20. For: $AgNO_{3(aq)} + NaBr_{(aq)} \rightarrow AgBr_{(s)} + NaNO_{3(aq)}$

$$\frac{(93.3\text{ g AgBr})(1\text{ mole AgBr})(1\text{ mole AgNO}_3)(169.9\text{ g AgNO}_3)}{(187.8\text{ g AgBr})(1\text{ mole AgBr})(1\text{ mole AgNO}_3)} = 84.4\text{ g AgNO}_3$$

$$\frac{(93.3\text{ g AgBr})(1\text{ mole AgBr})(1\text{ mole NaBr})(102.9\text{ g NaBr})}{(187.8\text{ g AgBr})(1\text{ mole AgBr})(1\text{ mole NaBr})} = 51.1\text{ g NaBr}$$

21. For: $KHC_4H_4O_{6(aq)} + NaHCO_{3(aq)} \rightarrow KNaC_4H_4O_{6(aq)} + H_2O_{(l)} + CO_{2(g)}$

$$\frac{(50.0\text{ g KHC}_4H_4O_6)(1\text{ mole KHC}_4H_4O_6)(1\text{ mole NaHCO}_3)(84.0\text{ g NaHCO}_3)}{(188.1\text{ g KHC}_4H_4O_6)(1\text{ mole KHC}_4H_4O_6)(1\text{ mole NaHCO}_3)}$$

$$= 22.3\text{ g NaHCO}_3$$

22. a. The equation is: $2\,Mg_{(s)} + O_{2(g)} \rightarrow 2\,MgO_{(s)}$

b. $\dfrac{(0.32\text{ g Mg})(1\text{ mole Mg})(1\text{ mole O}_2)}{(24.3\text{ g Mg})(2\text{ moles Mg})} = 0.0066\text{ moles O}_2$

c. $\dfrac{(0.0066\text{ moles O}_2)(32.0\text{ g O}_2)}{(1\text{ mole O}_2)} = 0.21\text{ g O}_2$

23. The equation is: $2\,Na_{(s)} + 2\,H_2O_{(l)} \rightarrow 2\,NaOH_{(aq)} + H_{2(g)}$

$$\frac{(15.0\text{ g Na})(1\text{ mole Na})(1\text{ mole H}_2)(2.0\text{ g H}_2)}{(23.0\text{ g Na})(2\text{ moles Na})(1\text{ mole H}_2)} = 0.65\text{ g H}_2$$

24. The equation is: $2 C_2H_{2(g)} + 5 O_{2(g)} \rightarrow 4 CO_{2(g)} + 2 H_2O_{(g)}$

$\dfrac{(104 \text{ g } C_2H_2)(1 \text{ mole } C_2H_2)(4 \text{ moles } CO_2)}{(26.0 \text{ g } C_2H_2)(2 \text{ moles } C_2H_2)} = 8.00 \text{ moles } CO_2$

$\dfrac{(104 \text{ g } C_2H_2)(1 \text{ mole } C_2H_2)(2 \text{ moles } H_2O)}{(26.0 \text{ g } C_2H_2)(2 \text{ moles } C_2H_2)} = 4.00 \text{ moles } H_2O$

25. The equation is: $16 Al_{(s)} + 3 S_{8(s)} \rightarrow 8 Al_2S_{3(s)}$

$\dfrac{(600.0 \text{ g } Al_2S_3)(1 \text{ mole } Al_2S_3)(16 \text{ moles } Al)(27.0 \text{ g } Al)}{(150.3 \text{ g } Al_2S_3)(8 \text{ mole } Al_2S_3)(1 \text{ mole } Al)} = 216 \text{ g } Al$

26. The equation is: $2 NaNO_{3(s)} \rightarrow 2 NaNO_{2(s)} + O_{2(g)}$

$\dfrac{(1.50 \text{ g } O_2)(1 \text{ mole } O_2)(2 \text{ moles } NaNO_3)(85.0 \text{ g } NaNO_3)}{(32.0 \text{ g } O_2)(1 \text{ mole } O_2)(1 \text{ mole } NaNO_3)} = 7.97 \text{ g } NaNO_3$

27. The equation is: $2 C_8H_{18(l)} + 25 O_{2(g)} \rightarrow 16 CO_{2(g)} + 18 H_2O_{(g)}$

$\dfrac{(500.0 \text{ g } C_8H_{18})(1 \text{ mole } C_8H_{18})(25 \text{ mole } O_2)(32.0 \text{ g } O_2)}{(114.0 \text{ g } C_8H_{18})(2 \text{ moles } C_8H_{18})(1 \text{ mole } O_2)} = 1750 \text{ g } O_2$

28. Since % yield = $\dfrac{\text{actual yield}}{\text{theoretical yield}}$ x 100%,

$\qquad$ % yield = $\dfrac{12.1 \text{ kg}}{14.7 \text{ kg}}$ x 100% = 82.3%

29. The equation is: $2 C_2H_{6(g)} + 7 O_{2(g)} \rightarrow 4 CO_{2(g)} + 6 H_2O_{(g)}$

The theoretical yield is given by: $\dfrac{(72.0 \text{ g } C_2H_6)(1 \text{ mole } C_2H_6)(4 \text{ moles } CO_2)(44.0 \text{ g } CO_2)}{(30.0 \text{ g } C_2H_6)(2 \text{ moles } C_2H_6)(1 \text{ mole } CO_2)}$

$\qquad\qquad\qquad\qquad\qquad\qquad\qquad\qquad = 211 \text{ g } CO_2$

% yield = $\dfrac{105 \text{ g}}{211 \text{ g}}$ x 100% = 49.8%

30. The theoretical yield is given by: $\dfrac{(25.0 \text{ g } SO_2)(1 \text{ mole } SO_2)(2 \text{ moles } SO_3)(80.1 \text{ g } SO_3)}{(64.1 \text{ g } SO_2)(2 \text{ moles } SO_2)(1 \text{ mole } SO_3)}$

$\qquad\qquad\qquad\qquad\qquad\qquad\qquad\qquad = 31.2 \text{ g } SO_3$

% yield = $\dfrac{28.2 \text{ g}}{31.2 \text{ g}}$ x 100% = 90.4%

31. $\dfrac{(25.0 \text{ g SO}_2)(1 \text{ mole SO}_2)(2 \text{ moles SO}_3)}{(64.1 \text{ g SO}_2)(2 \text{ moles SO}_2)} = 0.390$ moles SO_3

$\dfrac{(6.00 \text{ g O}_2)(1 \text{ mole O}_2)(2 \text{ moles SO}_3)}{(32.0 \text{ g O}_2)(\ 1 \text{ mole O}_2\ )} = 0.375$ moles SO_3

Since O_2 would produce fewer moles of SO_3, O_2 is the limiting reactant.

32. $\dfrac{(5.23 \text{ g ZnCl}_2)(\ 1 \text{ mole ZnCl}_2\ )(2 \text{ mole AgCl})}{(136.4 \text{ g ZnCl}_2)(1 \text{ mole ZnCl}_2)} = 0.0767$ mole $AgCl$

$\dfrac{(2.12 \text{ g AgNO}_3)(\ 1 \text{ mole AgNO}_3\ )(\ 2 \text{ mole AgCl}\ )}{(169.9 \text{ g AgNO}_3)(2 \text{ mole AgNO}_3)} = 0.0125$ mole $AgCl$

Since $AgNO_3$ would produce fewer moles of $AgCl$, $AgNO_3$ is the limiting reactant.

33. $\dfrac{(3.50 \text{ g NaNH}_2)(1 \text{ mole NaNH}_2)(\ 1 \text{ mole NaN}_3\ )}{(39.0 \text{ g NaNH}_2)(3 \text{ mole NaNH}_2)} = 0.0299$ mole NaN_3

$\dfrac{(3.50 \text{ g NaNO}_3)(1 \text{ mole NaNO}_3)(\ 1 \text{ mole NaN}_3\ )}{(85.0 \text{ g NaNO}_3)(1 \text{ mole NaNO}_3)} = 0.0412$ mole NaN_3

Since $NaNH_2$ would produce fewer moles of NaN_3, $NaNH_2$ is the limiting reactant.

The theoretical yield of NaN_3 is then:

$$\dfrac{(0.0299 \text{ mole NaN}_3)(65.0 \text{ g NaN}_3)}{(1 \text{ mole NaN}_3)} = 1.94 \text{ g NaN}_3$$

% yield = $\dfrac{1.20 \text{ g}}{1.94 \text{ g}}$ x 100% = 61.9%

34. $\dfrac{(16.14 \text{ g Mg(OH)}_2)(1 \text{ mole Mg(OH)}_2)(\ 1 \text{ mole MgCl}_2\ )}{(58.3 \text{ g Mg(OH)}_2)(1 \text{ mole Mg(OH)}_2)} = 0.277$ mole $MgCl_2$

$\dfrac{(10.97 \text{ g HCl})(1 \text{ mole HCl})(1 \text{ mole MgCl}_2)}{(36.5 \text{ g HCl})(\ 2 \text{ mole HCl}\ )} = 0.150$ mole $MgCl_2$

Since HCl would produce fewer moles of $MgCl_2$, HCl is the limiting reactant.

The theoretical yield of $MgCl_2$ is then:

$$\dfrac{(0.150 \text{ mole MgCl}_2)(95.3 \text{ g MgCl}_2)}{(1 \text{ mole MgCl}_2)} = 14.3 \text{ g MgCl}_2$$

% yield = $\dfrac{12.23}{14.3}$ x 100% = 85.5%

35. $\dfrac{(4.51 \text{ g } C_6H_5Cl)(1 \text{ mole } C_6H_5Cl)(1 \text{ mole DDT })}{(112.5 \text{ g } C_6H_5Cl)(2 \text{ moles } C_6H_5Cl)} = 0.0200$ mole DDT

$\dfrac{(9.00 \text{ g } C_2HOCl_3)(1 \text{ mole } C_2HOCl_3)(1 \text{ mole DDT })}{(147.5 \text{ g } C_2HOCl_3)(1 \text{ mole } C_2HOCl_3)} = 0.0610$ mole DDT

Since C_6H_5Cl would produce fewer moles of DDT, C_6H_5Cl is the limiting reactant.

The theoretical yield of DDT is then:

$$\dfrac{(0.0200 \text{ mole DDT})(354.5 \text{ g DDT})}{(1 \text{ mole DDT })} = 7.09 \text{ g DDT}$$

% yield $= \dfrac{6.54 \text{ g}}{7.09 \text{ g}}$ x 100% = 92.2%

36. a. $2\, C_8H_{18(l)} + 25\, O_{2(g)} \rightarrow 16\, CO_{2(g)} + 18\, H_2O_{(g)}$
b. $Sr_{(s)} + Cl_{2(g)} \rightarrow SrCl_{2(s)}$
c. $Ba_{(s)} + 2\, H_2O_{(l)} \rightarrow Ba(OH)_{2(s)} + H_{2(g)}$
d. $Pb(C_2H_3O_2)_{2(aq)} + K_2SO_{4(aq)} \rightarrow PbSO_{4(s)} + 2\, KC_2H_3O_{2(aq)}$
e. $PI_{3(s)} + 3\, H_2O_{(l)} \rightarrow 3\, HI_{(g)} + H_3PO_{3(s)}$

37. The equation is: $CaO_{(s)} + H_2O_{(l)} \rightarrow Ca(OH)_{2(s)}$

$\dfrac{(100.0 \text{ g CaO})(1 \text{ mole CaO})(1 \text{ mole } Ca(OH)_2)(74.1 \text{ g } Ca(OH)_2)}{(56.1 \text{ g CaO})(1 \text{ mole CaO })(1 \text{ mole } Ca(OH)_2)} = 132 \text{ g } Ca(OH)_2$

38. The equation is: $2\, C_4H_{10(g)} + 13\, O_{2(g)} \rightarrow 8\, CO_{2(g)} + 10\, H_2O_{(g)}$

$\dfrac{(7.62 \text{ g } C_4H_{10})(1 \text{ mole } C_4H_{10})(8 \text{ moles } CO_2)(44.0 \text{ g } CO_2)}{(58.0 \text{ g } C_4H_{10})(2 \text{ moles } C_4H_{10})(1 \text{ mole } CO_2)} = 23.1 \text{ g } CO_2$

39. The equation is: $CaO_{(s)} + H_2O_{(l)} \rightarrow Ca(OH)_{2(s)}$

A weight gain of 0.289 g means a mole gain of $\dfrac{(0.289 \text{ g } H_2O)(1 \text{ mole } H_2O)}{(18.0 \text{ g } H_2O)} = 0.0161$ mole H_2O

Since the mole ratio is 1 mole $Ca(OH)_2$/1 mole H_2O, this is the same as the number of moles of $Ca(OH)_2$ formed.

40. The theoretical yield is given by:

$\dfrac{(10.75 \text{ g } CaSO_4)(1 \text{ mole } CaSO_4)(1 \text{ mole } CaCO_3)(100.1 \text{ g } CaCO_3)}{(136.2 \text{ g } CaSO_4)(1 \text{ mole } CaSO_4)(1 \text{ mole } CaCO_3)} = 7.901 \text{ g } CaCO_3$

% yield $= \dfrac{7.02 \text{ g}}{7.901 \text{ g}}$ x 100% = 88.8%

41. $\dfrac{(10.20 \text{ g Al}_2O_3)(1 \text{ mole Al}_2O_3)(3 \text{ moles H}_2O)}{(102.0 \text{ g Al}_2O_3)(1 \text{ mole Al}_2O_3)} = 0.3000 \text{ mole H}_2O$

$\dfrac{(7.50 \text{ g HNO}_3)(1 \text{ mole HNO}_3)(3 \text{ moles H}_2O)}{(63.0 \text{ g HNO}_3)(6 \text{ moles HNO}_3)} = 0.0595 \text{ mole H}_2O$

Since HNO_3 would produce fewer moles of H_2O, HNO_3 is the limiting reactant. Using all the HNO_3 would require the use of:

$\dfrac{(7.50 \text{ g HNO}_3)(1 \text{ mole HNO}_3)(1 \text{ mole Al}_2O_3)(102.0 \text{ g Al}_2O_3)}{(63.0 \text{ g HNO}_3)(6 \text{ moles HNO}_3)} = 2.02 \text{ g Al}_2O_3$

The amount of Al_2O_3 left is 10.20 g - 2.02 g = 8.18 g Al_2O_3

42. $\dfrac{(1.49 \text{ g Cu})(1 \text{ mole Cu})(1 \text{ mole CuSO}_4)(159.6 \text{ g CuSO}_4)}{(63.5 \text{ g Cu})(1 \text{ mole Cu})(1 \text{ mole CuSO}_4)} = 3.74 \text{ g CuSO}_4$ in the sample

% purity = $\dfrac{\text{actual content}}{\text{assumed content}}$ x 100% = $\dfrac{3.74 \text{ g}}{5.52 \text{ g}}$ x 100% = 67.8%

43. $\dfrac{(5.55 \text{ g N}_2)(1 \text{ mole N}_2)(2 \text{ moles NH}_3)}{(28.0 \text{ g N}_2)(1 \text{ mole N}_2)} = 0.396 \text{ mole NH}_3$

$\dfrac{(1.30 \text{ g H}_2)(1 \text{ mole H}_2)(2 \text{ moles NH}_3)}{(2.0 \text{ g H}_2)(3 \text{ moles H}_2)} = 0.433 \text{ mole NH}_3$

Since N_2 would produce fewer moles of NH_3, N_2 is the limiting reactant.

The theoretical yield of NH_3 is then:

$\dfrac{(0.396 \text{ mole NH}_3)(17.0 \text{ g NH}_3)}{(1 \text{ mole NH}_3)} = 6.73 \text{ g NH}_3$

% yield = $\dfrac{\text{actual yield}}{\text{theoretical yield}}$ x 100%

actual yield = $\dfrac{(\% \text{ yield})(\text{theoretical yield})}{100\%} = \dfrac{(56.3\%)(6.73 \text{ g})}{100\%} = 3.79 \text{ g NH}_3$

Sample Quiz Questions

1. Express the following equation in a complete sentence.

$$4 NH_{3(g)} + 5 O_{2(g)} \rightarrow 4 NO_{(g)} + 6 H_2O_{(g)}$$

a. Four molecules of gaseous ammonia react with five molecules of gaseous oxygen to yield four molecules of gaseous nitrogen monoxide and six molecules of gaseous water.
b. Four molecules of liquid ammonia react with five molecules of gaseous oxygen to yield four molecules of gaseous nitrogen monoxide and six molecules of liquid water.
c. Four molecules of gaseous nitrogen monoxide and six molecules of gaseous water react to yield four molecules of gaseous ammonia and five molecules of gaseous water.
d. Four molecules of liquid ammonia react with five molecules of liquid oxygen to yield four molecules of liquid nitrogen monoxide and six molecules of liquid water.
e. Four molecules of ammonia react with five molecules of oxygen to yield four molecules of nitrogen monoxide and six molecules of water.

2. Express the following statement as a complete chemical equation.

Three molecules of solid sodium bromide react with a molecule of liquid phosphoric acid to yield three molecules of gaseous hydrogen bromide and a molecule of solid sodium phosphate.

a. $NaBr_{(s)} + 3 H_3PO_{4(l)} \rightarrow HBr_{(g)} + 3 Na_3PO_{4(s)}$
b. $3 HBr_{(g)} + Na_3PO_{4(s)} \rightarrow 3 NaBr_{(s)} + H_3PO_{4(l)}$
c. $3 NaBr_{(s)} + H_3PO_{4(l)} \rightarrow 3 HBr_{(g)} + Na_3PO_{4(s)}$
d. $HBr_{(g)} + Na_3PO_{4(s)} \rightarrow NaBr_{(s)} + H_3PO_{4(l)}$
e. $3 NaBr_{(aq)} + H_3PO_{4(aq)} \rightarrow 3 HBr_{(g)} + Na_3PO_{4(aq)}$

3. A sample of 10.00 g of NO produces 15.33 g of NO_2 when it reacts with oxygen. What mass of O_2 is required for the reaction?

$$2 NO_{(g)} + O_{2(g)} \rightarrow 2 NO_{2(g)}$$

a. 25.33 g
b. 5.33 g
c. 10.00 g
d. 5.00 g
e. 7.66 g

4. The decomposition of a sample of hydrogen peroxide, H_2O_2, produced 5.14 g of water and 4.57 g of oxygen. What was the mass of the hydrogen peroxide sample?

$$2 H_2O_{2(l)} \rightarrow 2 H_2O_{(l)} + O_{2(g)}$$

a. 9.71 g
b. 4.86 g
c. 0.57 g
d. 7.42 g
e. 14.85 g

5. A 3.50 g sample of Fe_3O_4 reacts with 0.12 g of oxygen to form Fe_2O_3. What is the mass of the Fe_2O_3 made?

$$4 Fe_3O_{4(s)} + O_{2(g)} \rightarrow 6 Fe_2O_{3(s)}$$

   a. 21.21 g
   b. 3.54 g
   c. 3.29 g
   d. 4.34 g
   e. 3.62 g

6. Classify the reaction: $Zn_{(s)} + 2 AgNO_{3(aq)} \rightarrow Zn(NO_3)_{2(aq)} + 2 Ag_{(s)}$
    a. combination reaction.
    b. decomposition reaction.
    c. single replacement reaction.
    d. double replacement reaction.
    e. combustion reaction.

7. Classify the reaction: $MgSO_4 \cdot 7H_2O_{(s)} \rightarrow MgSO_{4(s)} + 7 H_2O_{(g)}$
    a. combination reaction.
    b. decomposition reaction.
    c. single replacement reaction.
    d. double replacement reaction.
    e. combustion reaction.

8. Predict the products of the reaction: $Pb(NO_3)_{2(aq)} + 2 NaI_{(aq)} \rightarrow$
       a. $PbNa_2 + 2 INO_3$
       b. $PbI_2 + NaNO_3$
       c. $PbI + 2 NaNO_3$
       d. $PbNO_3 + NaI$
       e. $PbI_2 + 2 NaNO_3$

9. Predict the reactants needed for the reaction: $\rightarrow K_3PO_{4(aq)} + 3 H_2O_{(l)}$
       a. $(OH)_3PO_4 + 3 KH$
       b. $3 KOH + H_3PO_4$
       c. $K_2HPO_4 + K(OH)_2$
       d. $KOH + H_3PO_4$
       e. $(OH)_3PO_4 + KH$

10. Supply the missing quantity in the reaction: $C_{16}H_{32}O_{2(s)} + \underline{\hspace{1cm}}_{(g)} \rightarrow 16 CO_{2(g)} + 16 H_2O_{(g)}$
       a. 23 O
       b. 24 O_2
       c. 46 O
       d. 23 O_2
       e. 16 O_2

11. Balance the following equation: $H_2C_2O_4 + NaOH \rightarrow Na_2C_2O_4 + H_2O$
   a. $2\ H_2C_2O_4 + 4\ NaOH \rightarrow 2\ Na_2C_2O_4 + 4\ H_2O$
   b. $2\ H_2C_2O_4 + NaOH \rightarrow 2\ Na_2C_2O_4 + H_2O$
   c. $H_2C_2O_4 + 2\ NaOH \rightarrow Na_2C_2O_4 + 2\ H_2O$
   d. $H_2C_2O_4 + NaOH \rightarrow Na_2C_2O_4 + H_2O$
   e. $H_2C_2O_4 + 2\ NaOH \rightarrow Na_2C_2O_4 + H_2O$

12. Balance the following equation: $H_3PO_3 + NH_4OH \rightarrow (NH_4)_3PO_3 + H_2O$
   a. $H_3PO_3 + NH_4OH \rightarrow (NH_4)_3PO_3 + H_2O$
   b. $3\ H_3PO_3 + NH_4OH \rightarrow 3\ (NH_4)_3PO_3 + H_2O$
   c. $2\ H_3PO_3 + 6\ NH_4OH \rightarrow 2\ (NH_4)_3PO_3 + 6\ H_2O$
   d. $H_3PO_3 + 3\ NH_4OH \rightarrow (NH_4)_3PO_3 + 3\ H_2O$
   e. $3\ H_3PO_3 + 3\ NH_4OH \rightarrow (NH_4)_3PO_3 + 3\ H_2O$

13. Balance the following equation: $C_{12}H_4Cl_4O_2 + H_2O \rightarrow C_6H_4Cl_2O_2$
   a. $C_{12}H_4Cl_4O_2 + 2\ H_2O \rightarrow 2\ C_6H_4Cl_2O_2$
   b. $C_{12}H_4Cl_4O_2 + H_2O \rightarrow 2\ C_6H_4Cl_2O_2$
   c. $C_{12}H_4Cl_4O_2 + 2\ H_2O \rightarrow C_6H_4Cl_2O_2$
   d. $2\ C_{12}H_4Cl_4O_2 + 4\ H_2O \rightarrow 4\ C_6H_4Cl_2O_2$
   e. $2\ C_{12}H_4Cl_4O_2 + H_2O \rightarrow 2\ C_6H_4Cl_2O_2$

14. According to the equation,

$$S_{8(s)} + 8\ O_{2(g)} \rightarrow 8\ SO_{2(g)}$$

how many moles of O_2 are required to react with 50.0 g of sulfur?
   a. 400 moles
   b. 1.56 moles
   c. 0.0243 mole
   d. 0.195 mole
   e. 49.8 moles

15. According to the equation for decomposing the mineral fluorapatite,

$$Ca_{10}F_2(PO_4)_{6(s)} + 7\ H_2SO_{4(l)} \rightarrow 2\ HF_{(g)} + 3\ Ca(H_2PO_4)_{2(s)} + 7\ CaSO_{4(s)}$$

how many moles of H_2SO_4 are required to produce 125 g of $CaSO_4$?
   a. 6.42 moles
   b. 0.131 mole
   c. 12.9 moles
   d. 0.918 mole
   e. 90.0 moles

16. According the equation,

$$3\,CS_{2(g)} + 6\,NaOH_{(aq)} \rightarrow 2\,Na_2CS_{3(aq)} + Na_2CO_{3(aq)} + 3\,H_2O_{(l)}$$

what mass of NaOH is required to react with 4.50 g of CS_2?
   a. 0.787 g
   b. 4.72 g
   c. 2.36 g
   d. 0.0591 g
   e. 0.118 g

17. According to the equation,

$$TiO_{2(s)} + 2\,Cl_{2(g)} + 2\,C_{(s)} \rightarrow TiCl_{4(g)} + 2\,CO_{(g)}$$

what mass of CO can be produced from 756 g of TiO_2?
   a. 1.32×10^2 g
   b. 9.46 g
   c. 2.65×10^2 g
   d. 1510 g
   e. 5.30×10^2 g

18. According to the equation,

$$Na_2SO_{4(s)} + 4\,C_{(s)} \rightarrow Na_2S_{(s)} + 4\,CO_{(g)}$$

what mass of carbon is required to react with 12.7 g of Na_2SO_4?
   a. 0.357 g
   b. 50.8 g
   c. 4.29 g
   d. 0.268 g
   e. 1.07 g

19. According to the equation,

$$2\,NaBr_{(aq)} + Cl_{2(g)} \rightarrow Br_{2(l)} + 2\,NaCl_{(aq)}$$

what mass of Br_2 can be made when 75.0 g of NaBr and 75.0 g of Cl_2 are allowed to react?
   a. 116 g
   b. 169 g
   c. 75.0 g
   d. 150 g
   e. 58.2 g

20. According to the equation,

$$4 KO_{2(s)} + 2 H_2O_{(g)} + 4 CO_{2(g)} \rightarrow 4 KHCO_{3(s)} + 3 O_{2(g)}$$

what mass of oxygen can be made when 1.00 kg of KO_2 and 500.0 g of carbon dioxide are allowed to react with excess water?
    a. 3.38 x 10^2 g
    b. 4.50 x 10^2 g
    c. 1.50 x 10^3 g
    d. 2.73 x 10^2 g
    e. 3.63 x 10^2 g

21. According to the equation,

$$4 NH_{3(g)} + 6 NO_{(g)} \rightarrow 5 N_{2(g)} + 6 H_2O_{(l)}$$

what mass of nitrogen can be made if 10.0 g of NH_3 and 30.0 g of NO are allowed to react?
    a. 20.6 g
    b. 23.3 g
    c. 16.5 g
    d. 28.0 g
    e. 40.0 g

22. According to the equation,

$$2 Al_{(s)} + 3 MgO_{(s)} \rightarrow 3 Mg_{(s)} + Al_2O_{3(s)}$$

what mass of both products can be made if 75.0 g of aluminum and 150.0 g of MgO are allowed to react?
    a. 101 g Mg; 142 g Al_2O_3
    b. 202 g Mg; 283 g Al_2O_3
    c. 90.4 g Mg; 127 g Al_2O_3
    d. 90.4 g Mg; 380 g Al_2O_3
    e. 33.8 g Mg; 142 g Al_2O_3

23. Consider the equation for the decomposition of the mineral mispickel,

$$FeSAs_{(s)} \rightarrow FeS_{(s)} + As_{(s)}$$

When 132 g of FeSAs is allowed to react, 49.9 g of As is formed. What is the percentage yield of the reaction?
    a. 60.7%
    b. 37.8%
    c. 46.0%
    d. 70.0%
    e. 82.2%

24. Consider the reaction for making ethyl alcohol from sugar,

$$C_6H_{12}O_{6(aq)} \rightarrow 2\,C_2H_5OH_{(aq)} + 2\,CO_{2(g)}$$

The reaction typically has a percentage yield of 78.2%. What mass of sugar must be used in order to get an actual yield of 100.0 g of C_2H_5OH?

    a. 5.01×10^2 g
    b. 1.96×10^2 g
    c. 1.28×10^2 g
    d. 2.50×10^2 g
    e. 3.91×10^2 g

25. Consider one of the reactions involved in the biological metabolism of sugar,

$$C_6H_{12}O_{6(aq)} + 6\,O_{2(g)} \rightarrow 6\,CO_{2(g)} + 6\,H_2O_{(l)}$$

When 15.0 g of $C_6H_{12}O_6$ and 20.0 g of oxygen are allowed to react, 17.8 g of CO_2 are made. What is the percentage yield of the reaction?

    a. 80.9%
    b. 93.8%
    c. 64.7%
    d. 75.0%
    e. 89.0%

Answers to the Sample Quiz Questions

1. (a), 2. (c), 3. (b), 4. (a), 5. (e), 6. (c), 7. (b), 8. (e), 9. (b), 10. (d), 11. (c), 12. (d), 13. (a), 14. (b), 15. (d), 16. (b), 17. (e), 18. (c), 19. (e), 20. (d), 21. (a), 22. (c), 23. (e), 24. (d), 25. (a)

GASES

GASES

Chapter Overview

Chapter 10 describes the properties of gases and the mathematical relationships between the properties. The chapter begins with a qualitative examination of the properties of gases, such as having mass, occupying volume, exerting pressure, being compressible, and being able to diffuse.

The quantitative relationships of Boyle, Charles, and Gay-Lussac are then developed from their empirical bases. They are subsequently tied together with the combined gas equation. As part of this treatment, it is stressed that it is not necessary to learn all the individual relationships; by identifying which quantities remain constant in a calculation, the combined equation can be rearranged and simplified to give the desired expression. Avogadro's hypothesis is used to introduce the idea of molecules of gas rather than mass and the comparability of gas data at STP. Finally, the ideal gas equation is described as a quantitative combination of all the individual gas laws. The compatibility of the units of measure is stressed. As before, it is shown how each of the individual gas laws can be derived from the ideal gas equation as needed.

After the empirical behavior of gases has been fully examined, the kinetic molecular theory is discussed to give the behavior a theoretical explanation.

Finally, two important ancillary relationships are covered. Dalton's law of partial pressures is discussed and the densities of gases are discussed in qualitative and quantitative terms.

The chapter closes with an optional section dealing with the use of gas properties, particularly the ideal gas equation, in stoichiometric calculations.

Solutions to the Study Questions and Problems

1. **a. Pressure** is the force per unit area that a gas exerts on the walls of its vessel. **b.** A **torr** is a unit of expressing pressure. One torr equals one mm Hg and there are 760 torr in one atmosphere. Each of these equivalences is exact. **c. Compressibility** is the ability to reduce a large volume of a gas into a small volume. This compression increases pressure. **d. Diffusion** is the ability of two or more gases to intermingle and form a homogeneous mixture.

2. The six major properties of gases are:

      1. mass - All gases have mass.
      2. volume - Gases occupy space.
      3. pressure - Gases exert pressure on the walls of their containers.
      4. compressibility - Gases are compressible.
      5. expansion and contraction - Gases expand and contract with temperature changes.
      6. diffusion - Gases form homogeneous mixtures.

3. Using a balance, determine the mass of an evacuated vessel. Next, let gas enter the vessel and reweigh it. The second weighing will show a mass increase which can only be attributed to the mass of the gas which was allowed into the vessel.

4. When the temperature of a gas is raised, it will expand. This expansion spreads out the molecules, leaving fewer molecules in a given volume. The consequence is a reduction in density of the gas. When a gas is cooled, the opposite occurs. The gas contracts putting more molecules in a given volume and increasing the density.

5. When an aerosol can is heated, the gas remaining in the can tries to expand and there is a resulting increase in pressure since the gas must keep the constant volume of the can. The can will explode if the pressure becomes too great.

6. As the air in the balloon is heated, it expands and becomes less dense. Because the air in the balloon is less dense than that of the surrounding air, it will rise, taking the balloon and its passengers with it.

7. When mass and temperature are held constant, the pressure and volume of a sample of gas are inversely proportional as stated in Boyle's law:

$$P \propto 1/V$$
$$PV = k$$

and

$$P_iV_i = k = P_fV_f$$
$$P_iV_i = P_fV_f$$

8. We breathe by expanding and contracting our lungs with the action of the diaphragm. When the lungs expand, their volume increases and the pressure in them drops. Outside air then rushes in to equalize the pressure. When the lungs contract, their volume decreases and the pressure increases. Air then leaves the lungs in order to equalize the pressure.

9. Air in a filled balloon is at a higher pressure than external air and so it will escape in order to equalize the pressure if it can.

10. By Boyle's law, $P_iV_i = P_fV_f$,

$$V_f = P_iV_i/P_f$$
$$V_f = (0.750 \text{ atm})(360 \text{ mL})/(1.00 \text{ atm})$$
$$V_f = 270 \text{ mL}$$

11. In each case, $V_f = (4.00 \text{ atm})(4.00 \text{ L})/P_f$.

    a. $V_f = (4.00 \text{ atm})(4.00 \text{ L})/(1.00 \text{ atm}) = 16.0 \text{ L}$
    b. $V_f = (4.00 \text{ atm})(4.00 \text{ L})/(0.400 \text{ atm}) = 40.0 \text{ L}$
    c. $V_f = (4.00 \text{ atm})(4.00 \text{ L})/(10.0 \text{ atm}) = 1.60 \text{ L}$

12. In each case, $P_f = (1.00 \text{ atm})(200.0 \text{ mL})/V_f$.

    a. $P_f = (1.00 \text{ atm})(200.0 \text{ mL})/(250.0 \text{ mL}) = 0.800 \text{ atm}$
    b. $P_f = (1.00 \text{ atm})(200.0 \text{ mL})/(100.0 \text{ mL}) = 2.00 \text{ atm}$
    c. $P_f = (1.00 \text{ atm})(200.0 \text{ mL})/(1000.0 \text{ mL}) = 0.200 \text{ atm}$

13. In each case, $P_f = (1.75 \text{ atm})(25.0 \text{ L})/V_f$.

    a. $P_f = (1.75 \text{ atm})(25.0 \text{ L})/(10.0 \text{ L}) = 4.38 \text{ atm}$
    b. $P_f = (1.75 \text{ atm})(25.0 \text{ L})/(35.0 \text{ L}) = 1.25 \text{ atm}$
    c. $P_f = (1.75 \text{ atm})(25.0 \text{ L})/(2.50 \text{ L}) = 17.5 \text{ atm}$

14. By Boyle's law, $P_i V_i = P_f V_f$,

$$P_f = P_i V_i / V_f$$
$$P_f = (1.00 \text{ atm})(10.0 \text{ L})/(1.00 \text{ L})$$
$$P_f = 10.0 \text{ atm}$$

15. If mass and pressure are held constant, then volume and temperature are directly proportional by Charles' law:

$$V \propto T$$
$$V/T = k$$

and

$$V_i/T_i = k = V_f/T_f$$
$$V_i/T_i = V_f/T_f$$

16. Kelvin plotted gas volume *vs.* Celsius temperature and found a temperature at which volume apparently reached zero. He speculated that at that temperature, -273.15 °C, a gas would have no volume and the energy of the molecules would be zero.

17. **Absolute zero** is the lowest temperature possible for a gas which, from Kelvin's work, is assumed to be -273.15 °C. **Absolute temperature** is the temperature relative to absolute zero in the units of Kelvins (K), where 1 Kelvin = 1 °C. Therefore, $T_{(K)} = T_{(°C)} + 273.15$.

18. By Charles' law, $V_i/T_i = V_f/T_f$,

$$V_f = V_i T_f / T_i$$
$$V_f = (79.5 \text{ L})(273 \text{ K})/(318 \text{ K})$$
$$V_f = 68.2 \text{ L}$$

19. In each case, $V_f = (100.0 \text{ mL})T_f/(363 \text{ K})$.

    a. $V_f = (100.0 \text{ mL})(323 \text{ K})/(363 \text{ K}) = 88.9 \text{ mL}$
    b. $V_f = (100.0 \text{ mL})(418 \text{ K})/(363 \text{ K}) = 115 \text{ mL}$
    c. $V_f = (100.0 \text{ mL})(263 \text{ K})/(363 \text{ K}) = 72.4 \text{ mL}$

20. Celsius and Fahrenheit are related by: $T_{(°F)} = 1.8 \cdot T_{(°C)} + 32$ and $T_{(°C)} = (T_{(°F)} - 32) \cdot 5/9$

For the outside air: $T_{(°C)} = (68 - 32) \cdot 5/9 = 20. \; °C = 293 \text{ K}$
For lung air: $T_{(°C)} = (98.6 - 32) \cdot 5/9 = 37 \; °C = 310 \text{ K}$

$$V_f = (6.00 \times 10^3 \text{ mL})(293 \text{ K})/(310 \text{ K})$$
$$V_f = 5.67 \times 10^3 \text{ mL}$$

21. If mass and volume are held constant, pressure is directly proportional to temperature:

$$P \propto T$$
$$P/T = k$$

and

$$P_i/T_i = k = P_f/T_f$$
$$P_i/T_i = P_f/T_f$$

22. Since $P_i/T_i = P_f/T_f$,

$$T_f = P_f T_i/P_i$$
$$T_f = (2.50 \text{ atm})(273 \text{ K})/(1.80 \text{ atm})$$
$$T_f = 379 \text{ K} = 106 \; °C$$

23. **a.** $P_f = (3.00 \text{ atm})(373.2 \text{ K})/298 \text{ K}) = 3.75 \text{ atm}$
    b. $T_f = (2.50 \text{ atm})(298 \text{ K})/(3.00 \text{ atm}) = 248 \text{ K} = -25 \; °C$
    c. $T_f = (3.50 \text{ atm})(298 \text{ K})/(3.00 \text{ atm}) = 348 \text{ K} = 75 \; °C$

24. $T_i = 32 \; °F = 0 \; °C = 273 \text{ K}$
    $T_f = 110.0 \; °F = 43.3 \; °C = 316 \text{ K}$

$$P_i/T_i = P_f/T_f$$
$$P_f = P_i T_f/T_i$$
$$P_f = (2280 \text{ torr})(316 \text{ K})/(273 \text{ K})$$
$$P_f = 2640 \text{ torr}$$

25. By the combined gas law, $P_i V_i/T_i = P_f V_f/T_f$,

$$V_f = P_i V_i T_f/T_i P_f$$
$$V_f = \frac{(1.10 \text{ atm})(450.0 \text{ mL})(273.15 \text{ K})}{(35 + 273 \text{ K})(1.00 \text{ atm})}$$
$$V_f = 439 \text{ mL}$$

26. By the combined gas law, $P_iV_i/T_i = P_fV_f/T_f$,

$P_f = P_iV_iT_f/T_iV_f$
$P_f = \dfrac{(0.800\ atm)(1.00\ L)(90.0 + 273.2\ K)}{(-5.0 + 273.2\ K)(3.00\ L)}$
$P_f = 0.361\ atm$

27. By the combined gas law, $P_iV_i/T_i = P_fV_f/T_f$,

$V_f = P_iV_iT_f/T_iP_f$
$V_f = \dfrac{(0.75\ atm)(155\ mL)(45.0 + 273.15\ K)}{(30.0 + 273.15\ K)(0.50\ atm)}$
$V_f = 240\ mL$

28. By the combined gas law, $P_iV_i/T_i = P_fV_f/T_f$,

$T_f = P_fV_fT_i/P_iV_i$
$T_f = \dfrac{(1.00\ atm)(1.00\ L)(80.0 + 273.15\ K)}{(0.700\ atm)(0.8000\ L)}$
$T_f = 631\ K = 357\ °C$

29. Avogadro's hypothesis was that, if temperature and pressure are held constant, then equal volumes of gases contain equal numbers of molecules. He based his hypothesis on the assumptions that 1) gases are indeed composed of molecules and 2) molecules of a gas occupy a fixed volume at a given temperature and pressure.

30. STP stands for standard temperature and pressure. Standard temperature is defined to be exactly 0 °C or 273.15 K. Standard pressure is defined to be exactly 760 torr or 1 atmosphere.

31. The volume of one mole of a gas at STP is called the **molar volume**. This is a constant value of 22.4 L for all gases.

32. $\dfrac{(4.16 \times 10^{20}\ molecules)(1\ mole)(22.4\ L)}{(6.02 \times 10^{23}\ molecules)(1\ mole)} = 0.0155\ L = 15.5\ mL$

33. The ideal gas equation says that pressure times volume is equal to the number of moles times the temperature (in Kelvin) times the proportionality constant, R, for any gas sample. Real gases do not strictly obey the ideal gas equation but under ordinary conditions of pressure (less than about 10 atmospheres) and temperature (significantly above the boiling point of the gas), the ideal gas equation can be used without any substantial error.

34. By the ideal gas equation, $PV = nRT$,

$P = nRT/V$
$P = (0.300\ mole)(0.0821\ L\text{-}atm/mole\text{-}K)(90.0 + 273.15\ K)/(10.0\ L)$
$P = 0.894\ atm$

35. By the ideal gas equation, $PV = nRT$,

$n = PV/RT$
$n = \dfrac{(1.25\ atm)(0.6000\ L)}{(0.0821\ L\text{-}atm/mole\text{-}K)(60.0 + 273.15\ K)}$
$n = 0.0274\ mole$

36. By the ideal gas equation, PV = nRT,

$$n = PV/RT$$
$$n = \frac{(1.50 \text{ atm})(47.3 \text{ L})}{(0.0821 \text{ L-atm/mole-K})(27 + 273.15 \text{ K})}$$
$$n = 2.88 \text{ moles}$$

$$\text{mass of } N_2 = \frac{(2.88 \text{ moles})(28.0 \text{ g } N_2)}{(1 \text{ mole } N_2)} = 80.6 \text{ g } N_2$$

37. By the ideal gas equation, PV = nRT,

$$V = n\text{RT}/P$$
$$V = \frac{(0.100 \text{ mole})(0.0821 \text{ L-atm/mole-K})(25 + 273.15 \text{ K})(760 \text{ torr})}{(2.00 \text{ torr})(1 \text{ atm})}$$

$$V = 9.30 \times 10^2 \text{ L}$$

38. The molar mass of CO_2 is 1(12.0 g/mole) + 2(16.0 g/mole) = 44.0 g/mole.

$$n = \frac{(10.0 \text{ g } CO_2)(1 \text{ mole } CO_2)}{(44.0 \text{ g } CO_2)} = 0.227 \text{ mole}$$

$$V = n\text{RT}/P$$
$$V = \frac{(0.227 \text{ mole})(0.0821 \text{ L-atm/mole-K})(25 + 273.15 \text{ K})}{(1.75 \text{ atm})}$$

$$V = 3.18 \text{ L}$$

39. The kinetic molecular theory is constructed around six major features:

1. All gases are composed of molecules.
2. These individual molecules are so small that the volume each occupies is negligible.
3. Molecules of the gas are very far apart and most of the volume occupied by a gas sample is empty.
4. Molecules of the gas are always in motion and therefore possess kinetic energy.
5. The molecules of the gas collide with each other and the container walls in perfectly elastic collisions.
6. The average kinetic energy of the gas molecules is proportional to absolute temperature.

40. The relationship of the kinetic molecular to the observed properties of gases is:

1. Gases have mass since they are composed of molecules.
2. Gases occupy space because they are in constant motion.
3. Gases exert pressure due to the collisions with the container walls.
4. Gases can be compressed since most of the space between molecules is empty.
5. Gases will diffuse due to the motion of the molecules and the lack of attraction between molecules.

41. In the kinetic molecular theory's explanation of Boyle's law, when the volume of the container is decreased, the number of collisions is increased since the molecules are more crowded, thus increasing the pressure.

42. In the kinetic molecular theory's explanation of Charles' law, when the temperature of a gas is increased, the average kinetic energy and the average velocity of the molecules increases. The higher velocities mean an increase in the force of each collision, causing an increase in volume to keep the pressure constant.

43. Real gases deviate from ideal behavior because of two factors overlooked by the kinetic molecular theory. The atoms and molecules do occupy some space; their volume is not negligible. They also possess some short range attractions for each other; when they pass close to one another, molecules do attract each other and reduce their velocities.

44. Dalton's law of partial pressures says that the total pressure of a gas mixture is the sum of the pressures of all the component gases of the mixture. The pressure of each component gas is termed a partial pressure.

45. Partial pressure is the pressure exerted by a component gas of a mixture.

46. Since $P_{total} = P_1 + P_2 + ...$, for this mixture:

$$P_{total} = P_{oxygen} + P_{cyclopropane}$$
$$P_{cyclopropane} = P_{total} - P_{oxygen}$$
$$P_{cyclopropane} = 760.0 \text{ torr} - 570 \text{ torr} = 190 \text{ torr} = 0.25 \text{ atm}$$

47. The percentage composition of lung gases in terms of moles follows from Dalton's law:

$$P_{total} = P_{oxygen} + P_{carbon\ dioxide} + P_{water} + P_{nitrogen}$$
$$P_{total} = 100.0 \text{ torr} + 40.0 \text{ torr} + 47.0 \text{ torr} + 573.0 \text{ torr}$$
$$P_{total} = 760.0 \text{ torr}$$

In the gas laws, it is shown that $P \propto$ moles. Therefore, the percentage composition by pressure is the same as the percentage composition by moles:

$$\% \ O_2 = \frac{100.0 \text{ torr}}{760.0 \text{ torr}} \times 100\% = 13.16\%$$
$$\% \ CO_2 = \frac{40.0 \text{ torr}}{760.0 \text{ torr}} \times 100\% = 5.26\%$$
$$\% \ H_2O = \frac{47.0 \text{ torr}}{760.0 \text{ torr}} \times 100\% = 6.18\%$$
$$\% \ N_2 = \frac{573.0 \text{ torr}}{760.0 \text{ torr}} \times 100\% = 75.39\%$$

By assuming a total of one mole of gas molecules in the sample, the weight percentages can be easily determined from the mole percentages using the molar masses of the component gases:

For O_2: $\frac{(0.1316 \text{ mole})(32.0 \text{ g } O_2)}{(1 \text{ mole } O_2)} = 4.21 \text{ g } O_2$ $\frac{(4.21 \text{ g})}{(28.7 \text{ g})} \times 100\% = 14.7\% \ O_2$

For CO_2: $\frac{(0.0526 \text{ mole})(44.0 \text{ g } CO_2)}{(1 \text{ mole } CO_2)} = 2.31 \text{ g } CO_2$ $\frac{(2.31 \text{ g})}{(28.7 \text{ g})} \times 100\% = 8.05\% \ CO_2$

For H_2O: $\frac{(0.0618 \text{ mole})(18.0 \text{ g } H_2O)}{(1 \text{ mole } H_2O)} = 1.11 \text{ g } H_2O$ $\frac{(1.11 \text{ g})}{(28.7 \text{ g})} \times 100\% = 3.87\% \ H_2O$

For N_2: $\frac{(0.7539 \text{ mole})(28.0 \text{ g } N_2)}{(1 \text{ mole } N_2)} = 21.1 \text{ g } N_2$ $\frac{(21.1 \text{ g})}{(28.7 \text{ g})} \times 100\% = 73.5\% \ N_2$

total mass = 28.7 g

48. Since the total pressure remains constant and the only components which change in partial pressure are carbon dioxide and oxygen, the situation can be summarized as:

$$P_{oxygen(initial)} + P_{carbon\ dioxide(initial)} = P_{oxygen(final)} + P_{carbon\ dioxide(final)}$$
$$P_{oxygen(final)} = P_{oxygen(initial)} + P_{carbon\ dioxide(initial)} - P_{carbon\ dioxide(final)}$$
$$P_{oxygen(final)} = 100.0\ torr + 40.0\ torr - 60.0\ torr$$
$$P_{oxygen(final)} = 80.0\ torr$$

Oxygen's partial pressure drops to 80.0 torr.

49. The density of gases is low compared to liquids and solids because the gas molecules are spaced very far apart compared to those in solids and liquids.

50. Since $n = \dfrac{mass}{molar\ mass}$, then $PV = \dfrac{(mass)RT}{(molar\ mass)}$

The expression for density is

$$d = \frac{mass}{V} = \frac{P(molar\ mass)}{RT}$$

a. For CO_2, $d = \dfrac{(1.00\ atm)(44.0\ g/mole)}{(0.0821\ L\text{-}atm/mole\text{-}K)(273.15\ K)} = 1.96\ g/L$

b. For Cl_2, $d = \dfrac{(1.00\ atm)(71.0\ g/mole)}{(0.0821\ L\text{-}atm/mole\text{-}K)(273.15\ K)} = 3.17\ g/L$

c. For SO_3, $d = \dfrac{(1.00\ atm)(80.1\ g/mole)}{(0.0821\ L\text{-}atm/mole\text{-}K)(273.15\ K)} = 3.58\ g/L$

51. Since $d = mass/V$,

$$d \times V = mass$$
$$d_i V_i = mass = d_f V_f$$
$$d_i V_i = d_f V_f$$

and

$$d_f = d_i V_i / V_f$$
$$d_f = (1.80\ g/L)(5.00\ L)/(1.00\ L)$$
$$d_f = 9.00\ g/L$$

52. The molar mass of C_2N_2 is $2(12.0\ g/mole) + 2(14.0\ g/mole) = 52.0\ g/mole$

$$\frac{(7.00\ g\ C_2N_2)(1\ mole\ C_2N_2)(2\ mole\ HCN)(0.0821\ L\text{-}atm/mole\text{-}K)(273.15\ K)(1000\ mL)}{(52.0\ g\ C_2N_2)(1\ mole\ C_2N_2)(1.00\ atm)\qquad\qquad (1\ L\ )}$$
$$= 6.04 \times 10^3\ mL\ HCN$$

$$\frac{(7.00\ g\ C_2N_2)(1\ mole\ C_2N_2)(1\ mole\ NO_2)(0.0821\ L\text{-}atm/mole\text{-}K)(273.15\ K)(1000\ mL)}{(52.0\ g\ C_2N_2)(1\ mole\ C_2N_2)(1.00\ atm)\qquad\qquad (1\ L\ )}$$
$$= 3.02 \times 10^3\ mL\ NO_2$$

53. The molar mass of Al_4C_3 is $4(27.0 \text{ g/mole}) + 3(12.0 \text{ g/mole}) = 144.0 \text{ g/mole}$

$$\frac{(2.00 \text{ g } Al_4C_3)(1 \text{ mole } Al_4C_3)(3 \text{ mole } CH_4)(0.0821 \text{ L-atm/mole-K})(273.15 \text{ K})(1000 \text{ mL})}{(144.0 \text{ g } Al_4C_3)(1 \text{ mole } Al_4C_3)(1.00 \text{ atm})(1 \text{ L})}$$
$$= 934 \text{ mL } CH_4$$

54. The molar mass of C_8H_{18} is $8(12.0 \text{ g/mole}) + 18(1.0 \text{ g/mole}) = 114.0 \text{ g/mole}$

$$\frac{(0.750 \text{ g } C_8H_{18})(1 \text{ mole } C_8H_{18})(16 \text{ mole } CO_2)(0.0821 \text{ L-atm/mole-K})(400.0 + 273.15 \text{ K})}{(114.0 \text{ g } C_8H_{18})(2 \text{ mole } C_8H_{18})(10.0 \text{ atm})}$$
$$= 0.291 \text{ L } CO_2$$

55. From Avogadro, since pressure and temperature are constant,

$$n \propto V$$
$$V/n = k$$

and

$$V_i/n_i = k = V_f/n_f$$
$$V_i/n_i = V_f/n_f$$

Therefore, using the coefficients of the equation as the relative number of moles:

$$V_f = V_i n_f/n_i$$
$$V_f = (475 \text{ L})(4.00 \text{ moles})/(4.00 \text{ moles})$$
$$V_f = 475 \text{ L NO}$$

56. An increase in temperature will increase the diffusion rate as the molecules will possess a higher velocity at the higher temperature. The gas molecules will spread out (or diffuse) more rapidly throughout the volume.

57. The tank contains

$$n = \frac{(150.0 \text{ atm})(12.0 \text{ L})}{(0.0821 \text{ L-atm/mole-K})(27 + 273.15 \text{ K})} = 73.0 \text{ moles He}$$

Each balloon can contain

$$n = \frac{(1.00 \text{ atm})(10.0 \text{ L})}{(0.0821 \text{ L-atm/mole-K})(27 + 273.15 \text{ K})} = 0.406 \text{ mole He/balloon}$$

Therefore, $\frac{(73.0 \text{ moles He})(1 \text{ balloon})}{(0.406 \text{ mole He})} = 1.80 \times 10^2$ balloons can be filled.

58. The initial temperature is $(-40.0 - 32.0) \cdot 5/9 = -40.0 \text{ °C}$ or 233.2 K.

$$T_f = V_f T_i/V_i$$
$$T_f = (2.50 \text{ L})(233.2 \text{ K})/(2.00 \text{ L})$$
$$T_f = 292 \text{ K} = 18.8 \text{ °C}$$

and

$$T_{(°F)} = 1.80(18.8) + 32.0$$
$$T_{(°F)} = 65.8 \text{ °F}$$

59. In each case, $T_f = V_f T_i / V_i$.

  a. $T_f = (225 \text{ mL})(92+273.15 \text{ K})/75.0 \text{ mL}) = 1095 \text{ K} = 822 \text{ °C}$
  b. $T_f = (30.0 \text{ mL})(92+273.15 \text{ K})/75.0 \text{ mL}) = 146 \text{ K} = -127 \text{ °C}$
  c. $T_f = (89.2 \text{ mL})(92+273.15 \text{ K})/75.0 \text{ mL}) = 434 \text{ K} = 161 \text{ °C}$

60. Here, $T_f = (120 - 32) \cdot 5/9 = 49 \text{ °C} = 322 \text{ K}$.

$$P_f = P_i T_f / T_i$$
$$P_f = (2.0 \text{ atm})(322 \text{ K})/(27 + 273.15 \text{ K})$$
$$P_f = 2.2 \text{ atm}$$

Therefore, it should not explode since the pressure is well below 3.0 atm.

61.
$$P_f = P_i V_i T_f / T_i V_f$$
$$P_f = \frac{(1.50 \text{ atm})(1.00 \text{ L})(180 + 273.15 \text{ K})}{(25 + 273.15 \text{ K})(4.50 \text{ L})}$$
$$P_f = 0.507 \text{ atm}$$

62. The expression is:

$$\text{molar mass} = (\text{mass})RT/PV$$
$$\text{molar mass} = \frac{(1.56 \text{ g})(0.0821 \text{ L-atm/mole-K})(50.0+273.15 \text{ K})}{(0.984 \text{ atm})(1.00 \text{ L})}$$
$$\text{molar mass} = 42.1 \text{ g/mole}$$

63. The expression is:

$$\text{molar mass} = (\text{mass})RT/PV$$
$$\text{molar mass} = \frac{(4.08 \text{ g})(0.0821 \text{ L-atm/mole-K})(32+273.15 \text{ K})}{(0.850 \text{ atm})(2.00 \text{ L})}$$
$$\text{molar mass} = 60.1 \text{ g/mole}$$

64. For the initially collected neon, $P_{total} = P_{Ne} + P_{water}$
$$P_{Ne} = 0.985 \text{ atm} - 0.0373 \text{ atm}$$
$$P_{Ne} = 0.948 \text{ atm}$$

Then,

$$P_f = P_i V_i T_f / T_i V_f$$
$$P_f = \frac{(0.948 \text{ atm})(1.00 \text{ L})(45 + 273.15 \text{ K})}{(28 + 273.15 \text{ K})(2.00 \text{ L})}$$
$$P_f = 0.501 \text{ atm}$$

65.
$$V_f = V_i n_f / n_i$$
$$V_f = (10.0 \text{ mL CO})(1 \text{ mole O}_2)/(2 \text{ moles CO})$$
$$V_f = 5.00 \text{ mL O}_2$$

Sample Quiz Questions

1. A sample of a gas is confined in a 3.51 L vessel at a pressure of 575 torr. What will the pressure be if the volume is decreased to 2.50 L?
    a. 410.0 torr
    b. 0.00124 atm
    c. 807 torr
    d. 1060 torr
    e. 0.539 atm

2. A sample of a gas is confined in a 54.22 L vessel at at pressure of 3.02 atm. What volume will be required to increase the pressure of the gas to 10.00 atm?
    a. 0.557 L
    b. 16.4 L
    c. 1.80 L
    d. 0.0610 L
    e. 180 L

3. A sample of a gas occupies 15.3 L at -15.0 °C. What volume will the gas occupy if the temperature is increased to 300.0 K?
    a. 13.2 L
    b. 306 L
    c. 0.765 L
    d. 17.8 L
    e. 27.5 L

4. A sample of a gas occupies a volume of 356 L at 522 °C. At what temperature will the gas occupy a volume of 999 L?
    a. 2230 °C
    b. 1460 °C
    c. 1960 °C
    d. 283 K
    e. 1740 K

5. A sample of a gas is confined at a pressure of 15.0 atm and a temperature of 36.0 K. What will the pressure be if the temperature is changed to 4.00 K?
    a. 1.67 atm
    b. 135 atm
    c. 13.4 atm
    d. 1270 atm
    e. 0.0744 atm

6. A sample of a gas is confined at a pressure of 1.05 atm and a temperature of 28.0 °C. What temperature is required to raise the pressure to 5.00 atm?
    a. 1160 K
    b. 1430 K
    c. 406 K
    d. 133 K
    e. 1710 K

7. A sample of 1.50 moles of CO_2 occupies a volume of 40.0 L at a particular pressure and temperature. How many moles of CO_2 must be added to increase the volume to 50.0 L?
    a. 0.38 mole
    b. 0.30 mole
    c. 1.88 moles
    d. 1.20 moles
    e. 3.38 moles

8. A sample of 0.605 mole of O_2 occupies a volume of 15.0 L at a particular pressure and temperature. If the number of moles of O_2 is increased to 1.00 mole, what volume will the gas occupy?
    a. 9.08 L
    b. 22.4 L
    c. 24.8 L
    d. 25 L
    e. 40.3 L

9. A sample of a gas is confined in a 3.00 L vessel at 1.02 atm and 298 K. If the volume of the vessel is reduced to 2.00 L and the temperature is increased to 315 K, what will the resulting pressure be?
    a. 0.719 atm
    b. 2.57 atm
    c. 1.45 atm
    d. 1.08 atm
    e. 1.62 atm

10. A sample of a gas is confined in a 8.03 L vessel at 1.07 atm and 298 K. If the pressure of the vessel is reduced to 0.330 atm and the temperature is increased to 375 K, what will the resulting volume be?
    a. 20.7 L
    b. 32.8 L
    c. 0.484 L
    d. 4.08 L
    e. 3.12 L

11. A sample of SiH_4 was collected in a 250.0 mL vessel at 22.0 °C and 0.0128 atm. What volume will the SiH_4 occupy at STP?
    a. 2.96 L
    b. 0.00346 L
    c. 3.46 L
    d. 0.00296 L
    e. 0.0397 L

12. A sample of a gas was collected in a 1.00 L vessel at 300.0 K and 0.772 atm. At what temperature will the volume be 2.00 L and the pressure be 1.00 atm?
    a. 463 K
    b. 389 K
    c. 777 K
    d. 600 K
    e. 194 K

13. A sample of 30.5 g of N_2 is confined in a 20.0 L vessel at 298 K. What is the pressure of the N_2?
    a. 1.22 atm
    b. 37.3 atm
    c. 34.3 atm
    d. 0.112 atm
    e. 1.33 atm

14. A sample of 2.00 moles of CO_2 is confined at 3.00 atm and 0.0 °C. What volume does the gas occupy?
    a. 14.9 L
    b. 44.8 L
    c. 7.47 L
    d. 134 L
    e. 33.6 L

15. A sample of 0.0223 g of a gas is confined in a 1.00 L vessel at 0.00554 atm and 273 K. What is the molar mass of the gas?
    a. 0.000247 g/mole
    b. 22.4 g/mole
    c. 4050 g/mole
    d. 0.0111 g/mole
    e. 90.2 g/mole

16. A sample of 1.00 mole of a gas is confined in a 20.0 L vessel At what temperature will the pressure in the vessel be 2.00 atm?
    a. 214 K
    b. 40.0 K
    c. 244 K
    d. 487 K
    e. 273 K

17. Which of the following is not a valid part of the kinetic molecular theory?
    a. Kinetic energy is related to absolute temperature.
    b. Gas molecules have significant volumes.
    c. Gases are composed of molecules.
    d. Collisions of gas molecules are elastic.
    e. Molecules are always in motion and therefore possess kinetic energy.

18. Which of the following is true of gases according to the kinetic molecular theory?
    a. Gas molecules essentially have no mass.
    b. Gases can be compressed because their atoms are soft.
    c. Gases readily diffuse.
    d. There is little empty space between molecules.
    e. Collisions of molecules can be readily prevented.

19. A gaseous mixture is analyzed giving the pressures of the components to be 0.205 atm N_2, 75.0 torr CO_2, 5 torr He, and 83 torr CO. What is the total pressure of the mixture?
    a. 163 torr
    b. 708 torr
    c. 760 torr
    d. 319 torr
    e. 150 torr

20. A gaseous mixture of hydrogen, oxygen, and nitrogen exerts a total pressure of 1.00 atm. If the partial pressure of H_2 is 15.0 torr and the partial pressure of oxygen is 152 torr, what is the partial pressure of nitrogen?
 a. 593 torr
 b. 760 torr
 c. 168 torr
 d. 608 torr
 e. 927 torr

21. What is the density of $SO_{2(g)}$ at STP?
 a. 1.00 g/L
 b. 0.0446 g/L
 c. 0.350 g/L
 d. 2.86 g/L
 e. 0.235 g/L

22. A gas is found to have a density of 2.05 g/L at STP. What is the molar mass of the gas?
 a. 10.9 g/mole
 b. 1620 g/mole
 c. 6820 g/mole
 d. 133 g/mole
 e. 45.9 g/mole

23. Consider the equation:

$$2\,NO_{2(g)} \rightarrow N_2O_{4(g)}$$

What volume of N_2O_4 at STP is formed when 100.0 g of NO_2 are used in the reaction?
 a. 97.4 L
 b. 24.4 L
 c. 11.2 L
 d. 48.7 L
 e. 100.0 L

24. Consider the equation:

$$H_{2(g)} + I_{2(g)} \rightarrow 2\,HI_{(g)}$$

What volume of H_2 at 22 °C and 15.0 atm is required to produce 256 g of HI?
 a. 3.23 L
 b. 0.121 L
 c. 6.48 L
 d. 128 L
 e. 1.62 L

Answers to the Sample Quiz Questions

1. (c), 2. (b), 3. (d), 4. (c), 5. (a), 6. (b), 7. (a), 8. (c), 9. (e), 10. (b), 11. (d), 12. (c), 13. (e), 14. (a), 15. (e), 16. (d), 17. (b), 18. (c), 19. (d), 20. (a), 21. (d), 22. (e), 23. (b), 24. (e)

LIQUIDS AND SOLIDS

CHAPTER
11

Chapter Overview

Chapter 11 discusses the properties of liquids and solids, much as Chapter 10 dealt with gases. Since the interactions of particles in the condensed phases are so much more complex than in gases, this chapter is very descriptive in nature and limits calculations to those dealing with the energetics of heating and cooling and phases changes.

The chapter begins with a discussion of intermolecular forces to build a foundation for the observed properties of liquids and solids. The specific properties of liquids are then covered, including density, surface tension, viscosity, and vaporization. The concepts of boiling points and heats of vaporization and their calculation are discussed here. Following the description of liquids are sections covering the analogous properties of solids, including the structures of solid materials, melting, heats of fusion, and melting points. The calculations associated with the energetics of the melting process are also covered.

The chapter closes with an optional section which treats energy calculations in considerably more detail than in the previous sections of the chapter. This section ties together the energetics of phase changes with those of heating and cooling and so broadens the range of properties and temperatures which can be described.

Solutions to the Study Questions and Problems

1. **a. Liquefaction** is the process in which a gas is condensed into a liquid and includes those cases where extreme pressure is required to perform the phase change. **b. Condensation** is generally synonymous with liquefaction although it excludes the application of pressure. **c. Dipolar attractions** are intermolecular forces which exist between polar molecules due to the separation of charge. **d. London dispersion forces** are intermolecular forces which exist between molecules, both polar and nonpolar, due to the creation of instantaneous dipoles by fluctuating electron clouds. **e. Hydrogen bonds** are intermolecular forces which represent an extreme case of dipolar attraction in which hydrogen atoms are bonded to oxygen, nitrogen, or fluorine atoms. This situation gives extremely polar bonds with high partial charges and so constitute the strongest of the intermolecular forces.

2. The three kinds of intermolecular forces are dipolar attractions, hydrogen bonds, and London dispersion forces. All three are based on polarity. The weakest, London dispersion forces, operates by the attraction between instantaneously induced dipoles. The instantaneous dipoles are created as the electron clouds shift in response to a nearby charge. Adjacent molecules then allign themselves so as to reinforce the shift. The partial charges are very small since the ability of the electron clouds to distort is limited. The dipolar attractions are intermediate in strength. They arise from the existence of permanent dipoles within the molecules; the molecules are polar. In this case, the partial charges are larger than in London dispersion forces since the dipoles are permanent and more pronounced. The strongest of the forces, hydrogen bonding, arises from the dipolar attraction of molecules containing H–N, H–O, or H–F bonds. These particular bonds are extremely polar and show unusually large partial charges which are so unique so as to make this type of interaction be considered a separate kind.

3. **a.** In CCl_4, there would only be London dispersion forces since the molecule is nonpolar. **b.** In CH_3OH, there will be London dispersion forces, dipolar attractions, and hydrogen bonding since the molecule is polar and contains O–H bonds. **c.** In Ne, there will only be London dispersion forces (very weak ones) since, as a monatomic element, there cannot be any fixed polarity and only a very small induced dipole. **d.** In CH_3CH_3, there will only be London dispersion forces since the molecule is nonpolar. (Note the end-to-end symmetry of the molecule.) **e.** In N_2, there will only be London dispersion forces since the molecule is nonpolar. **f.** In CH_3NH_2, there will be London dispersion forces, dipolar attractions, and hydrogen bonding since the molecule is polar and contains N–H bonds. (The C–N bond is slightly polar.)

4. The two classes of liquids are polar and nonpolar liquids. As their names imply, the basis for differentiation is whether the molecules exhibit polarity. Polar liquids are composed of polar molecules and are held together by dipolar attractions and by London dispersion forces and, if the molecules contain hydrogen bonded to oxygen, nitrogen, or fluorine, by hydrogen bonding. Nonpolar liquids are composed of nonpolar molecules and are held together only by London dispersion forces.

5. Since boiling requires the breaking of the intermolecular forces holding the molecules together as the liquid sample, weaker intermolecular forces should require less energy to overcome. This translates to lower temperature. Nonpolar liquids are held together only by London dispersion forces which are the weakest forces and so they should and, all other things being equal, do boil at lower temperatures than polar liquids.

6. Boiling point is related to the strength of intermolecular forces. Since hydrogen bonding is a stronger intermolecular force than dipolar attractions, liquids which exhibit hydrogen bonding should have higher boiling points than those polar molecules which do not exhibit hydrogen bonding.

7. Liquids are generally less dense than solids because the molecules in liquids are farther apart than the molecules in solids. The additional space is required in order for the molecules of liquid to travel through the sample.

8. Water is unusually dense since it has hydrogen bonding. The hydrogen bonding is a strong attractive force which pulls the molecules closer together. Having more molecules within a given volume results in higher density.

9. Oil floats on water because it is less dense than water so it rises to the top of the water.

10. Surface tension is the force acting on the surface of a liquid which tends to minimize surface area. It is a state of imbalanced intermolecular forces which arises from the inability of the surface molecules to extend their intermolecular forces in all directions and makes the intermolecular forces at the surface relatively strong compared to within the bulk of the liquid.

11. Surface tension is affected by the molecular structure of the liquid because molecular structure affects the strength of the intermolecular forces in the liquid and the intermolecular forces determine the surface tension.

12. When water coats glass, it is because the strength of the intermolecular forces between water molecules and glass molecules is competitive with or stronger than the intermolecular forces between adjacent water molecules. This allows the water to actually increase its surface area since there is more energy advantage to spreading out and maximizing the glass contact.

13. Viscosity is a liquid's resistance to flow. Therefore, a "thick" liquid like tar has a high viscosity since it resists flowing well while a "thin" liquid like alcohol has a low viscosity since it doesn't resist flowing very well. To the contrary, alcohol flows very well.

14. The molecular structure of a liquid has a profound effect on its viscosity. The stronger the intermolecular forces between molecules, the more resistance there is to flowing and the higher the viscosity. Those factors which lead to strong intermolecular forces, such as polarity and hydrogen bonds, will necessarily lead to higher viscosities.

15. An increase in temperature decreases viscosity while a decrease in temperature increases viscosity. An increase in temperature causes an increase in the average kinetic energy of the molecules which weakens the intermolecular forces and allows a liquid to flow more easily.

16. a. Vaporization is the conversion of molecules in the liquid phase to the gas phase. **b. Evaporation** is the term given to vaporization if the process leads to a significant loss of the amount of liquid. (Consider the evaporation of a puddle of water after a rain shower.) **c. Sublimation** is the conversion of molecules in the solid phase to the gas phase without first passing through the liquid phase. (Consider how snow can noticeably disappear even at 0 °F.) **d.** A **dynamic equilibrium** is a process in which the molecules continue to move yet there is no net change. Using vaporization and condensation as an example, individual molecules in a closed container will continue to pass from liquid to gas and from gas to liquid. (That's the "dynamic" part.) There is no net change in the amount of liquid or the amount of vapor, though. (That's the "equilibrium" part.) **e.** The **vapor pressure of a liquid** is pressure exerted by a vapor in equilibrium with its liquid. Due to the equilibrium with its liquid, vapor molecules do not behave exactly like other gases, though. **f.** A liquid is said to be **volatile** when it has a high vapor pressure, a low boiling point, and evaporates easily.

17. The dynamic equilibrium that exists between a liquid and its vapor in a closed container is characterized by vaporization of liquid molecules simultaneously with condensation of vapor molecules. Further, in equilibrium, the rate of vaporization is the same as the rate of condensation. That means that the same number of liquid molecules are vaporizing in a given period of time as the number of vapor molecules that are condensing in the same period. The net effect is that the total number of liquid molecules remains constant as does the number of vapor molecules.

18. Vapor pressure reflects the ease with which molecules can escape the liquid phase. When the intermolecular forces are strong, the molecules in the liquid phase travel at a slower velocity and find it more difficult to escape, reducing the rate of vaporization and the vapor pressure. When the intermolecular forces are weak, the molecules in the liquid phase can move at higher velocities and escape more easily, increasing the rate of vaporization and the vapor pressure.

19. Water has a lower vapor pressure at any given temperature than ethyl alcohol and ethyl ether because the intermolecular forces at work in water are stronger than those at work in ethyl alcohol and ethyl ether. All three substances have hydrogen bonding, but water is able to form a more extensive network of hydrogen bonds because it is the smallest and simplest molecule of the three.

20. Ethyl ether must be tightly capped because it is a very volatile liquid, meaning that, if not confined, it will evaporate easily. If left without being tightly sealed, the ethyl ether soon will disappear through evaporation.

21. Increasing temperature increases vapor pressure due to an increase in the average kinetic energy of the molecules in the liquid phase and the increased ease with which they can escape from the liquid. Cooling has the opposite effect.

22. The **boiling point** of a liquid is that temperature at which the vapor pressure of the liquid equals the barometric pressure.

23. As atmospheric pressure decreases, so does the boiling point of a liquid. As atmospheric pressure increases, so does the boiling point of a liquid. The boiling point varies like this since the boiling point is the temperature at which the vapor pressure of the liquid equals the atmospheric pressure. When atmospheric pressure is reduced, a lower vapor pressure is required to boil and a lower temperature is required to generate that vapor pressure. When atmospheric pressure is increased, a higher vapor pressure is required to boil and a higher temperature is required to generate that vapor pressure.

24. On a mountain, the atmospheric pressure is lower (610 torr) than it is at lower altitudes (760 torr at sea level, on average). Therefore, in order to boil water on the mountain, only a vapor pressure of 610 torr needs to be attained. A vapor pressure of 610 torr is generated at a lower temperature than is required to generate a vapor pressure of 760 torr (100 °C for water).

25. Water boils at a higher temperature than most other liquids of similar formula weight because it exhibits such strong hydrogen bonding. The stronger intermolecular force reduces the vapor pressure at any given temperature and, therefore, a higher temperature is required to generate a high enough vapor pressure to boil.

26. During the boiling process, the heat being added (*e.g.*, from a stove or a burner) is not being converted into warming the liquid. It is supplying the energy necessary for the molecules of liquid to break their intermolecular forces, and vaporize en masse. Both warming a liquid and boiling it involve increasing the kinetic energy of the molecules but, in warming, the molecules are not accelerated to velocities sufficient for the average molecule to break its intermolecular forces. During boiling, the kinetic energy being supplied to the molecules is sufficient for the average molecule to break its intermolecular forces and escape.

27. The **molar heat of vaporization** of a liquid is the amount of heat required to vaporize one mole of a boiling liquid at one atmosphere of pressure. The symbol given to this quantity, which is characteristic of a liquid, is ΔH_{vap}.

28. As the strength of intermolecular forces increases, so does ΔH_{vap}. As the strength of intermolecular forces increases, the amount of work required to break those forces increases. It is that increase of required work which is reflected in the value of ΔH_{vap}.

29. Water's molar heat of vaporization is high because of its strong intermolecular forces. The exceptional strength of these intermolecular forces directly relates to the high ΔH_{vap} of water.

30. Perspiration cools the body because evaporation requires heat. As the perspiration evaporates, it obtains the necessary heat from the area surrounding the molecules, including the skin. This drain of heat from the skin by the evaporating molecules is what cools us.

31. From Table 11-7, the molar heat of vaporization of water is 40.6 kJ/mole. Therefore:

$$\frac{(3.75 \text{ g } H_2O)(1 \text{ mole } H_2O)(\quad 40.6 \text{ kJ}\quad)}{(18.0 \text{ g } H_2O)(1 \text{ mole } H_2O)} = 8.46 \text{ kJ}$$

32. $\dfrac{(3.00 \times 10^{23} \text{ molecules } H_2O)(\quad\quad 1 \text{ mole } H_2O\quad\quad)(\quad 40.6 \text{ kJ}\quad)}{(6.02 \times 10^{23} \text{ molecules } H_2O)(1 \text{ mole } H_2O)} = 20.2 \text{ kJ}$

33. Solids are rigid and have fixed volumes because the particles, whether atoms, ions, or molecules, are close enough together and the intermolecular forces are strong enough to keep them from moving through the sample. The only motion in solids is some degree of vibration. Since the individual particles cannot move, the entire sample remains rigid.

34. The two types of solids are crystalline solids and amorphous solids. Crystalline solids show a high degree of long reaching internal organization as shown by their crystal lattices. This organization is a repeating geometric pattern of particles in all three dimensions. Amorphous solids do not show this internal organization. If any patterns exist, they are so short that they are not outwardly apparent. Amorphous solids are characterized by disorder.

35. When crystals form very slowly, the particles have the opportunity to find their most stable positions in the lattice, those which preserve the pattern. If a crystal forms more rapidly, there is a rush of particles to find their positions, resulting in more defects as particles get added, trapping their predecessors before they can find the more organized positions.

36. The five types of crystals and their distinguishing features are:

1. Ionic crystals - These crystals are composed of oppositely charged ions in orderly three-dimensional arrays.
2. Molecular crystals - These crystals are composed of molecules in orderly three-dimensional arrays.
3. Covalent crystals - These crystals are composed of orderly three-dimensional arrays of atoms which are covalently bonded to one another.
4. Metallic crystals - These crystals are composed of orderly three-dimensional arrays of metal atoms which are bonded to one another by what is called a metallic bond. The metallic bond is described as having metal cations in the arrays, swimming in a sea of electrons.
5. Atomic crystals - These crystals are composed of orderly three-dimensional arrays of atoms. It differs from the metallic crystal in that these atoms do not release electrons as in the metals.

37. Molecular crystals generally have lower melting points than ionic crystals since the molecular crystals are held together with intermolecular forces which are weak compared to the cation-anion attraction which holds ionic crystals together.

38. Graphite is slippery because the giant "molecules" occur as plates with strong covalent bonds in two dimensions, not three. The plates can then be slid across each other, acting as a lubricant.

39. Covalent crystals have very high melting points due to the strength of the covalent bonds which must be broken to melt them and due to the number of bonds which must be broken.

40. The forces which correspond to the five types of lattices are:

1. In ionic crystals, the forces are ionic attractions between oppositely charged cations and anions (the ionic bond). Examples would include almost any metal-nonmetal compound, such as $NaCl$, BaF_2, $CsNO_3$, etc.
2. In molecular crystals, the forces can be one or more of the intermolecular forces (dipolar attractions, hydrogen bonding, or London dispersion forces). Examples would include ice, diatomic elements, and other nonmetallic compounds.
3. In covalent crystals, the forces are covalent bonds between atoms, forming long networks of bonded atoms. Examples would include diamond, graphite, and quartz.
4. In metallic crystals, the forces are the attraction of metal atoms to loosely held electrons of neighboring atoms. These electrons are fairly "free" and their mobility accounts for the electrical conductivity of metals. Examples would be virtually any solid metal or metal alloy.
5. In atomic crystals, the forces are London dispersion forces only. Since the atoms have no bonds, they cannot be polar. Examples are limited to the noble gases.

41. The two causes of the internal disorder seen in amorphous solids are 1) the rapid cooling of the liquid to form the solid, which prevents the formation of the well-ordered arrays of particles, and 2) the existence of polymers, which are long chains of covalently bonded atoms (often hundreds or thousands of atoms long) which, due to their size, cannot pack neatly into a crystal lattice.

42. Glass is considered an amorphous solid because the Si–O linkages are irregularly spaced. (See Figure 11-17 in the text.) This irregularity prevents the formation of a crystal.

43. A polymer is a material which consists of long chain molecules with many smaller units (called monomers) repeating for the length of the molecule. Many polymers are amorphous solids due to irregularities in the repeating pattern or complexity of the pattern which prevents it from solidifying in a neat, organized fashion characteristic of crystals.

44. While being heated, particles in a crystalline solid gain kinetic energy which allows them to vibrate more. As the heating continues, the particles vibrate more and more until they have enough kinetic energy to break the lattice forces which held them in place. At the point where the kinetic energy of the particles is sufficent to break the lattice forces, melting occurs. Now, as a liquid, the particles are free enough to move around within the sample.

45. The dynamic equilibrium which exists between solid and liquid at the melting point is very similar to the one that exist between liquid and vapor at the boiling point. Here, the rate of melting is equal to the rate of freezing, meaning that equal numbers of solid particles melt and liquid particles freeze in a given period of time. The effect is that there is no net change in the number of solid particles or liquid particles.

46. The **melting point** of a solid is that temperature at which the solid and liquid are at equilibrium with each other.

47. During the melting process, the energy which is put into the sample is being consumed by the breakage of the lattice forces holding the material together rather than into warming the solid. While there are particles of solid left to consume the energy, the temperature will remain constant. Only after all of the solid has been melted will the energy being applied go toward warming of the liquid sample.

48. The **molar heat of fusion**, ΔH_{fus}, is the amount of energy required to melt one mole of a crystalline solid at its melting point.

49. The molar heat of fusion is usually smaller than the molar heat of vaporization of the same substance since melting requires the amount of energy required to disrupt a crystal lattice. The particles are still left in contact with one another so there are still intermolecular forces. Vaporization requires the amount of energy necessary to break the intermolecular forces and, therefore, separate the particles. Intermolecular forces are generally stronger than lattice forces.

50. Since molar heat of fusion is the energy required to disrupt the lattice forces of a crystal, the stronger the lattice forces, the more energy will be required to break them and, therefore, the higher the molar heat of fusion.

51. From Table 11-8, the molar heat of fusion of water is 5.98 kJ/mole. Therefore:

$$\frac{(50.0 \text{ g } H_2O)(1 \text{ mole } H_2O)(\ 5.98 \text{ kJ}\ )}{(18.0 \text{ g } H_2O)(1 \text{ mole } H_2O)} = 16.6 \text{ kJ}$$

52. The molar mass of benzene is 6(12.0 g/mole) + 6(1.0 g/mole) = 78.0 g/mole. Therefore:

$$\text{heat} = \frac{(\quad \text{mass} \quad)(\Delta H_{fus})}{(\text{molar mass})}$$

$$\Delta H_{fus} = \frac{(\text{heat})(\text{molar mass})}{(\quad \text{mass} \quad)}$$

$$\Delta H_{fus} = \frac{(1.892 \text{ kJ})(78.0 \text{ g/mole})}{(\quad 15.0 \text{ g} \quad)}$$

$$\Delta H_{fus} = 9.84 \text{ kJ/mole}$$

53. Melting points of pure crystalline solids tend to be sharp (well-defined) since the individual forces holding the particles in place tend to be very similar throughout the crystal. Therefore, the particles gain suffcient energy to break the lattice forces at very nearly the same temperature.

54. As lattice forces increase, so do melting points. This is because the melting point reflects the energy required to break the lattice forces. The stronger the lattice forces, the more energy is required to break them and the higher the temperature required to supply that amount of energy.

55. Amorphous solids have broad melting ranges rather than sharp melting points because the forces within the solid vary with the amount of disorganization which exists in different parts of the sample. Therefore, different amounts of energy are required to melt different parts of the sample and a range of temperatures is required to provide those energies.

56. The heating curve of H_2O from -25 °C to 125 °C showing all the phase transitions and temperature increases is:

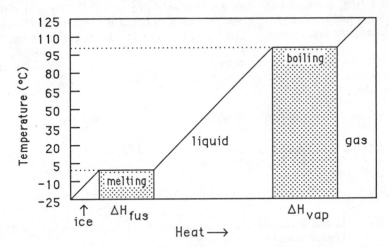

57. The amount of water in moles is: $\dfrac{(25.0 \text{ g})(1 \text{ mole})}{(18.0 \text{ g})} = 1.39$ moles

For warming ice: $\dfrac{(0.492 \text{ cal})(25.0 \text{ g})(15 \text{ °C})}{(1 \text{ g-°C})} = 180$ cal

For melting ice: $\dfrac{(1.39 \text{ moles})(5.98 \text{ kJ})(1000 \text{ J})(1.000 \text{ cal})}{(1 \text{ mole })(1 \text{ kJ})(4.184 \text{ J})} = 1990$ cal

For warming liquid: $\dfrac{(1.000 \text{ cal})(25.0 \text{ g})(100.0 \text{ °C})}{(1 \text{ g-°C})} = 2.50 \times 10^3$ cal

For boiling water: $\dfrac{(1.39 \text{ moles})(40.6 \text{ kJ})(1000 \text{ J})(1.000 \text{ cal})}{(1 \text{ mole })(1 \text{ kJ})(4.184 \text{ J})} = 13500$ cal

The sum of the heat required for the processes is: 180 cal + 1990 cal + 2500 cal + 13500 cal =

18200 cal.

58. The number of moles of water is: $\dfrac{(4.60 \times 10^{23} \text{ molecules})(1 \text{ mole})}{(6.02 \times 10^{23} \text{ molecules})} = 0.764$ mole

The number of grams of water is: $\dfrac{(0.764 \text{ mole})(18.0 \text{ g})}{(1 \text{ mole})} = 13.8$ g

For warming ice: $\dfrac{(0.492 \text{ cal})(13.8 \text{ g})(8 \text{ °C})}{(1 \text{ g-°C})} = 50$ cal

For melting ice: $\dfrac{(0.764 \text{ moles})(5.98 \text{ kJ})(1000 \text{ J})(1.000 \text{ cal})}{(1 \text{ mole })(1 \text{ kJ})(4.184 \text{ J})} = 1090$ cal

For warming liquid: $\dfrac{(1.000 \text{ cal})(13.8 \text{ g})(100.0 \text{ °C})}{(1 \text{ g-°C})} = 1380$ cal

For boiling water: $\dfrac{(0.764 \text{ moles})(40.6 \text{ kJ})(1000 \text{ J})(1.000 \text{ cal})}{(1 \text{ mole })(1 \text{ kJ})(4.184 \text{ J})} = 7410$ cal

The sum of the heat required for the processes is: 50 cal + 1090 cal + 1380 cal + 7410 cal =

9930 cal.

59. The number of moles of O_2 is: $\dfrac{(100.0 \text{ g})(1 \text{ mole})}{(32.0 \text{ g})} = 3.125$ moles

For cooling gaseous O_2: $\dfrac{(0.228 \text{ cal})(100.0 \text{ g})(208 \text{ °C})(4.184 \text{ J})(1.000 \text{ kJ})}{(1 \text{ g-°C})\qquad\qquad(1.000 \text{ cal})(1000 \text{ J})} = 19.8$ kJ

For condensing O_2: $\dfrac{(3.125 \text{ moles})(6.82 \text{ kJ})}{(1 \text{ mole})} = 21.3$ kJ

For cooling liquid O_2: $\dfrac{(0.35 \text{ cal})(100.0 \text{ g})(17 \text{ °C})(4.184 \text{ J})(1.000 \text{ kJ})}{(1 \text{ g-°C})\qquad\qquad(1.000 \text{ cal})(1000 \text{ J})} = 2.5$ kJ

The sum of the heat required for the processes is: $19.8 \text{ kJ} + 21.3 \text{ kJ} + 2.5 \text{ kJ} = 43.6$ kJ

60. Freeze-drying is important in the preservation of many products, including plasma, since the technique involves fast freezing and then sublimation of the ice at low pressure and temperature, avoiding the damage to the product which would occur if the water was eliminated at higher temperatures.

61. a. The volumes of liquids and solids are both essentially constant. Neither can be significantly compressed to smaller volumes.
b. The shape of a liquid is that of its container (at least the bottom of it, depending on how full it is). The shape of a solid is independent of its container since solids are rigid.
c. The attractive forces are greater among solids. Both phases have intermolecular forces but, in addition, crystalline solids also have lattice forces.
d. The relative distances between particles is greater for liquids than for solids. This is because liquids lack the lattice forces which would make them rigidly organized and the molecules require the extra distance in order to move.
e. Molecules in liquids are much more mobile than molecules in solids. Molecules in liquids are in constant motion. Molecules in solids are held in place and can only vibrate.
f. Solids exhibit much more molecular organization than liquids due to the lattice forces. Molecules in liquids are not very organized and, due to their motion, what organization there may be is constantly changing.
g. The types of particles which can exist in solids and liquids are the same. The difference between the solid phase and the liquid phase is a physical, not chemical, difference.

62. Foods must be cooked longer at higher elevations since the boiling point of the cooking water is lower than at lower elevations. If complete cooking is related to the amount of heat put into the food, it will take longer cooking times at high elevation since less heat is being supplied to the food per minute of cooking time due to the lower boiling temperature.

63. Dry ice must be kept in a closed container since it (solid CO_2) easily sublimes at room pressure.

64. A razor blade can float due to the surface tension of the water. If the blade is placed in the water on edge, it will sink. In order to float, it must be laid flat on the water.

65. The molar mass of ammonia, NH_3, is: $1(14.0 \text{ g/mole}) + 3(1.0 \text{ g/mole}) = 17.0$ g/mole

$$\Delta H_{vap} = \frac{(\text{heat})(\text{molar mass})}{(\text{mass})}$$

$$\Delta H_{vap} = \frac{(13.7 \text{ kJ})(17.0 \text{ g/mole})}{(10.0 \text{ g})}$$

$$\Delta H_{vap} = 23.3 \text{ kJ/mole}$$

66. Quick-freezing protects food since, by freezing food as rapidly as possible, the ice formed is composed of very small crystals and amorphous solid. This prevents the cells from being ruptured during the process and keeps the original form of the food.

67. Ice is less dense than water because of the state of organization in the solid. In the cold liquid, the molecules are at their closest. Upon freezing, the molecules, in their efforts to form as many hydrogen bonds as possible, actually have to move to slightly larger distances from one another, reducing the density.

68. From Table 11-8, the ΔH_{fus} of I_2 is 17 kJ/mole.

The number of moles of I_2 in the sample is: $\dfrac{(1.00 \times 10^{23} \text{ molecules})(1 \text{ mole})}{(6.02 \times 10^{23} \text{ molecules})}$

$= 0.166 \text{ mole}$

$\dfrac{(0.166 \text{ mole})(17 \text{ kJ})}{(1 \text{ mole})} = 2.82 \text{ kJ}$

69. For liquid water: $\dfrac{(1.00 \text{ mole})(18.0 \text{ g})(1.000 \text{ cal})(63\ ^\circ C)}{(1.00 \text{ mole})(1.000 \text{ g-}^\circ C)} = 1130 \text{ cal}$

For condensing steam: $\dfrac{(1.00 \text{ mole})(40.6 \text{ kJ})(1000 \text{ J})(1.000 \text{ cal})}{(1 \text{ mole})(1.000 \text{ kJ})(4.184 \text{ J})} = 9.70 \times 10^3 \text{cal}$

Therefore, in cooling to 37 °C, liquid water only releases 1130 cal/mole while the steam cooled to 37 °C releases $1130 + 9.70 \times 10^3 = 10800$ cal, almost ten times as much heat as the liquid water.

Sample Quiz Questions

1. Which of the following exhibits only London dispersion forces?
   a. $IBr_{(l)}$
   b. $H_2SO_{4(l)}$
   c. $CCl_{4(l)}$
   d. $Al_2O_{3(s)}$
   e. $HF_{(l)}$

2. Which of the following exhibits hydrogen bonding?
   a. $CH_{4(l)}$
   b. $PH_{3(g)}$
   c. $NaH_{(s)}$
   d. $CH_3CH_2OH_{(l)}$
   e. $HI_{(g)}$

3. The forces which bind the molecules of a polar liquid, like CH_3Cl, together are
   a. London dispersion forces and dipolar attractions.
   b. generally large compared to the forces which bind ionic solids.
   c. London dispersion forces.
   d. hydrogen bonding.
   e. usually very weak.

4. Liquids are generally less dense than solids because
    a. the molecules in solids are farther apart.
    b. the intermolecular forces in liquids are stronger.
    c. to organize into a lattice, the distances between molecules increase.
    d. molecules in liquids tend to have less kinetic energy than molecules in solids.
    e. the molecules in liquids are farther apart.

5. Which of the following liquids should have the highest density? (all have about the same molecular weight)
    a. C_8H_{18}
    b. GeF_3
    c. BrCl
    d. $SiHCl_3$
    e. C_9H_9

6. Which of the following liquids should have the highest surface tension?
    a. CCl_4
    b. $CHCl_3$
    c. CH_2Cl_2
    d. CH_3OH
    e. CH_4

7. Which of the following liquids should have the lowest surface tension?
    a. CH_3OH
    b. CH_4
    c. CH_3F
    d. CH_2F_2
    e. CHF_3

8. Which of the following liquids should have the highest viscosity?
    a. $C_{10}H_{22}$
    b. C_8H_{18}
    c. C_6H_{14}
    d. C_4H_{10}
    e. C_2H_6

9. Viscosity generally
    a. increases with decreasing molecular weight.
    b. is the measure of a liquid's ability to flow.
    c. increases with increasing temperature.
    d. is unexpectedly low for water.
    e. increases with increasing intermolecular forces.

10. A dynamic equilibrium
    a. means that there is no change.
    b. exists when opposite processes occur at the same rate.
    c. exists between a liquid and its vapor in an open vessel.
    d. refers to the production of vapors by a liquid.
    e. exists when opposite processes occur simultaneously.

11. Vapor pressure generally
      a. is affected by the intermolecular forces of the liquid.
      b. is the same for most substances at a given temperature.
      c. increases as the kinetic energy of the liquid molecules decreases.
      d. is independent of temperature.
      e. increases with increasing intermolecular forces.

12. Boiling points generally
      a. decrease with increasing strength of the intermolecular forces in a liquid.
      b. increase with decreasing atmospheric pressure.
      c. decrease with decreasing atmospheric pressure.
      d. decrease with increasing viscosity.
      e. depend only on the atmospheric pressure.

13. Water boils
      a. more slowly at high altitudes.
      b. at a higher temperature in Death Valley than in Denver.
      c. at a constant temperature of 100 °C.
      d. at a lower temperature in Death Valley than in Denver.
      e. only if heated to a high temperature.

14. The molar heat of vaporization of chloroform, $CHCl_3$, is 31.9 kJ/mole. How much heat is required to vaporize 97.0 g of chloroform at its boiling point?
      a. 3090 kJ
      b. 0.267 kJ
      c. 39.3 kJ
      d. 25.9 kJ
      e. 3.75 kJ

15. A sample of 1.00 kg of glycerin, $C_3H_8O_3$, requires 828 kJ to vaporize at its boiling point. What is the molar heat of vaporization of glycerin?
      a. 9.00×10^3 kJ/mole
      b. 76.2 J/mole
      c. 7.62×10^4 kJ/mole
      d. 1.21 kJ/mole
      e. 76.2 kJ/mole

16. Crystalline solids
      a. show a high degree of organization.
      b. have lower melting points than amorphous solids.
      c. are less organized than amorphous solids.
      d. are usually made up of oppositely charged ions.
      e. have relatively low intermolecular forces compared to liquids.

17. Ionic crystals generally
      a. have weak intermolecular forces.
      b. conduct electricity.
      c. are unstable.
      d. have lower melting points than molecular crystals of the same size.
      e. have higher melting points than atomic crystals.

18. When melting of a crystal occurs,
   a. the particles in the solid are rigidly held in place but are vibrating rapidly.
   b. the kinetic energy of the particles exceeds the energy of the intermolecular forces.
   c. some particles require much less energy than others while some require much more.
   d. energy is given off.
   e. it is over a range of temperatures.

19. The molar heat of fusion for crystalline substances generally
   a. is higher for molecular crystals than for ionic crystals.
   b. decreases with increasing strength of intermolecular forces.
   c. is the amount of heat required to melt one gram of a substance at its melting point.
   d. is lower than the molar heat of vaporization for the same substance.
   e. is higher for atomic crystals than for molecular crystals.

20. The molar heat of fusion for iodine, I_2, is 17 kJ/mole. If 1.00 kg of iodine is melted at its melting oint, how much energy is required?
   a. 3.9 kJ
   b. 4.3 kJ
   c. 67 kJ
   d. 0.067 kJ
   e. 17000 kJ

21. Amorphous solids generally
   a. exhibit an organized packing of atoms within the crystal.
   b. melt suddenly at a well defined temperature.
   c. result from slow freezing of the liquid.
   d. are more stable than crystalline solids.
   e. melt over a range of temperatures.

22. The melting points of crystalline substances generally
   a. are lower than for amorphous solids of the same molecular weight.
   b. increase with increasing strength of the intermolecular forces in the solid.
   c. vary widely with changes in atmospheric pressure.
   d. are a broad range of temperatures, not a well defined temperature.
   e. increase with decreasing strength of the intermolecular forces in the solid.

23. Given that for H_2O, $\Delta H_{fus} = 5.98$ kJ/mole, $\Delta H_{vap} = 40.6$ kJ/mole, and the specific heat of liquid water is 1.00 cal/g-°C, calculate the amount of heat required to convert 55.5 g of water from ice at 0.00 °C to liquid water at 99.9 °C.
   a. 9950 cal
   b. 18.4 cal
   c. 4410 cal
   d. 5540 cal
   e. 1130 cal

Answers to the Sample Quiz Questions

1. (c), 2. (d), 3. (a), 4. (e), 5. (c), 6. (d), 7. (b), 8. (a), 9. (e), 10. (b), 11. (a), 12. (c), 13. (b), 14. (d), 15. (e), 16. (a), 17. (e), 18. (b), 19. (d), 20. (c), 21. (e), 22. (b), 23. (a)

WATER AND AQUEOUS SOLUTIONS

CHAPTER

12

Chapter Overview

Chapter 12 discusses the properties of water and its solutions, perhaps the most common reaction medium in chemistry. Given water's role in nature and in the history of chemistry, it is fitting that the behavior of water and aqueous solutions be emphasized. As the foundation for understanding aqueous solutions, the chapter first describes the properties of water and the properties of solutions, including the solution process and solubility.

The molarity and percent systems of expressing concentration are then covered as a way to quantitatively describe the amount of a solute in solution. The techniques of calculating dilutions and performing stoichiometric calculations are also covered here.

The chapter concludes with two optional sections. The first one discusses the colligative properties of solutions, vapor pressure lowering, boiling point elevation, freezing point lowering, and osmotic pressure. The second optional section describes the properties of colloids and suspensions.

Solutions to the Study Questions and Problems

1. The molecular arrangement of ice is more rigid than liquid water. Due to the formation of the crystal, there is more space between molecules in the ice than in the liquid water so ice is less dense than cold liquid water.

2. In liquid water, the molecules are in constant motion, breaking and reforming hydrogen bonds. A liquid water molecule, on average, forms three hydrogen bonds to other molecules. In ice, the molecules are held in a fixed arrangement with each molecule forming four hydrogen bonds to other molecules.

3. Ice is less dense than liquid water because there is more space between water molecules in the rigid arrangement of ice as compared to liquid water.

4. All of these properties increase with increasing strength of intermolecular forces. All of these relatively high values are due to the presence of hydrogen bonding in water.

5. **a.** A **solution** is a homogeneous mixture of two or more components. **b.** An **aqueous solution** is is one in which water is the solvent (*i.e.*, water is the major component). **c.** The **solvent** is the major component of a solution. **d.** The **solute** is the minor component or components of a solution (*i.e.*, the components other than the solvent).

6. A gaseous solution - the air we breathe.
    A liquid solution - apple juice or any uncarbonated, clear beverage.
    A solid solution - brass or steel.

7. A solution can be colorless or colored but all liquid solutions are clear and retain the clarity even in the presence of light. The term colorless means lack of color. Clarity relates to whether a mixture is cloudy (turbid).

8. Particles in solution usually have diameters less than one nanometer. The liquid and solid components of a mixture can be separated using evaporation; the liquid component(s) will evaporate leaving the solid component(s) behind.

9. To obtain salt from seawater, giant shallow pans are flooded with the water. The water evaporates leaving behind the nonvolatile salt.

10. When solid NaCl is dissolved in water, molecules of water surround the Na^+ and Cl^- ions. The intermolecular forces formed between water molecules and the ions are primarily ion-dipole interactions and are strong enough to overcome the lattice forces and the intermolecular attractions of the solid NaCl. The ions are therefore separated from the solid and float into the solution, still surrounded by the water molecules.

11. **Hydration** is the process in which liquid water molecules surround a solute particle in solution. **Solvation** is the more general term, where molecules of the liquid solvent, whatever it may be, surround a solute particle.

12.

$$\text{a. } MgCl_{2(s)} \xrightarrow{H_2O} Mg^{2+}_{(aq)} + 2\,Cl^-_{(aq)}$$

$$\text{b. } NaOH_{(s)} \xrightarrow{H_2O} Na^+_{(aq)} + OH^-_{(aq)}$$

$$\text{c. } Al_2(SO_4)_{3(s)} \xrightarrow{H_2O} 2\,Al^{3+}_{(aq)} + 3\,SO_4^{2-}_{(aq)}$$

$$\text{d. } LiNO_{3(s)} \xrightarrow{H_2O} Li^+_{(aq)} + NO_3^-_{(aq)}$$

13. **a.** The greater the surface area of the undissolved solute, the faster the rate of dissolving due to an increase in the number of attack sites. **b.** Agitation of the solution will increase the rate of dissolving due to the agitation's action of drawing newly dissolved solute particles away from the undissolved solute. **c.** An increase in temperature will increase the rate of dissolving due to an increase in the kinetic energy of the particles.

14. **a.** The **solubility** of a solute is the maximum amount of the solute that can dissolve in a set amount of the solvent at a set temperature. **b. Miscible** liquids are mutually soluble in all proportions; it makes no difference which is present in the greater amount. **c.** A **saturated solution** contains the maximum amount of solute dissolved in it and has some additional solid present to ensure this situation. There is a dynamic equilibrium between the dissolved and undissolved solute. **d.** The heat change that occurs when one mole of a solute dissolves is called the **molar heat of solution**, $\Delta H_{solution}$.

15. **Soluble** and **insoluble** are terms with very imprecise meanings. In general, if the solubility of a solute exceeds 1 g/100 mL of solvent, it is considered soluble. Solutes with solubilities less than 1 g/100 mL of solvent are considered insoluble.

16. In a saturated solution, the undissolved solute exists in a separate phase (usually solid) from the dissolved solute (a homogeneous solution with the solvent). A dynamic equilibrium exists in which solute particles move back and forth between the phases such that the total amount of dissolved solute remains constant as does the total amount of undissolved solute.

17. If the sign of the molar heat of solution is negative, the solution process is exothermic and gives off heat. If the sign of the molar heat of solution is positive, the solution process is endothermic and absorbs heat.

18. As a general rule, the more heat given off, the greater the solubility. Therefore, NaOH > NaI > NaCl.

19. Of the three, NaOH would make the best hot pack since it would release the greatest amount of heat.

20. **a.** Pressure only has a small effect if there is no appreciable volume change in the process. If there is an appreciable volume change, such as in dissolving a gas in a liquid, then an increase in pressure will increase the solubility of the gas. **b.** If the molar heat of solution is positive, meaning that the process is endothermic, then increasing the temperature will increase the solubility. If the molar heat of solution is negative, meaning that the process is exothermic, then increasing the temperature will decrease the solubility. **c.** In terms of being able to make predictions, if a solvent is composed of polar molecules, it will dissolve polar and ionic solutes. If the solvent forms hydrogen bonds, it will be especially effective at dissolving solutes which also form hydrogen bonds. If the solvent is composed of nonpolar molecules, it will dissolve nonpolar solutes.

21. The fizz in soda pop is dissolved CO_2. The CO_2 is put into the soda under high pressure, which increases the gas's solubility. When the soda pop is first opened, the pressure drops and some of the dissolved CO_2 bubbles out.

22. **Hydrophilic** means "water-loving" and hydrophilic substances are those that have a strong attraction for water. They are almost always polar or ionic. **Hydrophobic** means "water-hating" and hydrophobic substances are those that only have London dispersion forces to attract them to water. They are almost always nonpolar substances.

23. The statement "like dissolves like" means that polar solvents can dissolve polar or ionic solutes and that nonpolar solvents dissolve nonpolar solutes.

24. **Concentration** is the amount of solute in a given quantity of solution. **Molarity** specifies that the concentration be expressed in terms of the number of moles of solute per liter of solution.

25. a. The molar mass of NaCl is 1(23.0 g/mole) + 1(35.5 g/mole) = 58.5 g/mole

$$\frac{(10.0 \text{ g NaCl})(1 \text{ mole NaCl})}{(58.5 \text{ g NaCl})(1.00 \text{ L})} = 0.171 \text{ mole/L}$$

b. The molar mass of KCl is 1(39.1 g/mole) + 1(35.5 g/mole) = 74.6 g/mole

$$\frac{(20.0 \text{ g KCl})(1 \text{ mole KCl})}{(74.6 \text{ g KCl})(100.0 \text{ mL})} \frac{(1000 \text{ mL})}{(1 \text{ L})} = 2.68 \text{ mole/L}$$

c. The molar mass of LiBr is 1(6.9 g/mole) + 1(79.9 g/mole) = 86.8 g/mole

$$\frac{(15.0 \text{ g LiBr})(1 \text{ mole LiBr})}{(86.8 \text{ g LiBr})(500.0 \text{ mL})} \frac{(1000 \text{ mL})}{(1 \text{ L})} = 0.346 \text{ mole/L}$$

d. The molar mass of $Mg(NO_3)_2$ is 1(24.3 g/mole) + 2(14.0 g/mole) + 6(16.0 g/mole)
$$= 148.3 \text{ g/mole}$$

$$\frac{(25.0 \text{ g } Mg(NO_3)_2)(1 \text{ mole } Mg(NO_3)_2)}{(148.3 \text{ g } Mg(NO_3)_2)(650.0 \text{ mL})} \frac{(1000 \text{ mL})}{(1 \text{ L})} = 0.259 \text{ mole/L}$$

e. The molar mass of Na_3PO_4 is 3(23.0 g/mole) + 1(31.0 g/mole) + 4(16.0 g/mole)
$$= 164.0 \text{ g/mole}$$

$$\frac{(12.5 \text{ g } Na_3PO_4)(1 \text{ mole } Na_3PO_4)}{(164.0 \text{ g } Na_3PO_4)(300.0 \text{ mL})} \frac{(1000 \text{ mL})}{(1 \text{ L})} = 0.254 \text{ mole/L}$$

26. a. The molar mass of $C_6H_{12}O_6$ is 6(12.0 g/mole) + 12(1.0 g/mole) + 6(16.0 g/mole)
$$= 180.0 \text{ g/mole}$$

$$\frac{(0.500 \text{ mole } C_6H_{12}O_6)(1.00 \text{ L})(180.0 \text{ g } C_6H_{12}O_6)}{(1.00 \text{ L})(1 \text{ mole } C_6H_{12}O_6)} = 90.0 \text{ g } C_6H_{12}O_6$$

b. The molar mass of NaCl is 1(23.0 g/mole) + 1(35.5 g/mole) = 58.5 g/mole

$$\frac{(0.100 \text{ mole NaCl})(800.0 \text{ mL})(1.00 \text{ L})(58.5 \text{ g NaCl})}{(1.00 \text{ L})(1000 \text{ mL})(1 \text{ mole NaCl})} = 4.68 \text{ g NaCl}$$

c. The molar mass of Na_3PO_4 is 3(23.0 g/mole) + 1(31.0 g/mole) + 4(16.0 g/mole)
$$= 164.0 \text{ g/mole}$$

$$\frac{(0.250 \text{ mole } Na_3PO_4)(420.0 \text{ mL})(1.00 \text{ L})(164.0 \text{ g } Na_3PO_4)}{(1.00 \text{ L})(1000 \text{ mL})(1 \text{ mole } Na_3PO_4)} = 17.2 \text{ g } Na_3PO_4$$

d. The molar mass of $Al_2(HPO_4)_3$ is 2(27.0 g/mole) + 3(1.0 g/mole) +3(31.0 g/mole)
$$+ 12(16.0 \text{ g/mole}) = 342.0 \text{ g/mole}$$

$$\frac{(1.50 \text{ mole } Al_2(HPO_4)_3)(150.0 \text{ mL})(1.00 \text{ L})(342.0 \text{ g } Al_2(HPO_4)_3)}{(1.00 \text{ L})(1000 \text{ mL})(1 \text{ mole } Al_2(HPO_4)_3)}$$
$$= 77.0 \text{ g } Al_2(HPO_4)_3$$

26. e. The molar mass of $MgCl_2$ is 1(24.3 g/mole) + 2(35.5 g/mole) = 95.3 g/mole

$$\frac{(0.0200 \text{ mole } MgCl_2)}{(\qquad 1.00 \text{ L} \qquad)}(2.50 \text{ L})\frac{(95.3 \text{ g } MgCl_2)}{(1 \text{ mole } MgCl_2)} = 4.76 \text{ g } MgCl_2$$

f. The molar mass of KCl is 1(39.1 g/mole) + 1(35.5 g/mole) = 74.6 g/mole

$$\frac{(2.00 \text{ mole KCl})}{(\qquad 1.00 \text{ L} \qquad)}(750.0 \text{ mL})\frac{(1.00 \text{ L})}{(1000 \text{ mL})}\frac{(74.6 \text{ g KCl})}{(1 \text{ mole KCl})} = 112 \text{ g KCl}$$

27. a. (0.100 mole NaCl/L)(0.1500 L) = 0.0150 mole NaCl
b. (0.250 mole KNO_3/L)(0.2000 L) = 0.0500 mole KNO_3
c. (1.20 moles $MgCl_2$/L)(0.6000 L) = 0.720 mole $MgCl_2$
d. (0.750 mole LiBr/L)(0.4000 L) = 0.300 mole LiBr
e. (3.70 moles KOH/L)(0.7500 L) = 2.78 moles KOH
f. (0.100 mole NaOH/L)(0.4500 L) = 0.0450 mole NaOH

28. a. $\dfrac{17.0 \text{ g}}{150.0 \text{ mL}}$ x 100% = 11.3 %(w/v)

b. $\dfrac{24.3 \text{ g}}{1000 \text{ mL}}$ x 100% = 2.43 %(w/v)

c. $\dfrac{35.7 \text{ g}}{900.0 \text{ mL}}$ x 100% = 3.97 %(w/v)

d. $\dfrac{14.6 \text{ g}}{500.0 \text{ mL}}$ x 100% = 2.92 %(w/v)

e. $\dfrac{30.6 \text{ g}}{745 \text{ mL}}$ x 100% = 4.11 %(w/v)

f. $\dfrac{9.75 \text{ g}}{200.0 \text{ mL}}$ x 100% = 4.88 %(w/v)

29. For 5 %(w/v) H_2O_2:   5% = $\dfrac{\text{mass}}{80.0 \text{ mL}}$ x 100%

mass = $\dfrac{(80.0 \text{ mL})(5\%)}{(100\%)}$

mass = 4 grams H_2O_2

30. It must be assumed that 1.00 L of blood has a mass of 1000.0 g. Then, the mass of NaCl per liter of blood is:

$$\frac{(0.15 \text{ mole NaCl})}{(\qquad 1 \text{ L blood} \qquad)}\frac{(58.5 \text{ g NaCl})}{(1 \text{ mole NaCl})} = 8.8 \text{ g/L}$$

and then

$$\frac{(8.8 \text{ g})}{(1 \text{ L})}\frac{(1.00 \text{ L})}{(1000 \text{ mL})} \text{ x } 100\% = 0.88 \text{ %(w/v)}$$

31. a. $\underline{17.0 \text{ mL}}$ x 100% = 11.3 %(v/v)
    150.0 mL

    b. $\underline{24.7 \text{ mL}}$ x 100% = 9.88 %(v/v)
    250.0 mL

    c. $\underline{7.80 \text{ mL}}$ x 100% = 6.24 %(v/v)
    125 mL

    d. $\underline{37.4 \text{ mL}}$ x 100% = 4.99 %(v/v)
    750.0 mL

    e. $\underline{340.0 \text{ mL}}$ x 100% = 22.7 %(v/v)
    1500 mL

    f. $\underline{17.2 \text{ mL}}$ x 100% = 0.573 %(v/v)
    3000 mL

32. a. $\underline{17.0 \text{ g}}$ x 100% = 11.3 %(w/w)
    150.0 g

    b. $\underline{24.8 \text{ g}}$ x 100% = 2.76 %(w/w)
    900.0 g

    c. $\underline{12.3 \text{ g}}$ x 100% = 25.1 %(w/w)
    49.0 g

    d. $\underline{43.6 \text{ g}}$ x 100% = 15.9 %(w/w)
    275 g

    e. $\underline{2.35 \text{ g}}$ x 100% = 1.96 %(w/w)
    120.0 g

    f. $\underline{458 \text{ g}}$ x 100% = 14.1 %(w/w)
    3250 g

33. a. A **reagent** is a laboratory chemical used in reactions and for performing analyses. **b.** A **dilution** is made by adding solvent to a concentrated solution in order to reduce the concentration of the solute to a more desirable level. **c.** The **dilution factor** is a conversion factor which relates the volumes of the concentrated and dilute solutions by: $C_dV_d = C_cV_c$ and $V_d = V_c \cdot (C_c/C_d)$ where (C_c/C_d) is the dilution factor.

34. a. (0.1500 L)(0.100 M/0.0500 M) = 0.300 L
    b. (0.2000 L)(0.250 M/0.0500 M) = 1.00 L
    c. (0.6000 L)(1.20 M/0.0500 M) = 14.4 L
    d. (0.4000 L)(0.750 M/0.0500 M) = 6.00 L
    e. (0.7500 L)(3.70 M/0.0500 M) = 55.5 L
    f. (0.4500 L)(0.100 M/0.0500 M) = 0.900 L

35. a. (10.0 mL)(7.50%/2.00%) = 37.5 mL
    b. (25.0 mL)(14.3%/2.00%) = 179 mL
    c. (20.0 mL)(10.0%/2.00%) = 1.00 x 10^2 mL
    d. (5.00 mL)(17.5%/2.00%) = 43.8 mL
    e. (1.00 mL)(25.0%/2.00%) = 12.5 mL

36. In each part, $V_c = (0.0500 \text{ M})(1.00 \text{ L})/M_c$.

    a. $(0.0500 \text{ M})(1.00 \text{ L})/(0.100 \text{ M}) = 0.500 \text{ L}$
    b. $(0.0500 \text{ M})(1.00 \text{ L})/(0.250 \text{ M}) = 0.200 \text{ L}$
    c. $(0.0500 \text{ M})(1.00 \text{ L})/(1.20 \text{ M}) = 0.0417 \text{ L}$
    d. $(0.0500 \text{ M})(1.00 \text{ L})/(0.750 \text{ M}) = 0.0667 \text{ L}$
    e. $(0.0500 \text{ M})(1.00 \text{ L})/(3.70 \text{ M}) = 0.0135 \text{ L}$
    f. $(0.0500 \text{ M})(1.00 \text{ L})/(0.100 \text{ M}) = 0.500 \text{ L}$

37. The molar mass of H_2SO_4 is: $2(1.0 \text{ g/mole}) + 1(32.1 \text{ g/mole}) + 4(16.0 \text{ g/mole}) = 98.1 \text{ g/mole}$

$$\frac{(2.75 \text{ g } H_2SO_4)(1 \text{ mole } H_2SO_4)(2 \text{ moles NaOH})(1.00 \text{ L NaOH})}{(98.1 \text{ g } H_2SO_4)(1 \text{ mole } H_2SO_4)(0.150 \text{ mole NaOH})} = 0.374 \text{ L NaOH}$$

38. $$\frac{(0.300 \text{ moles } Pb(NO_3)_2)(0.165 \text{ L } Pb(NO_3)_2)(2 \text{ mole KCl})(1.00 \text{ L KCl})}{(1.00 \text{ L } Pb(NO_3)_2)(1 \text{ mole } Pb(NO_3)_2)(0.250 \text{ mole KCl})} = 0.396 \text{ L KCl}$$

39. The molar mass of Na_2SO_4 is: $2(23.0 \text{ g/mole}) + 1(32.1 \text{ g/mole}) + 4(16.0 \text{ g/mole}) = 142.1 \text{ g/mole}$

$$\frac{(3.75 \text{ g } Na_2SO_4)(1 \text{ mole } Na_2SO_4)(1 \text{ mole } Pb(NO_3)_2)}{(142.1 \text{ g } Na_2SO_4)(1 \text{ mole } Na_2SO_4)(0.5000 \text{ L})} = 0.0528 \text{ mole } Pb(NO_3)_2/\text{L}$$

40. The molar mass of CuS is: $1(63.5 \text{ g/mole}) + 1(32.1 \text{ g/mole}) = 95.6 \text{ g/mole}$

$$\frac{(0.195 \text{ g } CuS)(1 \text{ mole } CuS)(1 \text{ mole } CuSO_4)}{(95.6 \text{ g } CuS)(1 \text{ mole } CuS)(0.7500 \text{ L } CuSO_4)} = 0.00272 \text{ mole } CuSO_4/\text{L}$$

41. a. Colligative properties are properties of solutions that depend only on the number of solute particles and not on the identity of the solute. **b. Molarity** is a measure of concentration expressed in moles of solute per liter of solution. **c. Semipermeable membranes** are thin layers that only allow certain solute or solvent molecules to pass through. **d. Osmotic membranes** are a special class of semipermeable membranes that allow only water through. **e. Osmosis** is the process in which water molecules move through a semipermeable membrane from a region of higher water concentration to a region of lower water concentration. This is equivalent to saying that the water migrates from a region of lower solute concentration to a region of higher solute concentration. **f.** The amount of pressure needed to prevent water from crossing the osmotic membrane is called the **osmotic pressure**.

42. A nonvolatile solute lowers the vapor pressure of the solution because the nonvolatile solute particles are spread evenly throughout the solution and at the surface. Thus, fewer solvent molecules can reach the surface to escape and the vapor pressure drops.

43. The boiling point of a solution containing nonvolatile solute particles is higher than that of the pure solvent because the solute causes vapor pressure lowering. Since the boiling point is that temperature at which the vapor pressure equals atmospheric pressure, additional heat must be applied to raise the vapor pressure to the necessary amount, requiring a higher temperature.

44. The freezing point of a solution containing a nonvolatile solute is lower than that of the pure solvent.

45. a. The molar mass of C_2H_5OH is: $2(12.0$ g/mole$) + 6(1.0$ g/mole$) + 1(16.0$ g/mole$)$
$$= 46.0 \text{ g/mole}$$

$$\frac{(2.30 \text{ g } C_2H_5OH)(1 \text{ mole } C_2H_5OH)(1000 \text{ g})}{(\quad 400.0 \text{ g} \quad)(46.0 \text{ g } C_2H_5OH)(1.00 \text{ kg})} = 0.125 \text{ mole/kg}$$

b. The molar mass of H_2SO_4 is: $2(1.0$ g/mole$) + 1(32.1$ g/mole$) +4 (16.0$ g/mole$) = 98.1$ g/mole

$$\frac{(49.0 \text{ g } H_2SO_4)(1 \text{ mole } H_2SO_4)(1000 \text{ g})}{(\quad 200.0 \text{ g} \quad)(98.1 \text{ g } H_2SO_4)(1.00 \text{ kg})} = 2.50 \text{ mole/kg}$$

c. The molar mass of NaCl is: $1(23.0$ g/mole$) + 1(35.5$ g/mole$) = 58.5$ g/mole

$$\frac{(29.2 \text{ g NaCl})(1 \text{ mole NaCl})}{(\quad 2.00 \text{ kg} \quad)(58.5 \text{ g NaCl})} = 0.250 \text{ mole/kg}$$

d. The molar mass of $C_{12}H_{22}O_{11}$ is: $12(12.0$ g/mole$) + 22(1.0$ g/mole$) + 11(16.0$ g/mole$)$
$$= 342.0 \text{ g/mole}$$

$$\frac{(10.0 \text{ g } C_{12}H_{22}O_{11})(1 \text{ mole } C_{12}H_{22}O_{11})(1000 \text{ g})}{(\quad 300.0 \text{ g} \quad)(342.0 \text{ g } C_{12}H_{22}O_{11})(1.00 \text{ kg})} = 0.0975 \text{ mole/kg}$$

46. The molal freezing point depression constant for naphthalene is 6.80 °C-kg/mol and its freezing point is 80.2 °C.

$$\frac{(6.80 \text{ °C-kg/mole})(12.0 \text{ g})}{(80.2 \text{ °C} - 78.9 \text{ °C})(0.2500 \text{ kg})} = 250 \text{ g/mole}$$

47. Salty soil kills plants by dehydration. If the soil is salty, water should flow from a region of low salt content (the plant) to a region of high salt content (the soil). Therefore, the plant loses much of the water it requires for life and it dies.

48. a. A **colloid** is a type of solution, although not a true solution, in which solute particles are about 1 nm to 100 nm in diameter. The particles are uniformly distributed but, due to their size, tend to have a cloudy appearence. **b. Brownian motion** is a type of particle motion in which the particles travel in random directions. Due to collisions, the directions in which the particles travel constantly change and the particles do not settle to the bottom. **c.** The **Tyndall effect** is a colloidal property in which light is reflected by the suspended particles so that a beam of light going through a colloid can be seen from the side. **d.** A **suspension** is a mixture with larger particles than a colloid in which agitation keeps the particles from settling out. As true heterogeneous mixtures, they can be separated by filtration.

49. True solutions are clear because the solute particles are so small that they do not reflect light. Colloids contain particles which are large enough to reflect light and so they appear cloudy.

50. a. A suspension contains large particles which will settle out or can be filtered out; a solution is clear and filtration will not remove solute particles. **b.** A solution does not reflect light by the Tyndall effect; a colloidal dispersion does reflect light. **c.** Both will be cloudy but the suspension can be separated by filtration, the colloidal dispersion cannot.

51. Colloidal dispersions don't settle out because, due to Brownian motion, collisions of solute particles with solvent molecules keep them mixed.

52. Polar and ionic substances are most likely to dissolve in water due to the similar intermolecular forces exhibited by water (dipolar attractions and hydrogen bonding) and by polar and ionic substances.

53. Solubility increases as $\Delta H_{\text{solution}}$ decreases. For this list, the order would be $Na_2SO_4 > MgSO_4 > Al_2(SO_4)_3 \cdot 6H_2O$.

54. The $Al_2(SO_4)_3 \cdot 6H_2O$ would make the best cold pack since its molar heat of solution is the most endothermic. One mole of it should get the coldest of the three.

55. a. The molar mass of $Al_2(HPO_4)_3$ is 342.0 g/mole.

$$\frac{(10.0 \text{ g})}{(0.200 \text{ mole/L})(342.0 \text{ g/mole})} = 0.146 \text{ L}$$

b. The molar mass of Li_2CO_3 is 73.8 g/mole.

$$\frac{(10.0 \text{ g})}{(0.150 \text{ mole/L})(73.8 \text{ g/mole})} = 0.903 \text{ L}$$

c. The molar mass of NaCl is 58.5 g/mole.

$$\frac{(10.0 \text{ g})}{(2.00 \text{ mole/L})(58.5 \text{ g/mole})} = 0.0855 \text{ L}$$

d. The molar mass of K_2SO_4 is 174.3 g/mole.

$$\frac{(10.0 \text{ g})}{(0.150 \text{ mole/L})(174.3 \text{ g/mole})} = 0.382 \text{ L}$$

e. The molar mass of $C_6H_{12}O_6$ is 180.0 g/mole.

$$\frac{(10.0 \text{ g})}{(0.300 \text{ mole/L})(180.0 \text{ g/mole})} = 0.185 \text{ L}$$

f. The molar mass of $Ca(NO_3)_2$ is 164.1 g/mole.

$$\frac{(10.0 \text{ g})}{(2.50 \text{ mole/L})(164.1 \text{ g/mole})} = 0.0244 \text{ L}$$

56. You must assume that the density of each solution is 1.00 g/mL.

a. $\dfrac{(30.0\%)(175 \text{ g})}{(100\%)} = 52.5$ g NaOH

b. $\dfrac{(10.0\%)(900.0 \text{ g})}{(100\%)} = 90.0$ g NaCl

c. $\dfrac{(20.0\%)(775 \text{ g})}{(100\%)} = 155$ g $Mg(NO_3)_2$

d. $\dfrac{(15.0\%)(300.0 \text{ g})}{(100\%)} = 45.0$ g $CaCl_2$

e. $\dfrac{(12.5\%)(650.0 \text{ g})}{(100\%)} = 81.2$ g KBr

f. $\dfrac{(17.0\%)(450.0 \text{ g})}{(100\%)} = 76.5$ g K_2SO_4

57. 90 proof is equivalent to 45 %(v/v). Therefore:

$$\frac{(45\%)(1000.0 \text{ mL})}{(100\%)} = 450 \text{ mL ethyl alcohol}$$

58. $\frac{(0.1000 \text{ mole AgNO}_3)(0.02935 \text{ L AgNO}_3)(\text{ 1 mole NaCl })}{(\quad 1 \text{ L AgNO}_3 \quad) \qquad\qquad (1 \text{ mole AgNO}_3)(0.010000 \text{ L NaCl})} = 0.294 \text{ M NaCl}$

59. The molal freezing point depression constant for water is 1.86 °C-kg/mol and its freezing point is 0.0 °C.

$$\frac{(1.86 \text{ °C-kg/mole})(14.5 \text{ g})}{(0.0 \text{ °C} - -1.0 \text{ °C})(0.1500 \text{ kg})} = 180 \text{ g/mole}$$

60. Due to osmosis, water flows from the cucumber to the salt water, which is from high water (low salt) concentration to low water (high salt) concentration. The cucumber ends up having lost a lot of its water which causes its skin to collapse because it's covering less material.

61. Whole milk is more opaque than nonfat skim milk because of the milkfat in it. The fat in milk is a colloidal dispersion which does block light passage, thereby making it opaque.

Sample Quiz Questions

1. Hydrogen bonding in water causes
    a. an unexpectedly low freezing point.
    b. water to be a good solvent for I_2.
    c. stronger intermolecular forces in the liquid than in ice.
    d. an unexpectedly high vapor pressure.
    e. ice to be less dense than the liquid.

2. Water
    a. is a nonpolar liquid.
    b. is a poor solvent for ionic solutes.
    c. has an unexpectedly low boiling point.
    d. is a polar liquid.
    e. has a relatively low viscosity.

3. Clarity
    a. is the same as cloudiness.
    b. is the same as transparency.
    c. means lack of color.
    d. is sometimes observed in true solutions.
    e. is the same as colorlessness.

4. In solution, dissolved particles tend to be
    a. more than 10 nm in diameter.
    b. easily retrieved by filtration.
    c. between 1 and 10 nm in diameter.
    d. ions, not molecules.
    e. less than 1 nm in diameter.

5. Which of the following factors does not affect the initial rate of dissolving a solute in a solvent?
   a. the amount of solvent used
   b. temperature
   c. surface area of the undissolved solute
   d. agitation
   e. the amount of solute used

6. Solubility
   a. is an endothermic process.
   b. depends on agitation of the solution.
   c. is the maximum amount of solute which can dissolve in a solvent at a given temperature.
   d. is an exothermic process.
   e. refers to the amount of solute dissolved.

7. Solubility increases
   a. with an increase in the time allowed to dissolve.
   b. with increasing temperature if $\Delta H_{solution}$ is a positive value.
   c. with agitation.
   d. with the amount of solute used.
   e. with increasing temperature if $\Delta H_{solution}$ is a negative value.

8. Solubility decreases
   a. with an increase in pressure.
   b. with a decrease in temperature.
   c. with a solute and solvent which have similar intermolecular forces.
   d. with an increase in the value of $\Delta H_{solution}$.
   e. with a decrease in pressure.

9. Chemical structure
   a. affects the solubility of a solute in a given solvent.
   b. is the sole controlling factor in solubility at a given temperature.
   c. is not an important factor in solubility.
   d. is the same in the liquid and solid phases of most solvents.
   e. refers only to crystalline substances.

10. What is the molarity of the solute when 15.0 g of $Ba(NO_3)_2$ is dissolved in enough water to make 1450 mL of solution?
    a. 2.70 M
    b. 0.370 M
    c. 0.0396 M
    d. 0.0103 M
    e. 10.3 M

11. How many grams of LiF are required to make 700.0 mL of a 0.100 M solution?
    a. 1.43 g
    b. 0.0700 g
    c. 181 g
    d. 1.81 g
    e. 3.70 g

12. What volume of solution is needed to make a 0.750 M solution of CsCl if 16.3 g of solid CsCl is used?
   a. 72.6 mL
   b. 0.273 L
   c. 0.129 L
   d. 3921 mL
   e. 7.75 L

13. What is the concentration of a solution of 3.00 moles of HCl dissolved in enough water to make a 5.00 kg of the solution, expressed in percent by weight?
   a. 0.730 %(w/w)
   b. 21.8 %(w/w)
   c. 36.5 %(w/w)
   d. 0.0600 %(w/w)
   e. 2.18 %(w/w)

14. How many grams of H_2SO_4 are required to make 10.0 kg of a 5.00 %(w/w) solution?
   a. 5.00×10^2 g
   b. 98.1 g
   c. 1.00×10^2 g
   d. 0.0500 g
   e. 4.90 g

15. How many grams of $KClO_4$ are required to make 1250.0 mL of a 15.2 %(w/v) solution?
   a. 137 g
   b. 1.90×10^2 g
   c. 21.1 g
   d. 169 g
   e. 114 g

16. What is the percent by volume concentration of 86 proof liquor?
   a. 43 %(v/v)
   b. 8.6 %(v/v)
   c. 86 %(v/v)
   d. 95 %(v/v)
   e. 170 %(v/v)

17. Calculate the final concentration when 13.5 mL of a 0.554 M NaCl solution is diluted to a final volume of 250.0 mL.
   a. 0.0299 M
   b. 0.00222 M
   c. 0.0540 M
   d. 0.0975 M
   e. 10.3 M

18. Calculate the final volume required to dilute 35.0 mL of a 2.34 M solution of KClO to a final concentration of 2.10 M.
   a. 81.9 mL
   b. 31.4 mL
   c. 73.5 mL
   d. 39.0 mL
   e. 1110 mL

19. According the the equation,

$$2\,AgNO_{3(aq)} + K_2CrO_{4(aq)} \rightarrow Ag_2CrO_{4(s)} + 2\,KNO_{3(aq)}$$

how many grams of Ag_2CrO_4 can be made from the complete reaction of 15.0 mL of a 0.800 M solution of $AgNO_3$?
   a. 1.99 g
   b. 2.04 g
   c. 1.02 g
   d. 12.0 g
   e. 3.98 g

20. According to the equation,

$$2\,NH_4Cl_{(aq)} + BaSO_{4(aq)} \rightarrow BaCl_{2(s)} + (NH_4)_2SO_{4(aq)}$$

what volume of 0.500 M $BaSO_4$ solution is required to completely react with 100.0 mL of 0.750 M NH_4Cl solution?
   a. 50.0 mL
   b. 75.0 mL
   c. 3.00×10^2 mL
   d. 1.50×10^2 mL
   e. 75.0 mL

21. According to the equation,

$$H_{2(g)} + Cl_{2(g)} \rightarrow 2\,HCl_{(aq)}$$

what will the molarity of the HCl solution be if 1.00 L of it is made from the complete reaction of 15.0 g of H_2?
   a. 30.0 M
   b. 3.8 M
   c. 7.5 M
   d. 60.0 M
   e. 15 M

22. What is the molality of a solution of 15.75 g NaCl dissolved in 175 g of $CHCl_3$?
   a. 0.0900 m
   b. 21.2 m
   c. 1.54 m
   d. 2.76 m
   e. 90.0 m

23. The molal freezing point depression constant of water is 1.86 °C-kg/mole. A solution of 22.1 g of a substance was dissolved in 750.0 g of water and the freezing point of the solution was -2.35 °C. Determine the molar mass of the substance.
   a. 129 g/mole
   b. 23.3 g/mole
   c. 3.79 g/mole
   d. 29.5 g/mole
   e. 37.2 g/mole

24. Colloidal dispersions
        a. are generally clear.
        b. are not mixtures.
        c. don't reflect light as well as true solutions.
        d. don't settle out on sitting.
        e. are not stable.

Answers to the Sample Quiz Questions

1. (e), 2. (d), 3. (b), 4. (e), 5. (a), 6. (c), 7. (b), 8. (d), 9. (a), 10. (c), 11. (d), 12. (c), 13. (e), 14. (a), 15. (b), 16. (e), 17. (a), 18. (d), 19. (a), 20. (b), 21. (e), 22. (c), 23. (b), 24. (d)

CHEMICAL EQUILIBRIUM AND REACTION RATES

CHAPTER 13

Chapter Overview

Chapter 13 begins with reaction rates and ends with equilibrium. This order of coverage is useful from the viewpoint that equilibrium and LeChatelier's principle are best visualized as the competition between two reactions, one being the reverse of the other. This approach has already been utilized in the description of melting and boiling and so the student should be able to appreciate the development of the concepts.

The discussion of kinetics is primarily a conceptual one; the mathematical treatment is modest. However, first and second order reactions and their rate laws are covered in detail. Reaction rates are rationalized in terms of activation energies and several controlling factors, such as temperature, concentrations, and catalysts.

Equilibrium reactions are then discussed, building from the discussion of percentage yield given in Chapter 9. The occurrence of equilibrium constants is then described, followed by a discussion of LeChatelier's principle and the factors which invoke it, such as concentration changes and temperature changes. Calculations involving K_{eq} are also covered. The enthalpy of reaction, ΔH, is then introduced as a corollary to the equilibrium constant.

The chapter ends with a section which explicitly ties the rates of opposing reactions to the equilibrium constants of the reactions.

Solutions to the Study Questions and Problems

1. **Reversible reactions** proceed in both the forward and reverse directions at the same time.

2. Reversible reactions are at a dynamic equilibrium in that both the forward and the reverse reactions are proceeding at the same rate. Therefore, while there is a continuous transformation of chemical species between reactants and products, the net amounts of the reactants and products remain constant.

3. **a.** Starting with 1.00 M "X" and 0.00 M "Y":

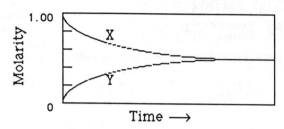

   b. Starting with 1.00 M "Y" and 0.00 M "X":

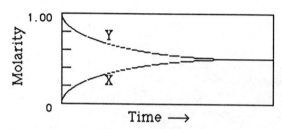

   c. Starting with 0.25 M "X" and 0.75 M "Y":

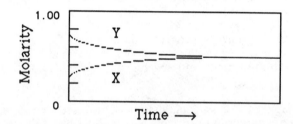

4. Spontaneous processes are not always rapid. A reaction may be favorable according to its enthalpy of reaction but the rate of the reaction may still be quite slow.

5. The **rate of reaction** is the concentration of formula units of a product formed in a given period of time or the concentration of formula units of a reactant consumed in a given period of time. The field of study which deals with measuring and interpreting reaction rates is called **chemical kinetics.**

6. **a.** The theoretical series of steps by which reactants are converted to products is called the **reaction pathway. b.** The amount of energy necessary to overcome the energy barrier between reactants and products is called the **activation energy. c.** The hypothetical structure that is midway between the reactants and products is known as the **activated complex** or **transition state.**

7. Reactions with relatively low activation energies will proceed at faster rates than those reactions with relatively high activation energies. Reaction rate and the magnitude of the activation energy are very closely related.

8. Reaction 2 has the higher activation energy because its rate of reaction is slower than that of reaction 1.

9. **a.** A **unimolecular reaction** is a reaction which has a reaction rate which depends only upon the concentration of one reactant. **b.** A **bimolecular reaction** is a reaction which has a reaction rate which depends on the concentrations of two reactants. **c.** The **rate equation** or **rate law** of a reaction is the mathematical expression of the relationship between reaction rate and the concentration of one or more reactants. **d.** The **rate constant**, k, is the proportionality constant relating reaction rate to concentration. **e.** A **catalyst** affects the rate of a reaction but is not consumed in the reaction. A catalyst can be recovered intact after the reaction is completed. **f.** **Catalysis** refers to the action of a catalyst, either increasing or decreasing the rate, in a chemical reaction.

10. **a.** An increase in temperature generally will increase the rate of a reaction as all of the reactant molecules possess more kinetic energy. **b.** Increasing the concentration of the reactants which appear in the rate law increases the rate of a chemical reaction. **c.** The nature of the reactants affects the rates of reactions because of the unique features of the structures of individual chemicals. **d.** Catalysis usually increases the rate of a reaction. Some catalysts do, however, retard reactions.

11. **a.** rate $= k[A][B]$ If the concentration of A is doubled, then rate $= k[2A][B]$, which shows that the rate will also be doubled.

b. rate $= k[A][B]$ If the concentration of B is doubled, then rate $= k[A][2B]$, which shows that the rate will also be doubled.

c. rate $= k[A][B]$ If the concentrations of A and B are doubled, then rate $= k[2A][2B]$, which shows that the rate will increase by a factor of 2 • 2 or four.

12. For: $H_{2(g)} + Cl_{2(g)} \rightarrow 2\,HCl_{(g)}$,

a. rate $= k[H_2][Cl_2]$

b. The units for the rate constant are Liters/mole-second (or some convenient time unit).

13. **a.** The catalyst also affects the reverse reaction to the same extent as the forward reaction. **b.** Because the forward and reverse reaction rates are affected to the same extent by the addition of a catalyst, the equilibrium constant is not affected.

14. The **equilibrium constant** is the ratio of the product concentrations to the reactant concentrations.

15. **a.** $K_{eq} = \dfrac{[NO]^4[H_2O]^6}{[NH_3]^4[O_2]^5}$

b. $K_{eq} = \dfrac{[N_2O_4]}{[NO_2]^2}$

c. $K_{eq} = \dfrac{[SO_2]^2[O_2]}{[SO_3]^2}$

d. $K_{eq} = \dfrac{[PCl_3][Cl_2]}{[PCl_5]}$

15. e. $K_{eq} = \dfrac{[HCl]^2}{[H_2][Cl_2]}$

16. $K_{eq} = \dfrac{[H_2]^2[S_2]}{[H_2S]^2}$

$K_{eq} = \dfrac{[0.20]^2[0.80]}{[1.0]^2}$

$K_{eq} = 0.032$ mole/liter

17. $K_{eq} = \dfrac{[HI]^2}{[H_2][I_2]}$

$K_{eq} = \dfrac{[0.60]^2}{[0.90][0.40]}$

$K_{eq} = 1.0$

18. $K_{eq} = \dfrac{[NO_2]^2}{[N_2O_4]}$

$K_{eq} = \dfrac{[0.0172]^2}{[0.00140]}$

$K_{eq} = 0.211$ mole/liter

19. The **position of equilibrium** refers to the relative concentrations of the products and reactants of a reaction at equilibrium.

20. If the equilibrium constant is greater than 1.0, the reaction favors the products; there are more products than reactants at equilibrium. If the equilibrium constant is less than 1.0, the reaction favors the reactants; there are more reactants than products at equilibrium.

21. **a.** The position of equilibrium lies to the right (product side). **b.** The position of equilibrium lies to the left (reactant side). **c.** The position of equilibrium lies to the right (product side). **d.** The position of equilibrium lies to the right (product side). **e.** The position of equilibrium lies to the left (reactant side).

22. **a.** This reaction is considered incomplete. **b.** This reaction is considered to be nonoccurring. **c.** This reaction is considered to be incomplete. **d.** This reaction is considered to have gone to completion. **e.** This reaction is considered to be incomplete.

23. If reaction conditions are altered, LeChatelier's principle predicts that the system readjusts the reaction rates of the forward and reverse reactions to relieve the strain and to establish a new equilibrium.

24. **a.** Increasing a reactant concentration causes a shift to the right (product side). **b.** Increasing a product concentration causes a shift to the left (reactant side). **c.** Decreasing a reactant concentration causes a shift to the left (reactant side). **d.** Deceasing a product concentration causes a shift to the right (product side).

25. a. $N_{2(g)} + O_{2(g)} = 2\,NO_{(g)}$

Increasing $[O_2]$ will drive the reaction to the right, decreasing $[N_2]$ and increasing $[NO]$.

b. $N_{2(g)} + 3\,H_{2(g)} = 2\,NH_{3(g)}$

Increasing $[NH_3]$ will drive the reaction to the left, increasing both $[N_2]$ and $[H_2]$.

c. $CO_{(g)} + H_2O_{(g)} = CO_{2(g)} + H_{2(g)}$

Increasing $[H_2]$ will drive the reaction to the left, increasing $[CO]$ and $[H_2O]$ and decreasing $[CO_2]$.

d. $PCl_{5(g)} = PCl_{3(g)} + Cl_{2(g)}$

Decreasing $[PCl_5]$ will drive the reaction to the left, decreasing both $[PCl_3]$ and $[Cl_2]$.

26. By Avogadro's law, $V_i/n_i = V_f/n_f$, a reduction in volume should be related to a reduction in the number of moles of gas. A decrease in container volume will then shift the reaction to whichever side has the fewer number of moles of gas.

a. A decrease in container volume will cause no shift due to equal numbers of moles of gas on both sides of the reaction. **b.** A decrease in container volume will cause a shift to the right due to fewer product gas moles. **c.** A decrease in container volume will cause no shift due to equal numbers of moles of gas on both sides of the reaction. **d.** A decrease in container volume will cause a shift to the left due to the fewer reactant gas moles.

27. For an exothermic reaction (Reactants = Products + heat), K_{eq} decreases with an increase in temperature since the added stress is on the product side. For an endothermic reaction (Reactants + heat = Products), K_{eq} increases with an increase in temperature since the added stress is on the reactant side.

28. $2\,H_{2(g)} + O_{2(g)} = 2\,H_2O_{(g)}$

a. The addition of water to the system will drive the reaction to the left, increasing $[H_2]$.
b. The removal of oxygen from the system will drive the reaction to the left, increasing $[H_2]$.
c. Increasing the temperature of the system will drive the reaction to the left, increasing $[H_2]$.

29. a. Enthalpy change is the heat absorbed or released by a chemical reaction. **b. A calorimeter** is a device used to measure the enthalpy change of a reaction.

30. In a calorimeter, a measured amount of water surrounds a vessel containing the reactants. The reactants are mixed and, after the reaction, the heat absorbed or released is measured by a change in the water temperature. From this value, the enthalpy change is calculated.

31. The equilibrium constant for a reaction can be found from the rates of the forward and reverse reactions by the relationships:

$$rate_{forward} = rate_{reverse}$$
$$k_f[\text{Reactants}] = k_r[\text{Products}]$$
$$\frac{k_f}{k_r} = K_{eq} = \frac{[\text{Products}]}{[\text{Reactants}]}$$

32. When a change is made in the concentration of one or more components in a reaction, the reaction rates for the forward and reverse reactions change as well; an increase in the concentration of a product causes the reverse reaction to be accelerated while an increase in the concentration of a reactant causes the forward reaction to be accelerated. When equilibrium is reestablished, the rates of the forward and reverse reactions are again equal.

33. The rate constants for a given reaction, k_f and k_r, vary only with temperature; they do not vary with concentrations, pressure, or the natures of the chemicals. Since $K_{eq} = k_f/k_r$, only temperature changes can affect the value of K_{eq}.

34. If the rate doubles for every 10 °C change in temperature, a 100 °C temperature change would cause the rate to double 10 times (100 °C/10 °C). Therefore, the total rate increase is:

$$2 \cdot 2 \cdot 2 \cdot 2 \cdot 2 \cdot 2 \cdot 2 \cdot 2 \cdot 2 \cdot 2 = 1024 \text{ times faster}$$

35. The reaction is: $A + B \rightarrow C$

    a. The rate law is: rate $= k[A][B]$

    b. rate $= k[A][B]$
    $$k = \frac{rate}{[A][B]} = \frac{2.5 \times 10^{-5}}{[0.20][0.30]} = 4.2 \times 10^{-4} \text{ L/mole-sec}$$

36. a. The enzyme must lower the activation energy of the reaction since it accelerates the reaction.
    b. The enzyme does not affect the equilibrium constant. The enzyme is a catalyst and catalysts only affect the rates of reaction, not the equilibrium constants.

37. The reactions which convert the CO, unburned gasoline, and other pollutants to CO_2 would not take place in the amount of time the gases are in the exhaust system without a catalyst. The addition of the catalyst accelerates the reactions enough for them to be essentially completed before the gases leave the exhaust system.

38. For $PCl_{5(g)} = PCl_{3(g)} + Cl_{2(g)}$,

    $$K_{eq} = \frac{[PCl_3][Cl_2]}{[PCl_5]}$$

    $$K_{eq} = \frac{[0.081 \text{ M}][0.081 \text{ M}]}{[0.158 \text{ M}]}$$

    $$K_{eq} = 0.042 \text{ mole/liter}$$

39. For $3\ C_2H_{2(g)} = C_6H_{6(g)}$,

$$K_{eq} = \frac{[C_6H_6]}{[C_2H_2]^3}$$

$$[C_6H_6] = K_{eq} \cdot [C_2H_2]^3$$

$$[C_6H_6] = (4.0\ L^2/mole^2)(0.70\ mole/L)^3$$

$$[C_6H_6] = 1.4\ mole/L$$

40. a. Adding Cl_2 to the system will drive the reaction to the left (reactant side). **b.** Increasing the temperature will drive the reaction to the right (product side). **c.** Removing PCl_3 from the system will drive the reaction to the right (product side).

Sample Quiz Questions

1.   A reversible reaction
   a. is a hypothetical reaction which helps explain activation energy.
   b. depends only on temperature.
   c. proceeds in both directions simultaneously.
   d. can lead to the formation of an equilibrium.
   e. can proceed in either direction depending on the conditions placed on it.

2.   At equilibrium,
   a. the rate constants for the forward and reverse reactions are equal.
   b. the reaction ceases.
   c. the concentrations of the reactants and products are equal.
   d. all of the reactants have been converted to products, barring a limiting reactant.
   e. the forward and reverse rates are equal.

3.   A transition state
   a. is a low energy interim product of a reaction.
   b. is the temperature at which the liquid and vapor phases are at equilibrium.
   c. has no dependency on the reactants of a reaction.
   d. is a reactive hypothetical chemical which shows characteristics of the reactants and products.
   e. has no dependency on the products of a reaction.

4.   The activation energy of a reaction
   a. is not related to the rate of the reaction.
   b. is the amount of energy required to intiate the reaction.
   c. is the amount of energy liberated by initiating the reaction.
   d. is a negative quantity.
   e. is the difference in energy content between the reactants and products of the reaction.

5. For the reaction

$$CH_3COCH_3 + I_2 \rightarrow CH_3COCH_2I + HI$$

tripling the concentration of CH_3COCH_3
   a. should triple the rate constant of the reaction.
   b. should double the rate of the reaction.
   c. should have no effect on the rate of the reaction.
   d. should drive the reaction to the left.
   e. should triple the rate of the reaction.

6. Consider the reaction

$$CH_2CH_2 + HBr \rightarrow CH_3CH_2Br$$

What is the expected rate law for the reaction?
   a. rate $= k[CH_2CH_2][HBr]$
   b. rate $= k[HBr]$
   c. rate $= k[CH_3CH_2Br]$
   d. rate $= k[CH_2CH_2]$
   e. rate $= k[CH_2CH_2][HBr]/[CH_3CH_2Br]$

7. The addition of a catalyst to a chemical reaction
   a. affects the rate of the forward reaction.
   b. always accelerates the reaction.
   c. affects the rate of the forward and reverse reactions.
   d. may not affect the reaction.
   e. affects the value of the equilibrium constant.

8. For the rate law

$$rate = k[A][B][C]$$

what are the units of the rate constant?
   a. $mole^3/liter^3$-second
   b. mole/liter-second
   c. $second^{-1}$
   d. $liter^2/mole^2$-second
   e. Rate constants have no units.

9. Consider the reaction

$$2 H_2S_{(g)} + 3 O_{2(g)} = 2 H_2O_{(g)} + 2 SO_{2(g)}$$

Write the expression for the equilibrium constant for the reaction.

a. $k_{eq} = \dfrac{[H_2S][O_2]}{[H_2O][SO_2]}$

b. $k_{eq} = \dfrac{[H_2O]^2[SO_2]^2}{[H_2S]^2[O_2]^3}$

c. $k_{eq} = \dfrac{[H_2S]^2[O_2]^3}{[H_2O]^2[SO_2]^2}$

d. $k_{eq} = \dfrac{[H_2O][SO_2]}{[H_2S][O_2]}$

e. $k_{eq} = \dfrac{[H_2O][SO_2]}{[H_2S][O_2]^3}$

10. Consider the reaction

$$CS_{2(g)} + 4 H_{2(g)} = CH_{4(g)} + 2 H_2S_{(g)}$$

Write the expression for the equilibrium constant for the reaction.

a. $K_{eq} = \dfrac{[CS_2][H_2]}{[CH_4][H_2S]}$

b. $K_{eq} = \dfrac{[CH_4][H_2S]^2}{[CS_2][H_2]^4}$

c. $K_{eq} = \dfrac{[CH_4][H_2S]}{[CS_2][H_2]^4}$

d. $K_{eq} = \dfrac{[CS_2][H_2]^4}{[CH_4][H_2S]^2}$

e. $K_{eq} = \dfrac{[CH_4][H_2S]}{[CS_2][H_2]}$

11. Consider the reaction

$$SnO_{2(s)} + 2\,H_{2(g)} \;=\; Sn_{(s)} + 2\,H_2O_{(g)}$$

Write the expression for the equilibrium constant for the reaction.

a. $K_{eq} = \dfrac{[Sn][H_2O]}{[SnO_2][H_2]}$

b. $K_{eq} = \dfrac{[SnO_2][H_2]}{[Sn][H_2O]}$

c. $K_{eq} = \dfrac{[Sn][H_2O]^2}{[SnO_2][H_2]^2}$

d. $K_{eq} = \dfrac{[SnO_2][H_2]^2}{[Sn][H_2O]^2}$

e. $K_{eq} = \dfrac{[Sn][H_2O]^2}{[SnO_2][H_2]}$

12. An equilibrium mixture for the reaction

$$O_{2(g)} + 4\,HCl_{(g)} \;=\; 2\,H_2O_{(g)} + 2\,Cl_{2(g)}$$

had the following concentrations:

$$[O_2] = 0.0223 \text{ mole/L}$$
$$[HCl] = 0.277 \text{ mole/L}$$
$$[H_2O] = 7.03 \text{ mole/L}$$
$$[Cl_2] = 0.880 \text{ mole/L}$$

Calculate the equilibrium constant. (The units have been omitted.)

a. 1.00×10^3

b. 1.00×10^6

c. 3.43×10^{-6}

d. 2.92×10^5

e. 9.98×10^{-4}

13. An equilibrium mixture for the reaction

$$2\,NO_{2(g)} + 7\,H_{2(g)} \;=\; 2\,NH_{3(g)} + 4\,H_2O_{(g)}$$

had the following concentrations:

$$[NO_2] = 0.0200\ mole/L$$
$$[H_2] = 0.0100\ mole/L$$
$$[NH_3] = 0.0200\ mole/L$$
$$[H_2O] = 0.0100\ mole/L$$

Calculate the equilibrium constant. (The units have been omitted.)
   a. 1.00×10^6
   b. 5.00×10^3
   c. 2.00×10^{-4}
   d. 1.00
   e. 1.00×10^{-6}

14. An equilibrium mixture for the reaction

$$2\,NOCl_{(g)} \;=\; 2\,NO_{(g)} + Cl_{2(g)}$$

had the following concentrations:

$$[NOCl] = 0.100\ mole/L$$
$$[NO] = 0.0750\ mole/L$$
$$[Cl_2] = 0.0250\ mole/L$$

Calculate the equilibrium constant. (The units have been omitted.)
   a. 71.1
   b. 0.0141
   c. 0.188
   d. 0.0188
   e. 0.00141

15. The position of equilibrium
   a. describes the relative rates of the forward and reverse reactions.
   b. depends on the concentrations of the reactants and products.
   c. is independent of temperature.
   d. depends on whether the reactants and products are solids, liquids, or gases.
   e. gives a measure of completeness of reaction.

16. Consider a reaction for which $K_{eq} = 0.798$ mole/L. Which of the following statements about the equilibrium is correct?
   a. The reaction essentially goes to completion.
   b. There are slightly more products than reactants in the mixture.
   c. The reaction essentially does not occur.
   d. The rates of the forward and reverse reactions are not equal.
   e. There are slightly more reactants than products in the mixture.

17. Consider the reaction

$$2 N_2O_{(g)} + 3 O_{2(g)} = 2 N_2O_{4(g)}$$

which is an endothermic reaction. What is the effect of increasing the concentration of N_2O?
   a. $[O_2]$ will decrease.
   b. The reaction will be driven to the left.
   c. $[N_2O_4]$ will decrease.
   d. $[O_2]$ will increase.
   e. There will be no effect.

18. Consider the reaction

$$CO_{(g)} + 2 H_{2(g)} = CH_3OH_{(g)}$$

which is an exothermic reaction. What is the effect of increasing the temperature?
   a. The reaction will be driven to the right.
   b. [CO] will decrease.
   c. $[CH_3OH]$ will increase.
   d. The reaction will be driven to the left.
   e. $[H_2]$ will decrease.

19. Enthalpy change
   a. is the energy difference between the transition state and the reactants in a reaction.
   b. is closely related to the rate of reaction.
   c. is the energy difference between the reactants and the products in a reaction.
   d. is independent of temperature.
   e. is the energy difference between the transition state and the products in a reaction.

20. For a given reaction, $k_f = 15.01$ second^{-1} and $k_r = 10.09$ liter/mole-second. What is the equilibrium constant?
   a. 1.488 mole/L
   b. 0.672 mole/L
   c. 1.488 L/mole
   d. 26.10 second^{-1}
   e. 0.672 L/mole

Answers to the Sample Quiz Questions

1. (c), 2. (e), 3. (d), 4. (b), 5. (e), 6. (a), 7. (c), 8. (d), 9. (b), 10. (b), 11. (c), 12. (d), 13. (a), 14. (b), 15. (e), 16. (e), 17. (a), 18. (d), 19. (c), 20. (a)

ACIDS, BASES, AND SALTS

CHAPTER
14

Chapter Overview

Chapter 14 discusses acids, bases, and salts. The material begins with descriptions of acids and bases according to the Arrhenius and the Bronsted-Lowry definitions, including acid-base conjugate pairs and amphoterism. The properties of acids and bases are also covered in terms of their common physical properties and their characteristic interactions with other materials. The more common household and industrial acids and bases are discussed in more detail.

The differentiation between strong and weak acids and bases is treated in depth, extending the equilibrium concepts of Chapter 13 to these types of compounds. This section includes calculations involving K_a and K_b and some math tips on how to perform the required algebra. Polyprotic acids are discussed in terms of their electron dot structures.

The anhydrides of acids and bases are then discussed with an emphasis on predicting the acid and base properties of the materials and their compositions.

A section on acid-base titrations and an optional section on expressing concentrations in normality then follow. These sections emphasize the algebraic relationships between acids and bases in reactions.

The chapter ends with sections on the salts which result from acid-base reactions, including predicting their composition, writing net ionic equations for acid-base reactions, and predicting whether the salts are soluble. The final section is optional and covers the concept of the solubility product constant, K_{sp}, and the calculations involved in relating the constants to concentrations.

Solutions to the Study Questions and Problems

1. **a.** In the **Arrhenius theory** of acids and bases, acids produce H^+ ions when dissolved in water and bases produce OH^- ions when dissolved in water. **b.** In the **Bronsted-Lowry** theory of acids and bases, an acid donates a proton and a base accepts a proton.

1. **c.** A **hydronium ion**, H_3O^+, is formed when a H^+ ion is released in aqueous solution. The H^+ bonds to a water molecule to form H_3O^+. **d.** A **conjugate acid** is the specie formed when a Bronsted-Lowry base has gained a proton. **e.** A **conjugate base** is the specie formed when a Bronsted-Lowry acid has donated a proton. **f.** Water is an **amphoteric** molecule. It can either gain or lose a proton and thus can be either an acid or a base.

2. There are no major differences between the Bronsted-Lowry and the Arrhenius theories in aqueous solution. The Bronsted-Lowry theory applies to non-aqueous solutions as well and is more general than the Arrhenius theory.

3. **a.** $HCl + H_2O = H_3O^+ + Cl^-$
    acid   base   acid   base

    b. $HNO_3 + H_2O = H_3O^+ + NO_3^-$
    acid   base   acid   base

    c. $HBr + H_2O = H_3O^+ + Br^-$
    acid   base   acid   base

    d. $HClO_4 + H_2O = H_3O^+ + ClO_4^-$
    acid   base   acid   base

4.

Acid	Conjugate Base	Base	Conjugate Acid
a. HI	I^-	**e.** HSO_4^-	H_2SO_4
b. $HClO_3$	ClO_3^-	**f.** OH^-	H_2O
c. $H_2PO_4^-$	HPO_4^{2-}	**g.** NH_3	NH_4^+
d. NH_4^+	NH_3	**h.** CO_3^{2-}	HCO_3^-

5. The major properties of acids are:

    1) They have a sour taste.
    2) They react with bases in neutralization reactions.
    3) They react with metals to produce hydrogen gas.
    4) Most of them are water soluble.
    5) They turn blue litmus to red.

    The major properties of bases are:

    1) They have a bitter taste.
    2) They have a slippery, soapy feel.
    3) They turn red litmus to blue.
    4) They react with acids in neutralization reactions.
    5) Most of them are water soluble.

6. An acid-base indicator is a substance which has one color in acidic solution and another color in basic solution. Litmus and phenolphthalein are examples.

7. For the neutralization of HCl with NaOH:

$$HCl_{(aq)} + NaOH_{(aq)} \rightarrow H_2O_{(l)} + NaCl_{(aq)}$$

8. Acids are designated as strong or weak depending on the extent to which they ionize or lose their protons in water. **Acid strength** then refers to this extent or the fraction of acid molecules which ionize. Strength should not be confused with total concentration of an acid.

9. Strong acids undergo almost complete ionization in water. An example would be hydrochloric acid (HCl) or nitric acid (HNO_3). Weak acids only undergo partial ionization in water. An example is acetic acid ($HC_2H_3O_2$) or nitrous acid (HNO_2).

10. Since HCl is a strong acid and essentially ionizes completely, the acid is considered to exist completely as $H_3O^+_{(aq)}$ and $Cl^-_{(aq)}$. Therefore, 6.0 M HCl yields 6.0 M H_3O^+.

11. $HC_2H_3O_{2(aq)} + H_2O_{(l)} = H_3O^+_{(aq)} + C_2H_3O_2^-_{(aq)}$

$$K_a = \frac{[H_3O^+][C_2H_3O_2^-]}{[HC_2H_3O_2]}$$

$$K_a = \frac{[0.0013][0.0013]}{[0.0987]}$$

$$K_a = 1.7 \times 10^{-5} M$$

12. $HCN_{(aq)} + H_2O_{(l)} = H_3O^+_{(aq)} + CN^-_{(aq)}$

$$K_a = \frac{[H_3O^+][CN^-]}{[HCN]}$$

$$K_a = \frac{[9.9 \times 10^{-6}][9.9 \times 10^{-6}]}{[0.20]}$$

$$K_a = 4.9 \times 10^{-10} M$$

13. $K_a = \frac{[H_3O^+][F^-]}{[HF]} = \frac{x^2}{[HF]}$

$$x^2 = K_a \cdot [HF]$$

$$x^2 = (6.8 \times 10^{-4})(0.099) = 6.7 \times 10^{-5}$$

$$x = 8.2 \times 10^{-3} M$$

14. **a.** A weak acid has a <u>strong</u> conjugate base.

   b. A strong acid has a <u>weak</u> conjugate base.

   c. A weak base has a <u>strong</u> conjugate acid.

   d. A strong base has a <u>weak</u> conjugate acid.

15. **Polyprotic acids** have more than one proton that they can donate.

16. $H_2SO_{4(aq)} + H_2O_{(l)} \rightarrow HSO_4^-{}_{(aq)} + H_3O^+{}_{(aq)}$

      acid   base   base   acid

   $HSO_4^-{}_{(aq)} + H_2O_{(l)} \rightarrow SO_4^{2-}{}_{(aq)} + H_3O^+{}_{(aq)}$

      acid   base   base   acid

17. $H_3PO_{4(aq)} + H_2O_{(l)} \rightarrow H_2PO_4^-{}_{(aq)} + H_3O^+{}_{(aq)}$

      acid   base   base   acid

   $H_2PO_4^-{}_{(aq)} + H_2O_{(l)} \rightarrow HPO_4^{2-}{}_{(aq)} + H_3O^+{}_{(aq)}$

      acid   base   base   acid

   $HPO_4^-{}_{(aq)} + H_2O_{(l)} \rightarrow PO_4^{3-}{}_{(aq)} + H_3O^+{}_{(aq)}$

      acid   base   base   acid

18. H_3PO_4 is a weaker acid than H_2SO_4 because the K_a of H_3PO_4 for the first H^+ dissociation is quite a bit smaller than the K_a of H_2SO_4 for the first H^+ dissociation. Structurally, this is caused by phosphorus being less electronegative than sulfur so that the O–H bonds in H_3PO_4 are less polar than those in H_2SO_4 and so less subject to ionization.

19. For a polyprotic acid, each successive K_a decreases because the negative charge formed on the conjugate base helps decrease the polarity of the remaining O–H bonds. Thus the second and further hydrogen ions don't dissociate as readily.

20. Strong bases readily provide hydroxide ions in aqueous solution or, by the Bronsted-Lowry definition, have a strong affinity for hydrogen ions. Weak bases do not provide hydroxide ions as readily in aqueous solution or, by the Bronsted-Lowry definition, have a low affinity for hydrogen ions.

21. KOH is a strong base and so is assumed to dissociate completely to give $K^+{}_{(aq)}$ and $OH^-{}_{(aq)}$. Therefore, the [OH$^-$] of a 2.0 M solution of KOH is also 2.0 M.

22. For $NH_{3(aq)} + H_2O_{(l)} = NH_4{}^+{}_{(aq)} + OH^-{}_{(aq)}$

$$K_b = \frac{[NH_4{}^+][OH^-]}{[NH_3]}$$

$$K_b = \frac{[0.0016][0.0016]}{[0.148]}$$

$$K_b = 1.7 \times 10^{-5} \text{ M}$$

23. $NaHCO_{3(aq)} + H_2O_{(l)} = Na^+{}_{(aq)} + H_2CO_{3(aq)} + OH^-{}_{(aq)}$

In this reaction, the Na^+ is a spectator ion. The $HCO_3{}^-$ anion is a base, reacting with water to form the conjugate acid, H_2CO_3, and OH^-.

24. Acid anhydrides are compounds which are converted to acids when mixed with water. For example, when CO_2 is dissolved in water, carbonic acid is produced:

$$CO_{2(aq)} + H_2O_{(l)} \rightarrow H_2CO_{3(aq)}$$

Basic anhydrides are converted to metal hydroxides when mixed with water. For example, when Na_2O is dissolved in water:

$$Na_2O_{(aq)} + H_2O_{(l)} \rightarrow 2\,NaOH_{(aq)}$$

25. a. CaO $\qquad CaO_{(aq)} + H_2O_{(l)} \rightarrow Ca(OH)_{2(aq)}$

b. Cl_2O $\qquad Cl_2O_{(aq)} + H_2O_{(l)} \rightarrow 2\,HClO_{(aq)}$

c. SiO_2 $\qquad SiO_{2(aq)} + H_2O_{(l)} \rightarrow H_2SiO_{3(aq)}$

d. ZnO $\qquad ZnO_{(aq)} + H_2O_{(l)} \rightarrow Zn(OH)_{2(aq)}$

e. B_2O_3 $\qquad B_2O_{3(aq)} + 3\,H_2O_{(l)} \rightarrow 2\,H_3BO_{3(aq)}$

26. a. $SrO_{(aq)} + H_2O_{(l)} \rightarrow Sr(OH)_{2(aq)}$

b. $Br_2O_{(aq)} + H_2O_{(l)} \rightarrow 2\,HBrO_{(aq)}$

c. $CoO_{(aq)} + H_2O_{(l)} \rightarrow Co(OH)_{2(aq)}$

d. $Cl_2O_{5(aq)} + H_2O_{(l)} \rightarrow 2\,HClO_{3(aq)}$

e. $SeO_{3(aq)} + H_2O_{(l)} \rightarrow H_2SeO_{4(aq)}$

27. The NO_2 in automobile exhausts can react with atmospheric moisture to form HNO_3; NO_2 is the acid anhydride of nitric acid. On the other hand, N_2 is a generally unreactive gas and comprises approximately 80% of the atmosphere, anyway.

28. A measured volume of an acid or base of unknown concentration is placed in a flask with a few drops of an appropriate acid-base indicator. Slowly, small amounts of a titrant (acid if the flask contains base and base if the flask contains acid) of known concentration are added to the flask until one drop causes a color change in the indicator. The total amount of the titrant used is then recorded as the endpoint volume and the concentration of the substance of unknown concentration can be calculated.

29. The reaction is: $H_2SO_{4(aq)} + 2\,NaOH_{(aq)} \rightarrow Na_2SO_{4(aq)} + 2\,H_2O_{(l)}$

$$\frac{(0.6000 \text{ mole NaOH})(0.03215 \text{ L NaOH})(1 \text{ mole } H_2SO_4)}{(\quad \text{L NaOH} \quad)\quad\quad(2 \text{ moles NaOH})(0.02500 \text{ L } H_2SO_4)} = 0.3858 \text{ M } H_2SO_4$$

30. The reaction is: $2\,HCl_{(aq)} + Ba(OH)_{2(aq)} \rightarrow BaCl_{2(aq)} + 2\,H_2O_{(l)}$

$$\frac{(0.1000 \text{ mole HCl})(0.01527 \text{ L HCl})(1 \text{ mole Ba(OH)}_2)}{(\quad \text{L HCl} \quad)\quad\quad(2 \text{ moles HCl})(0.02000 \text{ L Ba(OH)}_2)}$$
$$= 0.03818 \text{ M Ba(OH)}_2$$

31. The molar mass of $KHC_8H_4O_4$ (KHP) is: $1(39.1 \text{ g/mole}) + 5(1.0 \text{ g/mole}) + 8(12.0 \text{ g/mole})$

$$+ 4(16.0 \text{ g/mole}) = 204.1 \text{ g/mole}$$

Therefore, the number of moles of $KHC_8H_4O_4$ is $\dfrac{(0.6135 \text{ g})(1 \text{ mole})}{(204.1 \text{ g})} = 0.003006 \text{ mole KHP}$

$$\frac{(0.003006 \text{ mole KHP})(1 \text{ mole NaOH})}{(1 \text{ mole KHP})(0.02672 \text{ L NaOH})} = 0.1125 \text{ M NaOH}$$

32. The reaction is: $Mg(OH)_{2(aq)} + 2\,HCl_{(aq)} \rightarrow MgCl_{2(aq)} + 2\,H_2O_{(l)}$

The molar mass of $Mg(OH)_2$ is: $1(24.3 \text{ g/mole}) + 2(1.0 \text{ g/mole}) + 2(16.0 \text{ g/mole}) = 58.3 \text{ g/mole}$

$$\frac{(0.6000 \text{ mole HCl})(0.03064 \text{ L HCl})(1 \text{ mole Mg(OH)}_2)(58.3 \text{ g Mg(OH)}_2)}{(\quad \text{L HCl} \quad)\quad\quad(2 \text{ moles HCl})(1 \text{ mole Mg(OH)}_2)} = 0.536 \text{ g Mg(OH)}_2$$

$\dfrac{(0.536 \text{ g})}{(1.263 \text{ g})} \times 100\% = 42.4\ \%(w/w)\ Mg(OH)_2$

33. **a.** An **equivalent of an acid** is the amount of acid which neutralizes one mole of hydroxide ions. **b.** An **equivalent of a base** is the amount of a base that neutralizes one mole of hydrogen ions. **c.** A **monoprotic acid** contains only one donatable proton. **d.** A **diprotic acid** contains two donatable protons. **e.** A **triprotic acid** contains three donatable protons. **f. Normality** is a measure of concentration expressed as the number of equivalents per liter of solution.

34. **a.** H_2SO_4 is a diprotic acid. **b.** H_3PO_4 is a triprotic acid. **c.** HCl is a monoprotic acid. **d.** H_2CO_3 is a diprotic acid.

35. The molar mass of H_2SO_4 is: $2(1.0 \text{ g/mole}) + 1(32.1 \text{ g/mole}) + 4(16.0 \text{ g/mole}) = 98.1 \text{ g/mole}$

$$\frac{(392.4 \text{ g } H_2SO_4)(1 \text{ mole } H_2SO_4)(2 \text{ equivalents })}{(98.1 \text{ g } H_2SO_4)(1 \text{ mole } H_2SO_4)(2.00 \text{ L})} = 4.00 \text{ equiv/L or } 4.00 \text{ N } H_2SO_4$$

36. The molar mass of NaOH is: $1(23.0 \text{ g/mole}) + 1(1.0 \text{ g/mole}) + 1(16.0 \text{ g/mole}) = 40.0 \text{ g/mole}$

$$\frac{(20.0 \text{ g NaOH})(1 \text{ mole NaOH})(1 \text{ equivalent })}{(40.0 \text{ g NaOH})(1 \text{ mole NaOH})(0.2500 \text{ L})} = 2.00 \text{ equiv/L or } 2.00 \text{ N NaOH}$$

37. The molar mass of KOH is: $1(39.1 \text{ g/mole}) + 1(1.0 \text{ g/mole}) + 1(16.0 \text{ g/mole}) = 56.1 \text{ g/mole}$

$$\frac{(6.00 \text{ equivalents})(1 \text{ mole KOH})(0.6000 \text{ L KOH})(56.1 \text{ g KOH})}{(\text{ L KOH })(1 \text{ equivalent })(1 \text{ mole KOH})} = 202 \text{ g KOH}$$

38. $\dfrac{(0.01000 \text{ equivalents})(1000 \text{ meq })(0.1000 \text{ L})}{(1 \text{ L })(1 \text{ equivalent})} = 1.000 \text{ meq}$

39. $\dfrac{(0.150 \text{ equivalents})(1000 \text{ meq })(0.0500 \text{ L})}{(1 \text{ L })(1 \text{ equivalent})} = 7.50 \text{ meq}$

40. $\dfrac{(2.00 \text{ moles})(3 \text{ equivalents})}{(1 \text{ L })(1 \text{ mole })} = 6.00 \text{ equiv/L or } 6.00 \text{ N } H_3PO_4$

41. $\dfrac{(1.50 \text{ moles})(2 \text{ equivalents})}{(1 \text{ L })(1 \text{ mole })} = 3.00 \text{ equiv/L or } 3.00 \text{ N } H_2SO_4$

42. $\dfrac{(6.00 \text{ moles})(1 \text{ equivalents})}{(1 \text{ L })(1 \text{ mole })} = 6.00 \text{ equiv/L or } 6.00 \text{ N NaOH}$

43. Even though $M_aV_a = M_bV_b$ may have to be adjusted for the relative number of moles of each in the balanced equation, $N_aV_a = N_bV_b$ always works as is. Therefore,

$N_a = N_bV_b/V_a$

$N_a = (1.502 \text{ N KOH})(0.02005 \text{ L KOH})/(0.04000 \text{ L acid})$

$N_a = 0.7529 \text{ N acid}$

44. $V_b = N_aV_a/N_b$

$V_b = (1.000 \text{ N } HNO_3)(0.01500 \text{ L } HNO_3)/(0.4000 \text{ N base})$

$V_b = 0.03750 \text{ L base or } 37.50 \text{ mL base}$

45. a. A **salt** is an ionic compound formed by the reaction of an acid with a base. **b. Nonionic equations** are reaction equations that do not break down the compounds into their respective ions as they exist in solution. **c.** A **total ionic equation** contains all the compounds in a reaction broken down into their respective ions as they exist in solution. **d. Spectator ions** are ions which do not actually take part in a reaction. **e.** The **net ionic equation** cancels out the spectator ions and so only includes the species which actually participate in a reaction.

46. a. $2\,Na^+_{(aq)} + 2\,OH^-_{(aq)} + 2\,H^+_{(aq)} + SO_4^{2-}_{(aq)} \rightarrow 2\,Na^+_{(aq)} + SO_4^{2-}_{(aq)} + 2\,H_2O_{(l)}$

b. $2\,OH^-_{(aq)} + 2\,H^+_{(aq)} \rightarrow 2\,H_2O_{(l)}$

47. a. $Ca^{2+}_{(aq)} + 2\,OH^-_{(aq)} + 2\,H^+_{(aq)} + SO_4^{2-}_{(aq)} \rightarrow CaSO_{4(s)} + 2\,H_2O_{(l)}$

b. $Ca^{2+}_{(aq)} + 2\,OH^-_{(aq)} + 2\,H^+_{(aq)} + SO_4^{2-}_{(aq)} \rightarrow CaSO_{4(s)} + 2\,H_2O_{(l)}$ (same as part a)

48. Precipitates are insoluble solid products formed in chemical reactions.

49. a. Rb_2SO_4 is soluble. **b.** Ag_2O is insoluble. **c.** $PbSO_4$ is insoluble. **d.** $HgBr_2$ is soluble. **e.** $PbCO_3$ is insoluble.

50. a. $AlCl_{3(aq)} + 3\,NaOH_{(aq)} \rightarrow Al(OH)_{3(s)} + 3\,NaCl_{(aq)}$

b. $Ba(C_2H_3O_2)_{2(aq)} + K_2SO_{4(aq)} \rightarrow BaSO_{4(s)} + 2\,KC_2H_3O_{2(aq)}$

c. no reaction - All substances are soluble.

d. $FeCl_{2(aq)} + 2\,LiOH_{(aq)} \rightarrow Fe(OH)_{2(s)} + 2\,LiCl_{(aq)}$

51. a. $Al^{3+}_{(aq)} + 3\,Cl^-_{(aq)} + 3\,Na^+_{(aq)} + 3\,OH^-_{(aq)} \rightarrow Al(OH)_{3(s)} + 3\,Na^+_{(aq)} + 3\,Cl^-_{(aq)}$

b. $Ba^{2+}_{(aq)} + 2\,C_2H_3O_2^-_{(aq)} + 2\,K^+_{(aq)} + SO_4^{2-}_{(aq)} \rightarrow BaSO_{4(s)} + 2\,K^+_{(aq)} + 2\,C_2H_3O_2^-_{(aq)}$

d. $Fe^{2+}_{(aq)} + 2\,Cl^-_{(aq)} + 2\,Li^+_{(aq)} + 2\,OH^-_{(aq)} \rightarrow Fe(OH)_{2(s)} + 2\,Li^+_{(aq)} + 2\,Cl^-_{(aq)}$

52. a. $Al^{3+}_{(aq)} + 3\,OH^-_{(aq)} \rightarrow Al(OH)_{3(s)}$

b. $Ba^{2+}_{(aq)} + SO_4^{2-}_{(aq)} \rightarrow BaSO_{4(s)}$

d. $Fe^{2+}_{(aq)} + 2\,OH^-_{(aq)} \rightarrow Fe(OH)_{2(s)}$

53. a. For $Al(OH)_3$, $\quad K_{sp} = [Al^{3+}][OH^-]^3$

b. For Hg_2CrO_4, $\quad K_{sp} = [Hg_2^{2+}][CrO_4]$

c. For BaC_2O_4, $\quad K_{sp} = [Ba^{2+}][C_2O_4^{2-}]$

d. For $Sr_3(PO_4)_2$, $\quad K_{sp} = [Sr^{2+}]^3[PO_4^{3-}]^2$

54. $K_{sp} = [Cd^{2+}][OH^-]^2$

Using the symbol "S" for the solubility, then

$K_{sp} = [S][2 \cdot S]^2$ since dissolving 1 mole of compound gives one mole of Cd^{2+} and 2 moles of OH^-.

$K_{sp} = 4 \cdot S^3$

$K_{sp} = 4(1.7 \times 10^{-5})^3$

$K_{sp} = 2.0 \times 10^{-14} \, mole^3/L^3$

55. $K_{sp} = [Ce^{3+}][OH^-]^3$

Using the symbol "S" for the solubility, then

$K_{sp} = [S][3 \cdot S]^3$ since dissolving 1 mole of compound gives one mole of Ce^{3+} and 3 moles of OH^-.

$K_{sp} = 27 \cdot S^4$

$K_{sp} = 27(5.2 \times 10^{-6})^4$

$K_{sp} = 2.0 \times 10^{-20} \, mole^4/L^4$

56. For Ag_2CO_3, $K_{sp} = [Ag^+]^2[CO_3{}^{2-}]$

Using the symbol "S" for the solubility, $K_{sp} = [2 \cdot S]^2[S] = 4 \cdot S^3$

$S^3 = K_{sp}/4$

$S^3 = 8.2 \times 10^{-12}/4 = 2.0 \times 10^{-12}$

$S = 1.3 \times 10^{-4} \, mole/L$

For $CuCO_3$, $K_{sp} = [Cu^{2+}][CO_3{}^{2-}]$

Using the symbol "S" for the solubility, $K_{sp} = [S][S] = S^2$

$S^2 = K_{sp} = 2.5 \times 10^{-10}$

$S = 1.6 \times 10^{-5} \, mole/L$

Therefore, $CuCO_3$ has the lower solubility.

57. $K_{sp} = [Cr^{3+}][OH^-]^3$

$[Cr^{3+}] = K_{sp}/[OH^-]^3$

$[Cr^{3+}] = (3 \times 10^{-29})/(0.15)^3$

$[Cr^{3+}] = 9 \times 10^{-27}$ mole/L

58. As an acid: $H_2O_{(l)} \rightarrow H^+_{(aq)} + OH^-_{(aq)}$

As a base: $H_2O_{(l)} + H^+_{(aq)} \rightarrow H_3O^+_{(aq)}$

59. $K_a = \dfrac{[H_3O^+][CHO_2^-]}{[HCHO_2]} = \dfrac{x^2}{[HCHO_2]}$

$x^2 = K_a \cdot [HCHO_2] = 1.7 \times 10^{-4} \cdot 0.20 = 3.4 \times 10^{-5}$

$x = [H_3O^+] = 5.8 \times 10^{-3}$ mole/L

60. $\underset{\text{acid}}{H_2CO_{3(aq)}} + \underset{\text{base}}{H_2O_{(l)}} \rightarrow \underset{\text{base}}{HCO_3^-_{(aq)}} + \underset{\text{acid}}{H_3O^+_{(aq)}}$

$\underset{\text{acid}}{HCO_3^-_{(aq)}} + \underset{\text{base}}{H_2O_{(l)}} \rightarrow \underset{\text{base}}{CO_3^{2-}_{(aq)}} + \underset{\text{acid}}{H_3O^+_{(aq)}}$

61. $K_b = \dfrac{[CON_2H_5^+][OH^-]}{[CON_2H_4]}$

$K_b = \dfrac{[7.7 \times 10^{-8}][7.7 \times 10^{-8}]}{[0.40]}$

$K_b = 1.5 \times 10^{-14}$ mole/L

62. a. $CaO_{(s)} + SiO_{2(s)} \rightarrow CaSiO_{3(s)}$

b. $BaO_{(s)} + SO_{3(g)} \rightarrow BaSO_{4(s)}$

c. $B_2O_{3(s)} + 3\ Na_2O_{(s)} \rightarrow 2\ Na_3BO_{3(s)}$

63. Both SO_2 and SO_3 are acid anhydrides:

$$SO_{2(g)} + H_2O_{(l)} \rightarrow H_2SO_{3(aq)}$$

$$SO_{3(g)} + H_2O_{(l)} \rightarrow H_2SO_{4(aq)}$$

The SO_2 would be less damaging in the environment because the acid it forms is a very weak acid while the SO_3 forms a very strong and, therefore, corrosive acid.

64. $\dfrac{(1.000 \text{ mole } H_2SO_4)(0.04274 \text{ L } H_2SO_4)(2 \text{ moles NaOH})}{(1 \text{ L } H_2SO_4)(1 \text{ mole } H_2SO_4)(0.02000 \text{ L NaOH})} = 4.274 \text{ M NaOH}$

65. The molar mass of $H_2C_2O_4$ is: $2(1.0 \text{ g/mole}) + 2(12.0 \text{ g/mole}) + 4(16.0 \text{ g/mole}) = 90.0 \text{ g/mole}$

$\dfrac{(0.1845 \text{ mole NaOH})(0.02756 \text{ L NaOH})(1 \text{ mole } H_2C_2O_4)(90.0 \text{ g } H_2C_2O_4)}{(1 \text{ L NaOH})(2 \text{ moles NaOH})(1 \text{ mole } H_2C_2O_4)} = 0.229 \text{ g } H_2C_2O_4$

$\dfrac{(0.229 \text{ g})}{(0.2981 \text{ g})} \times 100\% = 76.8 \text{ \%(w/w)}$

66. The molar mass of H_3PO_4 is $3(1.0 \text{ g/mole}) + 1(31.0 \text{ g/mole}) + 4(16.0 \text{ g/mole}) = 98.0 \text{ g/mole}$

$\dfrac{(5.00 \text{ L})(2.00 \text{ equivalents})(1 \text{ mole})(98.0 \text{ g } H_3PO_4)}{(1 \text{ L})(3 \text{ equivalents})(1 \text{ mole } H_3PO_4)} = 327 \text{ g } H_3PO_4$

67. For HCl:

$\dfrac{(0.0150 \text{ L})(0.400 \text{ equivalents})}{(1 \text{ L})} = 0.00600 \text{ equivalents HCl}$

For NaOH:

$\dfrac{(0.0500 \text{ L})(0.100 \text{ equivalents})}{(1 \text{ L})} = 0.00500 \text{ equivalents NaOH}$

Since there were more equivalents of HCl, some HCl remains in excess and the resulting solution is acidic.

68. a. $Ca(OH)_{2(aq)} + 2 \text{ HBr}_{(aq)} \rightarrow CaBr_{2(aq)} + 2 H_2O_{(l)}$

b. $KOH_{(aq)} + HC_2H_3O_{2(aq)} \rightarrow KC_2H_3O_{2(aq)} + H_2O_{(l)}$

c. $NaOH_{(aq)} + HClO_{4(aq)} \rightarrow NaClO_{4(aq)} + H_2O_{(l)}$

d. $3 Mg(OH)_{2(aq)} + 2 H_3PO_{4(aq)} \rightarrow Mg_3(PO_4)_{2(s)} + 6 H_2O_{(l)}$

69. $K_{sp} = [Ca^{2+}][F^-]^2$

Using the symbol "S" as the solubility,

$K_{sp} = [S][2 \cdot S]^2 = 4 \cdot S^3$

$S^3 = K_{sp}/4 = 4.0 \times 10^{-11}/4 = 1.0 \times 10^{-11} \text{ mole}^3/L^3$

$S = 2.2 \times 10^{-4} \text{ mole/L}$

70. $K_{sp} = [Bi^{3+}]^2[S^{2-}]^3$

$[Bi^{3+}]^2 = K_{sp}/[S^{2-}]^3$

$[Bi^{3+}]^2 = (1.6 \times 10^{-72})/(0.10)^3 = 1.6 \times 10^{-69}$

$[Bi^{3+}] = 4.0 \times 10^{-35} \text{ mole/L}$

Sample Quiz Questions

1. An acid
    a. is a substance which releases hydroxide when dissolved in water.
    b. consists of a nonmetal and oxygen.
    c. is a compound which releases a proton when dissolved in water.
    d. is a compound which accepts a proton when dissolved in water.
    e. usually contains metal atoms.

2. Which of the following most properly illustrates the reaction of an acid with water?
    a. $PbCrO_{4(s)} \rightarrow Pb^{2+}{}_{(aq)} + CrO_{4(aq)}$
    b. $HClO_{2(aq)} + H_2O_{(l)} \rightarrow ClO_2{}^-{}_{(aq)} + H^+{}_{(aq)}$
    c. $Mg(OH)_{2(aq)} \rightarrow Mg^{2+}{}_{(aq)} + 2\ OH^-{}_{(aq)}$
    d. $HClO_{(aq)} + H_2O_{(l)} \rightarrow ClO^-{}_{(aq)} + H_3O^+{}_{(aq)}$
    e. $BaO_{(s)} + H_2O_{(l)} \rightarrow Ba(OH)_{2(aq)}$

3. In general, acids
    a. have a sour taste.
    b. have a bitter taste.
    c. have a soapy feel.
    d. are insoluble in water.
    e. turn red litmus to blue.

4. In general, bases
    a. turn blue litmus to red.
    b. react with metals to produce hydrogen gas.
    c. are insoluble in water.
    d. have a sour taste.
    e. have a bitter taste.

5.   What is $[H_3O^+]$ in a 3.00 M solution of $HClO_4$?
     a. 1.50 M
     b. 3.00 M
     c. 6.00 M
     d. It depends on the K_a of $HClO_4$.
     e. It depends on the volume of solution being considered.

6. K_a for HCN is 4.9×10^{-10}. If [HCN] = 0.275 M, what is $[H_3O^+]$?
     a. 1.3×10^{-10} M
     b. 0.28 M
     c. 1.2×10^{-5} M
     d. 0.076 M
     e. 1.8×10^{-20} M

7.   Consider the reaction

$$HClO_{(aq)} + H_2O_{(l)} \; = \; H_3O^+{}_{(aq)} + ClO^-{}_{(aq)}$$

K_a for the reaction is 3.2×10^{-8} mole/L. If $[H_3O^+]$ = 0.000300 M and [HClO] = 0.210 M, what is [ClO$^-$]?
     a. 4.6×10^{-11} M
     b. 6.7×10^{-9} M
     c. 1.1×10^{-4} M
     d. 4.3×10^{-7} M
     e. 2.2×10^{-5} M

8.   Consider the reaction

$$HNO_{2(aq)} + H_2O_{(l)} \; = \; H_3O^+{}_{(aq)} + NO_2^-{}_{(aq)}$$

If the following equilibrium concentrations exist,

$$[H_3O^+] = 0.00212 \text{ M}$$
$$[NO_2^-] = 0.00212 \text{ M}$$
$$[HNO_2] = 0.0100 \text{ M}$$

Calculate K_a.
     a. 4.5×10^{-6} M
     b. 0.212 M
     c. 4.5×10^{-4} M
     d. 4.5×10^{-8} M
     e. 1.00×10^2 M

9. For polyprotic acids, K_a values for the ionization of successive H^+ ions
    a. decrease due to an increase of negative charge on the central atom.
    b. decrease due to the fewer number of remaining H^+ atoms.
    c. remain fairly constant.
    d. increase due to the increasing polarity of the O–H bonds.
    e. increase due to repulsions between the H^+ ions.

10. The conjugate base of an acid
    a. is the molecule or ion left after the acid accepts a proton.
    b. is not stable under most conditions.
    c. is a stronger acid than the original acid.
    d. is the molecule or ion left after the acid donates a proton.
    e. cannot itself be an acid.

11. K_b for CO_3^{2-} is 2.1×10^{-4}. If the concentration of CO_3^{2-} is 0.075 M, what is $[OH^-]$?
    a. 1.6×10^{-5} M
    b. 0.075 M
    c. 1.4×10^{-2} M
    d. 4.0×10^{-3} M
    e. 2.5×10^{-10} M

12. K_b for triethylamine, $N(C_2H_5)_3$, is 5.2×10^{-4}. $[OH^-]$ and $[HN(C_2H_5)_3]$ are known to be 0.000103 M. Calculate $[N(C_2H_5)_3]$.
    a. 0.20 M
    b. 2.0×10^{-5} M
    c. 4.9×10^4 M
    d. 0.40 M
    e. 1.1×10^{-8} M

13. Consider the reaction

$$CN^-_{(aq)} + H_2O_{(l)} = HCN_{(aq)} + OH^-_{(aq)}$$

If the following equilibrium concentrations exist,

$$[OH^-] = 1.26 \times 10^{-3} \text{ M}$$
$$[HCN] = 1.26 \times 10^{-3} \text{ M}$$
$$[CN^-] = 0.100 \text{ M}$$

Calculate K_b.
    a. 0.0126
    b. 1.6×10^{-6}
    c. 1.6×10^{-4}
    d. 6.2×10^4
    e. 1.6×10^{-5}

14. Consider the reaction

$$N(CH_3)_{3(aq)} + H_2O_{(l)} \ = \ HN(CH_3)_3^+{}_{(aq)} + OH^-{}_{(aq)}$$

for which $K_b = 6.3 \times 10^{-5}$ M. If the following equilibrium concentrations exist,

$$[OH^-] = 0.0126 \text{ M}$$
$$[N(CH_3)_3] = 0.100 \text{ M}$$

Calculate $[HN(CH_3)_3^+]$.
- a. 6.3×10^{-6} M
- b. 5.0×10^{-4} M
- c. 7.9×10^{-6} M
- d. 5.0×10^{-3} M
- e. 7.9×10^{-7} M

15. An acid anhydride
- a. generally is composed of a metal and oxygen.
- b. is formed by reacting an acid with water.
- c. forms a base when reacted with water.
- d. is formed by reacting a base with water.
- e. forms an acid when dissolved in water.

16. The compound formed by Cl_2O_7 when it is reacted with water is
- a. $HClO_4$
- b. $HClO_3$
- c. $HClO_2$
- d. $HClO$
- e. H_2ClO_4

17. A 25.00 mL sample of a monoprotic acid required 33.24 mL of 0.500 M NaOH to titrate. Calculate the molarity of the acid.
- a. 0.376 M
- b. 0.0166 M
- c. 0.0125 M
- d. 0.665 M
- e. 0.752 M

18. What mass of HCl is required to react with 75.00 mL of 0.0125 M $Mg(OH)_2$?
- a. 0.0171 g
- b. 0.0684 g
- c. 0.00188 g
- d. 0.0342 g
- e. 6.00 g

19. What mass of HCl is required to react with 75.00 mL of 0.0125 N $Mg(OH)_2$?
- a. 0.0171 g
- b. 0.0684 g
- c. 0.00188 g
- d. 0.0342 g
- e. 6.00 g

20. A 35.00 mL sample of an acid required 15.05 mL of 0.225 M $Ba(OH)_2$ to react. Calculate the normality of the acid.
    a. 0.193 N
    b. 6.75 N
    c. 0.0964 N
    d. 3.38 N
    e. 0.0482 N

21. Which of the following salts should be soluble?
    a. $HgSO_4$
    b. Fe_2O_3
    c. Hg_2Cl_2
    d. $MgSO_4$
    e. $Ca(OH)_2$

22. Which of the following salts should not be soluble?
    a. $Co(ClO_4)_2$
    b. PbI_2
    c. Na_2O
    d. $(NH_4)_2SO_4$
    e. $Sr(OH)_2$

23. K_{sp} for $Zn(OH)_2$ is 1.8×10^{-14}. What is the solubility of $Zn(OH)_2$ in moles/L?
    a. 2.6×10^{-5} mole/L
    b. 6.6×10^{-6} mole/L
    c. 1.3×10^{-7} mole/L
    d. 6.7×10^{-8} mole/L
    e. 1.7×10^{-5} mole/L

24. K_{sp} for Ag_2S is 1.8×10^{-49}. If $[S^{2-}] = 0.0010$ M, what is $[Ag^+]$?
    a. 1.3×10^{-23} M
    b. 1.8×10^{-43} M
    c. 4.2×10^{-25} M
    d. 3.6×10^{-17} M
    e. 1.8×10^{-46} M

Answers to the Sample Quiz Questions

1. (c), 2. (d), 3. (a), 4. (e), 5. (b), 6. (c), 7. (e), 8. (c), 9. (a), 10. (d), 11. (d), 12. (b), 13. (e), 14. (b), 15. (e), 16. a(), 17. (d), 18. (b), 19. (d), 20. (a), 21. (d), 22. (b), 23. (e), 24. (a)

ELECTROLYTES, pH, AND BUFFERS

CHAPTER

15

Chapter Overview

Chapter 15 further extends the ideas of acids, bases, and soluble salts which were introduced in Chapter 14. The chapter begins with a description of electrolytes in general as substances which conduct electricity when melted or ionized in water. Electrolytes are then subdivided into strong and weak, based on the extent of ionization. This treatment is similar to that of strong and weak acids and bases in Chapter 14 but it is also pointed out that acids and bases are specific types of electrolytes.

The autoionization of water is then discussed and leads into the concept of the ion-product constant, K_w, and to the pH acidity scale. Since use of the pH scale requires the use of common logarithms, there are several practice problems and students are directed to Appendix A.4, Review of Basic Algebra, for general guidance on logarithms and to Appendix B, Decimal pH Values, for more detailed information. The section also includes numerous Math Tips on working logrithm problems with calculators. As the complement to pH, pOH is also discussed, as is the method of measuring pH.

This is followed by two optional sections dealing with more complex pH calculations, such as those involving non-integer pH values, the relationship between pH and the acid and base ionization constants, K_a and K_b, and percent ionization.

The chapter concludes with a qualitative description of buffers and their mode of operation.

Solutions to the Study Questions and Problems

1. **a.** Substances that conduct electricity when melted or dissolved in water are called **electrolytes**. **b. Strong electrolytes** are compounds that dissociate completely into ions when melted or dissolved in water. **c.** Substances that do not dissociate completely into ions when melted or dissolved in water are called **weak electrolytes**. **d.** If a substance produces no ions when melted or dissolved in water, it is a **nonelectrolyte**. Nonelectrolytes do not conduct electricity.

2. Most metals are good conductors of electricity because their outer shell electrons are held very loosely and so are easily moved from atom to atom. The passing of electrons from atom to atom is the flow of electricity.

3. Most nonmetals and molecular compounds are poor conductors of electricity because of two reasons: 1) either their outer shell electrons are held too tightly or 2) their outer shell electrons are shared with other atoms in covalent bonds.

4. Ionic compounds only conduct electricity when dissolved in water or melted because, in the solid state, they do not exist as individual ions; they are bound in crystal lattices by ionic bonds. When melted or dissolved in water, their individual ions are released and so can move and conduct electricity.

5. Strong electrolytes dissociate completely in water. An example of a strong electrolyte is is H_2SO_4. Weak electrolytes do not dissociate completely in water. An example is the weak electrolyte acetic acid, $HC_2H_3O_2$.

6. Weak electrolytes dissociate to some extent but not completely. An example is the weak base methylamine, CH_3NH_2. Nonelectrolytes do not dissociate to any appreciable extent and so do not conduct electricity. An example of a nonelectrolyte is sugar, $C_6H_{12}O_6$.

7. Pure water is a weak conductor of electricity because H_2O does not dissociate to any great extent. Tap water usually is a much better conductor of electricity because of the dissolved minerals which yield ions such as calcium, magnesium, chloride, and fluoride.

8. $$2 H_2O_{(l)} = H_3O^+_{(aq)} + OH^-_{(aq)}$$

9. The ionization constant of water, K_w, is called the ion-product constant of water.

10. $$2 H_2O_{(l)} = H_3O^+_{(aq)} + OH^-_{(aq)}$$

$$K_{eq} = \frac{[H_3O^+][OH^-]}{[H_2O]^2}$$

Since the concentration of H_2O is virtually a constant,

$$K_{eq}[H_2O]^2 = K_w = [H_3O^+][OH^-]$$

11. The symbol "p" in chemistry can be defined as "the negative log of". Therefore, pH is the negative log of $[H^+]$ or $[H_3O^+]$:

$$pH = - \log[H_3O^+]$$

pOH is the negative log of $[OH^-]$:

$$pOH = - \log[OH^-]$$

It also then follows that, since $K_w = [H_3O^+][OH^-] = 1.00 \times 10^{-14}$, then

$$- \log K_w = - \log[H_3O^+] + - \log[OH^-] = 14.000$$

$$pK_w = pH + pOH = 14.000$$

12. $K_w = [H_3O^+][OH^-]$

$[OH^-] = K_w/[H_3O^+]$

$[OH^-] = 1.00 \times 10^{-14}/1.00 \times 10^{-3}$

$[OH^-] = 1.00 \times 10^{-11}$ M

13. $pH = -\log[H_3O^+]$

a. $pH = -\log(0.100) = 1.000$
b. $pH = -\log(1.00 \times 10^{-12}) = 12.000$
c. $pH = -\log(1.00 \times 10^{-4}) = 4.000$
d. $pH = -\log(1.00 \times 10^{-9}) = 9.000$
e. $pH = -\log(1.00) = 0.000$
f. $pH = -\log(1.00 \times 10^{-6}) = 6.000$

14. Since pH + pOH = 14.000, pOH = 14.000 - pH

a. pOH = 14.000 - 1.000 = 13.000
b. pOH = 14.000 - 12.000 = 2.000
c. pOH = 14.000 - 4.000 = 10.000
d. pOH = 14.000 - 9.000 = 5.000
e. pOH = 14.000 - 0.000 = 14.000
f. pOH = 14.000 - 6.000 = 8.000

15. Because $K_w = 1.00 \times 10^{-14}$ at 25 °C, $pK_w = 14.000 = $ pH + pOH. Since pH + pOH is always equal to 14.000 at 25 °C, this is the logical upper limit of the scale.

16. For a 0.00100 M KOH solution,

a. $[OH^-] = 0.00100$ M, since KOH is a strong electrolyte.
b. $[H_3O^+] = K_w/[OH^-] = 1.00 \times 10^{-14}$ M^2/0.00100 M $= 1.00 \times 10^{-11}$ M
c. $pH = -\log(1.00 \times 10^{-11}) = 11.000$
d. $pOH = -\log(0.00100) = 3.000$

17. HCl is a strong acid. Therefore,

$[HCl] = [H_3O^+] = $ antilog(-1) = 1 × 10^{-1} = 0.1 M HCl sought in the dilute solution.

From here, this is a simple dilution problem:

$M_d V_d = M_c V_c$

$V_c = M_d V_d/M_c = (0.1\ M)(500.0\ mL)/(12.0\ M) = 4\ mL$

The solution is then made by diluting 4 mL of the 12.0 M HCl with enough water to make 500.0 mL of dilute solution. Notice that the pH value given only yields one significant figure.

18. CO_2 is the acid anhydride of H_2CO_3, which is a weak acid and dissociates to some extent in water:

$$CO_{2(g)} + H_2O_{(l)} \rightarrow H_2CO_{3(aq)}$$
and
$$H_2CO_{3(aq)} + H_2O_{(l)} \rightarrow H_3O^+_{(aq)} + HCO_3^-_{(aq)}$$

Therefore, the solution is slightly acidic.

19. Indicators are one color in their acid form and another color in their base form. If you add a small amount of an indicator to a solution, it is possible to estimate the pH of the solution based on the indicator's color. For more accurate estimates, mixtures of indicators are often used and, since colors are additive, a better estimate of pH can be gotten from the color.

20. pH paper is used for a low-cost, quick, approximate pH determination.

21. pH meters are more precise and more accurate but are considerably more expensive than pH paper. The meters are also subject to electronic and/or mechanical malfunctions and require maintenance and adjustment.

22. a. $pH = -\log(0.25) = 0.60$
   b. $pH = 14.000 - \log(0.35) = 13.54$
   c. $pH = 14.000 - \log(4.3 \times 10^{-6}) = 8.64$
   d. $pH = -\log(2.6 \times 10^{-3}) = 2.58$

23. a. $pH = -\log(6.8 \times 10^{-4}) = 3.17$
   b. $pH = 14.000 - \log(3.7 \times 10^{-2}) = 12.57$
   c. $pH = -\log(0.015) = 1.82$
   d. $pH = 14.000 - \log(6.5 \times 10^{-12}) = 2.81$

24. a. $[H_3O^+] = \text{antilog}(-3.05) = 8.9 \times 10^{-4} M$
   b. $[H_3O^+] = \text{antilog}(7.33 - 14.000) = 2.1 \times 10^{-7} M$
   c. $[H_3O^+] = \text{antilog}(-6.12) = 7.6 \times 10^{-7} M$
   d. $[H_3O^+] = \text{antilog}(11.45 - 14.000) = 2.8 \times 10^{-3} M$

25. a. $[OH^-] = \text{antilog}(0.37 - 14.000) = 2.3 \times 10^{-14} M$
   b. $[OH^-] = \text{antilog}(-3.42) = 3.8 \times 10^{-4} M$
   c. $[OH^-] = \text{antilog}(10.56 - 14.000) = 3.6 \times 10^{-4} M$
   d. $[OH^-] = \text{antilog}(-8.91) = 1.2 \times 10^{-9} M$

26. $HA_{(aq)} + H_2O_{(l)} = H_3O^+_{(aq)} + A^-_{(aq)}$

$K_a = \dfrac{[H_3O^+][A^-]}{[HA]}$

$[H_3O^+] = $ antilog$(-3.47) = 3.4 \times 10^{-4}$ M $= [HA]_{dissociated}$

$[HA]_{equilibrium} = [HA]_{initial} - [HA]_{dissociated} = 0.35$ M $- 3.4 \times 10^{-4}$ M ≈ 0.35 M

$K_a = \dfrac{(3.4 \times 10^{-4} \text{ M})(3.4 \times 10^{-4} \text{ M})}{(0.35 \text{ M})}$

$K_a = 3.3 \times 10^{-7}$ M

27. $B_{(aq)} + H_2O_{(l)} = BH^+_{(aq)} + OH^-_{(aq)}$

pOH $= 14.000 - 10.04 = 3.96$

$[OH^-] = $ antilog$(-3.96) = 1.1 \times 10^{-4}$ M

$[B]_{equilibrium} = [B]_{initial} - [B]_{dissociated} = 5.0 \times 10^{-3}$ M $- 1.1 \times 10^{-4}$ M $= 4.9 \times 10^{-3}$ M

$K_b = \dfrac{(1.1 \times 10^{-4} \text{ M})(1.1 \times 10^{-4} \text{ M})}{(4.9 \times 10^{-3} \text{ M})}$

$K_b = 2.5 \times 10^{-6}$ M

28. With 2.4 % ionization, $[H_3O^+] = (0.25$ M$)(0.024) = 0.0060$ M

$[HC_3H_5O_3]_{equilibrium} = [HC_3H_5O_3]_{initial} - [HC_3H_5O_3]_{dissociated} = 0.25$ M $- 0.0060$ M $= 0.24$ M

$K_a = \dfrac{(0.0060 \text{ M})(0.0060 \text{ M})}{(0.24 \text{ M})}$

$K_a = 1.5 \times 10^{-4}$ M

pH $= -\log(0.0060) = 2.22$

29. Hydrolysis is when a compound reacts with water to break apart the water molecules.

30. a. KNO_2 - Since $HNO_{2(aq)}$ is a weak acid, $NO_2^-_{(aq)}$ will be a strong base and the solution of KNO_2 will be basic.

$NO_2^-_{(aq)} + H_2O_{(l)} = HNO_{2(aq)} + OH^-_{(aq)}$

30. b. NH_4Br - $NH_4^+_{(aq)}$ is a weak acid. Since $HBr_{(aq)}$ is a strong acid, $Br^-_{(aq)}$ will be a weak base. The solution of NH_4Br will then be slightly acidic.

$$NH_4^+_{(aq)} + H_2O_{(l)} = NH_{3(aq)} + H_3O^+_{(aq)}$$

c. $NaC_2H_3O_2$ - Since $HC_2H_3O_{2(aq)}$ is a weak acid, $C_2H_3O_2^-_{(aq)}$ will be a strong base and the solution of $NaC_2H_3O_2$ will be basic.

$$C_2H_3O_2^-_{(aq)} + H_2O_{(l)} = HC_2H_3O_{2(aq)} + OH^-_{(aq)}$$

d. $LiHSO_4$ - Since $H_2SO_{4(aq)}$ is a strong acid, $HSO_4^-_{(aq)}$ will be a weak base and the solution of $LiHSO_4$ should be neutral.

31. Buffers are solutions that are able to maintain a constant pH despite the addition of moderate amounts of acids or bases. The two components of a buffer are called the **buffer pair**. The two components are either a weak acid and its salt or a weak base and its salt.

32. The weak acid acts as a source of ionized acid that can provide more H_3O^+ ions as needed to react with any OH^- ions added to the solution. The salt, which is completely dissociated, provides a source of conjugate base anions of the acid that can react with any H_3O^+ ions added to the solution. The system will then reestablish equilibrium as either H_3O^+ or OH^- are added.

33. The weak base acts as a source of unionized base that can provide more OH^- ions as needed to react with any H_3O^+ ions added to the solution. The salt, which is completely dissociated, provides cations to react with any OH^- ions added to the solution. The system will then reestablish equilibrium as either H_3O^+ or OH^- are added.

34. A solution of HCl and NaCl can't act as a buffer because HCl is a strong acid. Therefore, $Cl^-_{(aq)}$ is a weak base. Added H_3O^+ ions won't react with Cl^- and added OH^- ions will deplete existing H_3O^+.

35. The three buffer systems in the blood are:

1. carbonic acid/bicarbonate (H_2CO_3/HCO_3^-)
2. dihydrogen phosphate/hydrogen phosphate ($H_2PO_4^-$/HPO_4^{2-})
3. a mixture of proteins which remove or add H_3O^+ ions from blood as needed

The buffer pair in greatest concentration in the blood is the H_2CO_3/HCO_3^- pair. It is also the most important because it is involved with the expulsion of CO_2 from the body and it is particularly effective as a buffer at pH values near neutral, which is proper for the body.

36. When carbon dioxide is dissolved in water, which is the solvent in blood, carbonic acid forms:

$$CO_{2(g)} + H_2O_{(l)} = H_2CO_{3(aq)}$$

The carbonic acid then dissociates to a slight extent:

$$H_2CO_{3(aq)} + H_2O_{(l)} = H_3O^+_{(aq)} + HCO_3^-_{(aq)}$$

The carbonic acid acts as a source of H_3O^+ ions which can react with OH⁻ ions if needed. The HCO_3^- ions can react with any added H_3O^+ ions in the blood.

37. This represents an acid/base neutralization reaction,

$$Ba(OH)_{2(aq)} + H_2SO_{4(aq)} \rightarrow BaSO_{4(s)} + 2 H_2O_{(l)}$$

in which the salt is insoluble. Therefore, if equimolar amounts of the acid and the base are used, there will be no ions left in solution. The only species present will be the precipitate, $BaSO_{4(s)}$, and water, neither of which will conduct electricity.

38. a. $[H_3O^+]$ = antilog(-6.0) = 1 x 10^{-6} M
b. $[OH^-]$ = antilog(6.0 - 14.000) = 1 x 10^{-8} M
c. pOH = - log(1 x 10^{-8}) = 8.0

39. At any temperature, pure water should be neutral, $[H_3O^+]$ = $[OH^-]$. At 37 °C,

$$K_w = 2.42 \times 10^{-14} M^2 = [H_3O^+][OH^-] = x^2$$
$$[H_3O^+] = [OH^-] = x = 1.56 \times 10^{-7} M$$

40. $[H_3O^+]$ = antilog(-7.40) = 4.0 x 10^{-8} M

Assuming K_w = 2.42 x 10^{-14} M^2 at 37 °C (body temperature),

$$[OH^-] = 2.42 \times 10^{-14}/[4.0 \times 10^{-8}]$$
$$[OH^-] = 6.0 \times 10^{-7} M$$

41. $HA_{(aq)} + H_2O_{(l)} = H_3O^+_{(aq)} + A^-_{(aq)}$

$K_a = \dfrac{[H_3O^+][A^-]}{[HA]}$

$[H_3O^+] = \text{antilog}(-2.65) = 2.2 \times 10^{-3}\ M = [HA]_{\text{dissociated}}$

$[HA]_{\text{equilibrium}} = [HA]_{\text{initial}} - [HA]_{\text{dissociated}} = 0.24\ M - 2.2 \times 10^{-3}\ M \approx 0.24\ M$

$K_a = \dfrac{(2.2 \times 10^{-3}\ M)(2.2 \times 10^{-3}\ M)}{(0.24\ M)}$

$K_a = 2.0 \times 10^{-5}\ M$

42. With 33 % ionization, $[H_3O^+] = (0.200\ M)(0.33) = 0.066\ M$

$[HC_2HO_2Cl_2]_{\text{equilibrium}} = [HC_2HO_2Cl_2]_{\text{initial}} - [HC_2HO_2Cl_2]_{\text{dissociated}} = 0.200\ M - 0.066\ M$
$$= 0.134\ M$$

$K_a = \dfrac{(0.066\ M)(0.066\ M)}{(0.134\ M)}$

$K_a = 3.3 \times 10^{-2}\ M$

$pH = -\log(0.066) = 1.18$

43. The reaction is:

$$HC_7H_5O_{2(aq)} + H_2O_{(l)} = H_3O^+_{(aq)} + C_7H_5O_2^-_{(aq)}$$

At equilibrium, mass balance prevails:

$$HC_7H_5O_{2(aq)} + H_2O_{(l)} = H_3O^+_{(aq)} + C_7H_5O_2^-_{(aq)}$$
$$0.20\ M - X\ M \qquad\qquad X\ M \qquad X\ M$$

$$K_a = 6.2 \times 10^{-5}\ M = \frac{X^2}{0.20 - X}$$

$$1.2 \times 10^{-5} - (6.2 \times 10^{-5})(X) = X^2$$

$$0 = X^2 + (6.2 \times 10^{-5})X - 1.2 \times 10^{-5}$$

$$X = \frac{-(6.2 \times 10^{-5}) \pm \sqrt{\{(6.2 \times 10^{-5})^2 - 4(-1.2 \times 10^{-5})\}}}{2}$$

$$X = \frac{-(6.2 \times 10^{-5}) \pm \sqrt{\{4.8 \times 10^{-5}\}}}{2}$$

$$X = \frac{-(6.2 \times 10^{-5}) \pm \{6.9 \times 10^{-3}\}}{2}$$

Since $[H_3O^+]$ must be positive,

$$X = \frac{-(6.2 \times 10^{-5}) + \{6.9 \times 10^{-3}\}}{2}$$

$$X = [H_3O^+] = 3.4 \times 10^{-3}\ M$$

$$pH = -\log(3.4 \times 10^{-3}) = 2.47$$

$$\%\ ionization = \frac{3.4 \times 10^{-3}\ M}{0.20\ M} \times 100\% = 1.7\ \%$$

44. a. NaI - Na$^+$ is the cation of a strong base while I$^-$ is the anion of a strong acid. Both will therefore be weak and will not react with water. The solution will be neutral.

b. RbF - Rb$^+$ is the cation of a strong base while F$^-$ is the anion of a very weak acid. Therefore, F$^-$ will react with water to give a basic solution.

$$F^-_{(aq)} + H_2O_{(l)} = HF_{(aq)} + OH^-_{(aq)}$$

44. c. KH_2PO_4 - K^+ is the cation of a strong base while $H_2PO_4^-$ is the conjugate base of a weak acid. Therefore, $H_2PO_4^-$ will react with water to give a basic solution.

$$H_2PO_4^-{}_{(aq)} + H_2O_{(l)} = H_3PO_{4(aq)} + OH^-{}_{(aq)}$$

Note: $H_2PO_4^-$ is itself an acid but is so weak that it doesn't come into play here. K_a for H_3PO_4 is 7.5×10^{-3}. K_a for $H_2PO_4^-$ is 6.2×10^{-8}.

d. Na_2SO_3 - Na^+ is the cation of a strong base while SO_3^{2-} is the anion of a weak acid. Therefore, SO_3^{2-} will react with water to give a basic solution.

$$SO_3^{2-}{}_{(aq)} + H_2O_{(l)} = HSO_3^-{}_{(aq)} + OH^-{}_{(aq)}$$

45. a. HNO_2 and KNO_2 - Yes, it is a buffer pair made of a weak acid and its freely soluble salt.
b. HCN and $KClO$ - No, it is not a buffer pair. HCN is a weak acid but $KClO$ is not its salt.
c. NH_4NO_3 and HNO_3 - No, it is not a buffer pair. They have the same anion, but both are acids and HNO_3 is a strong acid.
d. KH_2PO_4 and K_2HPO_4 - Yes, it is a buffer pair made of a very weak acid and its freely soluble salt.

Sample Quiz Questions

1. An electrolyte
    a. is composed of molecules.
    b. conducts electricity when molten or dissolved.
    c. is generally a solid which must be molten to be useful.
    d. conducts heat.
    e. is generally a nonpolar liquid.

2. Electrolytes
    a. which dissociate completely are called weak.
    b. are uncommon substances.
    c. are nonconductors.
    d. which dissociate slightly are called weak.
    e. generally do not dissolve in water.

3. The ion-product constant for water
    a. accounts for the high conductivity of water.
    b. has the symbol K_a.
    c. is equivalent to $K_{eq} \cdot [H_2O]$.
    d. has the value 1.00×10^{-7} at 25 °C.
    e. shows that water is slightly acidic.

4. K_w

    a. has the form $K_w = [H_3O^+][OH^-]/[H_2O]$.
    b. is independent of temperature.
    c. is dependent on the addition of solutes to water.
    d. is roughly the same value for all solvents.
    e. has the form $K_w = [H_3O^+]][OH^-]$.

5. The pH of a solution is 3.88. What are $[H_3O^+]$ and $[OH^-]$?
    a. $[H_3O^+] = 7.6 \times 10^{-11}$ M; $[OH^-] = 1.3 \times 10^{-4}$ M
    b. $[H_3O^+] = 1.3 \times 10^{-4}$ M; $[OH^-] = 7.6 \times 10^{-11}$ M
    c. $[H_3O^+] = 1.3 \times 10^{-4}$ M; $[OH^-] = 7.6 \times 10^{-4}$ M
    d. $[H_3O^+] = 1.3 \times 10^{-11}$ M; $[OH^-] = 7.6 \times 10^{-11}$ M
    e. $[H_3O^+] = 1.0 \times 10^{-7}$ M; $[OH^-] = 1.0 \times 10^{-7}$ M

6. If $[H_3O^+]$ is 2.50×10^{-2} M in an aqueous solution, what is the pOH?
    a. 12.398
    b. 2.50
    c. 1.602
    d. 4.00×10^{-13}
    e. 1.00

7. If $[OH^-] = 0.500$ M in an aqueous solution, what is the pH?
    a. 0.301
    b. 4.00
    c. 2.00×10^{-14}
    d. 13.500
    e. 13.699

8. If $[H_3O^+] = 0.00300$ M in an aqueous solution, what is the pH?
    a. 3.00×10^{-3}
    b. 3.00
    c. 2.523
    d. 3.33×10^{-12}
    e. 11.477

9. If you need to prepare 1.00 L of a $HClO_4$ solution with pH = 3.00, how much of a stock 10.6 M $HClO_4$ solution would you need to use?
    a. 0.094 mL
    b. 0.0010 mL
    c. 1.0 mL
    d. 0.28 mL
    e. 9.4×10^{-5} mL

10. If you need to prepare 2.50 L of a NaOH solution with pH = 9.000, how much of a stock 0.200 M NaOH solution would you need to use?
     a. 12.5 mL
     b. 1.00×10^{-5} mL
     c. 0.0250 mL
     d. 0.125 mL
     e. 112 mL

11. What is the pH of an aqueous solution made by diluting 0.833 mL of 12.0 M HCl with enough water to make 1.00 L of dilute solution?
     a. 12.000
     b. 14.41
     c. 0.0100
     d. 10.0
     e. 2.000

12. What is the pH of an aqueous solution made by diluting 75.0 mL of 5.000 M KOH with enough water to make 1.75 L of dilute solution?
     a. 0.214
     b. 0.669
     c. 13.331
     d. 11.426
     e. 2.574

13. Nitrous acid, HNO_2, has $K_a = 4.5 \times 10^{-4}$ M. What is the pH of a solution of nitrous acid in which the equilibrium concentration of HNO_2 is 0.200 M?
     a. 2.02
     b. 3.35
     c. 9.49×10^{-3}
     d. 0.70
     e. 4.05

14. Carbonic acid, H_2CO_3, has $K_a = 4.3 \times 10^{-7}$ M. If the pH of a solution of carbonic acid is 3.000, what is the equilibrium concentration of H_2CO_3?
     a. 0.43 M
     b. 0.18 M
     c. 2.3 M
     d. 1.0×10^{-6} M
     e. 1.0×10^{-3} M

15. Carbonate, CO_3^{2-}, has $K_b = 2.1 \times 10^{-4}$ M. What is the pH of a solution of carbonate in which the equilibrium concentration of CO_3^{2-} is 0.500 M?
     a. 1.05×10^{-4}
     b. 1.989
     c. 0.0102
     d. 12.011
     e. 9.76×10^{-13}

16. Cyanide, CN^-, has $K_b = 1.6 \times 10^{-5}$ M. If the pH of a solution of cyanide is 12.000, what is the equilibrium concentration of CN^-?
    a. 1.2 M
    b. 6.2 M
    c. 0.16 M
    d. 1.6×10^{-9} M
    e. 6.2×10^{-8} M

17. An aqueous solution of formic acid, HCOOH, has pH = 1.888. The equilibrium concentration of HCOOH is found to be 0.987 M. What is the value of K_a for formic acid?
    a. 1.31×10^{-2}
    b. 1.00×10^{-7}
    c. 1.65×10^{-4}
    d. 7.83×10^{-13}
    e. 1.70×10^{-4}

18. An aqueous solution of ammonia, NH_3, has pH = 11.453. The equilibrium concentration of NH_3 is found to be 0.45 M. What is the value of K_b for ammonia?
    a. 2.8×10^{-3}
    b. 1.8×10^{-5}
    c. 3.5×10^{-12}
    d. 2.8×10^{-23}
    e. 8.1×10^{-6}

19. A buffer pair
    a. is composed of a weak acid and a strong base.
    b. is a buffer system using two acids and their conjugate bases.
    c. is used to alter the pH of a solution.
    d. is composed of a weak acid and its conjugate base or a weak base and its conjugate acid.
    e. is composed of a weak base and a strong acid.

20. Which of the following would constitute a buffer?
    a. HCN and KCN
    b. HCl and NaCl
    c. $HC_2H_3O_2$ and NaOH
    d. H_2SO_4 and Li_3PO_4
    e. H_2CO_3 and NH_4NO_3

Answers to the Sample Quiz Questions

1. (b), 2. (d), 3. (c), 4. (e), 5. (b), 6. (a), 7. (e), 8. (c), 9. (a), 10. (d), 11. (e), 12. (c), 13. (a), 14. (c), 15. (d), 16. (b), 17. (e), 18. (b), 19. (d), 20. (a)

OXIDATION AND REDUCTION

CHAPTER
16

Chapter Overview

Chapter 16 builds on the introductory coverage of oxidation numbers and ionic equations given in Chapters 6, 7, and 14. In this chapter, the emphasis is on the changes in oxidation numbers possible in chemical reactions. Therefore, the concepts of oxidation and reduction are presented in contexts more suitable for major topics.

Techniques of balancing redox equations are presented in detail by the oxidation state method and by the ion-electron or half-reaction method.

As a predictive tool in redox reactions, the activity series of the metals is also presented and fully rationalized. The series is reinforced with a discussion of metal displacement reactions.

Following these basic concepts, voltaic cells and electrolytic cells are discussed in detail, as are applications of redox reactions, such as batteries, electrolysis, and electroplating.

Solutions to the Study Questions and Problems

1. **a.** A **redox reaction** involves changes in the oxidation states of the elements in the reaction. **b. Oxidation** is the loss of electrons which is also accompanied by an increase in the oxidation number of the atom. **c. Reduction** is the gain of electrons which is also accompanied by a decrease in the oxidation number of the atom. **d.** An **oxidizing agent** or **oxidant** is the reactant that causes the other reactant to be oxidized. The oxidizing agent itself is reduced. **e.** A **reducing agent** or **reductant** is the reactant that causes the other reactant to be reduced. The reducing agent itself is oxidized.

2. **a.** $CO_2 + H_2O \rightarrow H_2CO_3$
     4 -2 1 -2 1 4 -2

    This is not a redox reaction since all the oxidation numbers remain the same.

2. **b.** $H_2S + 4 Br_2 + 4 H_2O \rightarrow H_2SO_4 + 8 HBr$
     1 -2   0   1 -2   1 6 -2   1 -1

This is a redox reaction. The S is oxidized from -2 (in H_2S) to +6 (in H_2SO_4) and the Br is reduced from 0 (in Br_2) to -1 (in HBr).

c. $H_3PO_4 + Al(OH)_3 \rightarrow AlPO_4 + 3 H_2O$
    1 5 -2   +3 -2 1   +3 5 -2   1 -2

This is not a redox reaction since all the oxidation numbers remain the same.

d. $2 AgNO_3 + H_2S \rightarrow Ag_2S + 2 HNO_3$
     1 5 -2   1 -2   1 -2   1 5 -2

This is not a redox reaction since all the oxidation numbers remain the same.

3. **a.** $3 P + 5 HNO_3 + 2 H_2O \rightarrow 5 NO + 3 H_3PO_4$
     0   1 5 -2   1 -2   2 -2   1 5 -2

P is oxidized from 0 (in P) to +5 (in H_3PO_4) and so P is the reducing agent. N is reduced from +5 (in HNO_3) to +2 (in NO) and so HNO_3 is the oxidizing agent.

b. $Sn + 4 HNO_3 \rightarrow SnO_2 + 4 NO_2 + 2 H_2O$
    0   1 5 -2   4 -2   4 -2   1 -2

Sn is oxidized from 0 (in Sn) to +4 (in SnO_2) and so Sn is the reducing agent. N is reduced from +5 (in HNO_3) to +4 (in NO_2) and so HNO_3 is the oxidizing agent.

c. $I_2 + 5 Cl_2 + 6 H_2O \rightarrow 2 HIO_3 + 10 HCl$
    0   0   1 -2   1 5 -2   1 -1

I is oxidized from 0 (in I_2) to +5 (in HIO_3) and so I_2 is the reducing agent. Cl is reduced from 0 (in Cl_2) to -1 (in HCl) and so Cl_2 is the oxidizing agent.

d. $K_2Cr_2O_7 + 6 FeCl_2 + 14 HCl \rightarrow 2 CrCl_3 + 2 KCl + 6 FeCl_3 + 7 H_2O$
    1 6 -2   2 -1   1 -1   3 -1   1 -1   3 -1   1 -2

Fe is oxidized from +2 (in $FeCl_2$) to +3 (in $FeCl_3$) and so $FeCl_2$ is the reducing agent. Cr is reduced from +6 (in $K_2Cr_2O_7$) to +3 (in $CrCl_3$) and so $K_2Cr_2O_7$ is the oxidizing agent.

4. **a.**

$$\overbrace{KMnO_4 + 2 KCl + H_2SO_4 \rightarrow MnSO_4 + K_2SO_4 + H_2O + Cl_2}^{-5}$$
          7   -1   2   0
                     $\underbrace{}_{+2}$

$$\overbrace{2 KMnO_4 + 10 KCl + H_2SO_4 \rightarrow 2 MnSO_4 + K_2SO_4 + H_2O + 5 Cl_2}^{2(-5)}$$
          7   -1   2   0
                     $\underbrace{}_{5(+2)}$

$2 KMnO_4 + 10 KCl + 8 H_2SO_4 \rightarrow 2 MnSO_4 + 6 K_2SO_4 + 8 H_2O + 5 Cl_2$

4. b.

$$\overset{\displaystyle\lceil\qquad\quad -2\qquad\quad\rceil}{\underset{0\qquad 1\qquad\qquad 5\qquad\ -1}{H_2O + P_4 + HClO \;\rightarrow\; 4\,H_3PO_4 + HCl}}$$

$$\lfloor\qquad +20\qquad\quad\rfloor$$

$$\overset{\displaystyle\lceil\qquad\qquad 10(-2)\qquad\qquad\rceil}{\underset{0\qquad\ 1\qquad\qquad 5\qquad\qquad -1}{H_2O + P_4 + 10\,HClO \;\rightarrow\; 4\,H_3PO_4 + 10\,HCl}}$$

$$\lfloor\qquad +20\qquad\qquad\rfloor$$

$$6\,H_2O + P_4 + 10\,HClO \;\rightarrow\; 4\,H_3PO_4 + 10\,HCl$$

c.

$$\overset{\displaystyle\lceil\qquad -3\qquad\rceil}{\underset{0\qquad 5\qquad\ \ 3\qquad 2}{4\,Sb + HNO_3 \;\rightarrow\; Sb_4O_6 + NO + H_2O}}$$

$$\lfloor\qquad +12\qquad\rfloor$$

$$\overset{\displaystyle\lceil\qquad 4(-3)\qquad\rceil}{\underset{0\qquad\ \ 5\qquad\quad 3\qquad 2}{4\,Sb + 4\,HNO_3 \;\rightarrow\; Sb_4O_6 + 4\,NO + H_2O}}$$

$$\lfloor\qquad +12\qquad\rfloor$$

$$4\,Sb + 4\,HNO_3 \;\rightarrow\; Sb_4O_6 + 4\,NO + 2\,H_2O$$

d.

$$\overset{\displaystyle\lceil\quad -2\quad\rceil}{\underset{4\qquad\ -1\qquad 2\quad 0}{PbO_2 + 2\,HI \;\rightarrow\; PbI_2 + I_2 + H_2O}}$$

$$\lfloor\quad +2\quad\rfloor$$

$$PbO_2 + 4\,HI \;\rightarrow\; PbI_2 + I_2 + 2\,H_2O$$

5. a.

$$\overset{\displaystyle\lceil\qquad -2\qquad\rceil}{\underset{0\qquad 6\qquad\ 2\qquad 4}{Cu + H_2SO_4 \;\rightarrow\; CuSO_4 + SO_2 + H_2O}}$$

$$\lfloor\quad +2\quad\rfloor$$

$$Cu + 2\,H_2SO_4 \;\rightarrow\; CuSO_4 + SO_2 + 2\,H_2O$$

b.

$$\overset{\displaystyle\lceil\qquad\quad -2\qquad\quad\rceil}{\underset{0\quad\ 4\qquad\qquad\qquad\ 2}{Pb + PbO_2 + 2\,H_2SO_4 \;\rightarrow\; 2\,PbSO_4 + H_2O}}$$

$$\lfloor\qquad +2\qquad\rfloor$$

$$Pb + PbO_2 + 2\,H_2SO_4 \;\rightarrow\; 2\,PbSO_4 + 2\,H_2O$$

5. c.
$$\begin{bmatrix} -2 \end{bmatrix}$$

$MnO_2 + HI \rightarrow MnI_2 + I_2 + H_2O$
4   -1   2   0
$$\begin{bmatrix} +1 \end{bmatrix}$$

$$\begin{bmatrix} -2 \end{bmatrix}$$
$MnO_2 + 2\,HI \rightarrow MnI_2 + I_2 + H_2O$
4   -1   2   0
$$\begin{bmatrix} 2(+1) \end{bmatrix}$$
$MnO_2 + 4\,HI \rightarrow MnI_2 + I_2 + 2\,H_2O$

d.
$$\begin{bmatrix} -3 \end{bmatrix}$$
$NF_3 + AlCl_3 \rightarrow N_2 + Cl_2 + AlF_3$
3   -1   0   0
$$\begin{bmatrix} +1 \end{bmatrix}$$

$$\begin{bmatrix} 2(-3) \end{bmatrix}$$
$2\,NF_3 + 2\,AlCl_3 \rightarrow N_2 + 3\,Cl_2 + AlF_3$
3   -1   0   0
$$\begin{bmatrix} 6(+1) \end{bmatrix}$$
$2\,NF_3 + 2\,AlCl_3 \rightarrow N_2 + 3\,Cl_2 + 2\,AlF_3$

6. A **half-reaction** is arrived at by breaking down the overall redox reaction into its two component parts, the oxidation half-reaction and the reduction half-reaction.

7. a. $AsH_{3(g)} + Ag^+_{(aq)} \rightarrow As_4O_{6(s)} + Ag_{(s)}$

$AsH_{3(g)} \rightarrow As_4O_{6(s)}$ (oxidation)
$Ag^+_{(aq)} \rightarrow Ag_{(s)}$ (reduction)

$4\,AsH_{3(g)} + 6\,H_2O_{(l)} \rightarrow As_4O_{6(s)} + 24\,H^+_{(aq)}$ (oxidation)
$Ag^+_{(aq)} \rightarrow Ag_{(s)}$ (reduction)

$4\,AsH_{3(g)} + 6\,H_2O_{(l)} \rightarrow As_4O_{6(s)} + 24\,H^+_{(aq)} + 24\,e^-$ (oxidation)
$Ag^+_{(aq)} + 1\,e^- \rightarrow Ag_{(s)}$ (reduction)

$4\,AsH_{3(g)} + 6\,H_2O_{(l)} \rightarrow As_4O_{6(s)} + 24\,H^+_{(aq)} + 24\,e^-$ (oxidation)
$24\,[Ag^+_{(aq)} + 1\,e^- \rightarrow Ag_{(s)}]$ (reduction)

$4\,AsH_{3(g)} + 6\,H_2O_{(l)} \rightarrow As_4O_{6(s)} + 24\,H^+_{(aq)} + 24\,e^-$ (oxidation)
$24\,Ag^+_{(aq)} + 24\,e^- \rightarrow 24\,Ag_{(s)}$ (reduction)

$4\,AsH_{3(g)} + 24\,Ag^+_{(aq)} + 6\,H_2O_{(l)} \rightarrow As_4O_{6(s)} + 24\,Ag_{(s)} + 24\,H^+_{(aq)}$

7.   b. $Zn_{(s)} + H_2MoO_{4(aq)} \rightarrow Zn^{2+}_{(aq)} + Mo^{3+}_{(aq)}$

$Zn_{(s)} \rightarrow Zn^{2+}_{(aq)}$ (oxidation)

$H_2MoO_{4(aq)} \rightarrow Mo^{3+}_{(aq)}$ (reduction)

$Zn_{(s)} \rightarrow Zn^{2+}_{(aq)}$ (oxidation)

$H_2MoO_{4(aq)} + 6\,H^+_{(aq)} \rightarrow Mo^{3+}_{(aq)} + 4\,H_2O_{(l)}$ (reduction)

$Zn_{(s)} \rightarrow Zn^{2+}_{(aq)} + 2\,e^-$ (oxidation)

$H_2MoO_{4(aq)} + 6\,H^+_{(aq)} + 3\,e^- \rightarrow Mo^{3+}_{(aq)} + 4\,H_2O_{(l)}$ (reduction)

$3\,[Zn_{(s)} \rightarrow Zn^{2+}_{(aq)} + 2\,e^-]$ (oxidation)

$2\,[H_2MoO_{4(aq)} + 6\,H^+_{(aq)} + 3\,e^- \rightarrow Mo^{3+}_{(aq)} + 4\,H_2O_{(l)}]$ (reduction)

$3\,Zn_{(s)} \rightarrow 3\,Zn^{2+}_{(aq)} + 6\,e^-$ (oxidation)

$2\,H_2MoO_{4(aq)} + 12\,H^+_{(aq)} + 6\,e^- \rightarrow 2\,Mo^{3+}_{(aq)} + 8\,H_2O_{(l)}$ (reduction)

$$3\,Zn_{(s)} + 2\,H_2MoO_{4(aq)} + 12\,H^+_{(aq)} \rightarrow 3\,Zn^{2+}_{(aq)} + 2\,Mo^{3+}_{(aq)} + 8\,H_2O_{(l)}$$

c. $Se_{(s)} + BrO_3^-{}_{(aq)} \rightarrow H_2SeO_{3(aq)} + Br^-_{(aq)}$

$Se_{(s)} \rightarrow H_2SeO_{3(aq)}$ (oxidation)

$BrO_3^-{}_{(aq)} \rightarrow Br^-_{(aq)}$ (reduction)

$Se_{(s)} + 3\,H_2O_{(l)} \rightarrow H_2SeO_{3(aq)} + 4\,H^+_{(aq)}$ (oxidation)

$BrO_3^-{}_{(aq)} + 6\,H^+_{(aq)} \rightarrow Br^-_{(aq)} + 3\,H_2O_{(l)}$ (reduction)

$Se_{(s)} + 3\,H_2O_{(l)} \rightarrow H_2SeO_{3(aq)} + 4\,H^+_{(aq)} + 4\,e^-$ (oxidation)

$BrO_3^-{}_{(aq)} + 6\,H^+_{(aq)} + 6\,e^- \rightarrow Br^-_{(aq)} + 3\,H_2O_{(l)}$ (reduction)

$3\,[Se_{(s)} + 3\,H_2O_{(l)} \rightarrow H_2SeO_{3(aq)} + 4\,H^+_{(aq)} + 4\,e^-]$ (oxidation)

$2\,[BrO_3^-{}_{(aq)} + 6\,H^+_{(aq)} + 6\,e^- \rightarrow Br^-_{(aq)} + 3\,H_2O_{(l)}]$ (reduction)

$3\,Se_{(s)} + 9\,H_2O_{(l)} \rightarrow 3\,H_2SeO_{3(aq)} + 12\,H^+_{(aq)} + 12\,e^-$ (oxidation)

$2\,BrO_3^-{}_{(aq)} + 12\,H^+_{(aq)} + 12\,e^- \rightarrow 2\,Br^-_{(aq)} + 6\,H_2O_{(l)}$ (reduction)

$$3\,Se_{(s)} + 2\,BrO_3^-{}_{(aq)} + 3\,H_2O_{(l)} \rightarrow 3\,H_2SeO_{3(aq)} + 2\,Br^-_{(aq)}$$

7. **d.** $H_3AsO_{3(aq)} + MnO_4^-{}_{(aq)} \rightarrow H_3AsO_{4(aq)} + Mn^{2+}{}_{(aq)}$

$H_3AsO_{3(aq)} \rightarrow H_3AsO_{4(aq)}$ (oxidation)

$MnO_4^-{}_{(aq)} \rightarrow Mn^{2+}{}_{(aq)}$ (reduction)

$H_3AsO_{3(aq)} + H_2O_{(l)} \rightarrow H_3AsO_{4(aq)} + 2\,H^+{}_{(aq)}$ (oxidation)

$MnO_4^-{}_{(aq)} + 8\,H^+{}_{(aq)} \rightarrow Mn^{2+}{}_{(aq)} + 4\,H_2O_{(l)}$ (reduction)

$H_3AsO_{3(aq)} + H_2O_{(l)} \rightarrow H_3AsO_{4(aq)} + 2\,H^+{}_{(aq)} + 2\,e^-$ (oxidation)

$MnO_4^-{}_{(aq)} + 8\,H^+{}_{(aq)} + 5\,e^- \rightarrow Mn^{2+}{}_{(aq)} + 4\,H_2O_{(l)}$ (reduction)

$5\,[H_3AsO_{3(aq)} + H_2O_{(l)} \rightarrow H_3AsO_{4(aq)} + 2\,H^+{}_{(aq)} + 2\,e^-]$ (oxidation)

$2\,[MnO_4^-{}_{(aq)} + 8\,H^+{}_{(aq)} + 5\,e^- \rightarrow Mn^{2+}{}_{(aq)} + 4\,H_2O_{(l)}]$ (reduction)

$5\,H_3AsO_{3(aq)} + 5\,H_2O_{(l)} \rightarrow 5\,H_3AsO_{4(aq)} + 10\,H^+{}_{(aq)} + 10\,e^-$ (oxidation)

$2\,MnO_4^-{}_{(aq)} + 16\,H^+{}_{(aq)} + 10\,e^- \rightarrow 2\,Mn^{2+}{}_{(aq)} + 8\,H_2O_{(l)}$ (reduction)

$5\,H_3AsO_{3(aq)} + 2\,MnO_4^-{}_{(aq)} + 6\,H^+{}_{(aq)} \rightarrow 5\,H_3AsO_{4(aq)} + 2\,Mn^{2+}{}_{(aq)} + 3\,H_2O_{(l)}$

8. **a.** $ClO^-{}_{(aq)} + I^-{}_{(aq)} \rightarrow Cl^-{}_{(aq)} + I_{2(s)}$

$I^-{}_{(aq)} \rightarrow I_{2(s)}$ (oxidation)

$ClO^-{}_{(aq)} \rightarrow Cl^-{}_{(aq)}$ (reduction)

$2\,I^-{}_{(aq)} \rightarrow I_{2(s)}$ (oxidation)

$ClO^-{}_{(aq)} + 2\,H^+{}_{(aq)} \rightarrow Cl^-{}_{(aq)} + H_2O_{(l)}$ (reduction)

$2\,I^-{}_{(aq)} \rightarrow I_{2(s)} + 2\,e^-$ (oxidation)

$ClO^-{}_{(aq)} + 2\,H^+{}_{(aq)} + 2\,e^- \rightarrow Cl^-{}_{(aq)} + H_2O_{(l)}$ (reduction)

$ClO^-{}_{(aq)} + 2\,I^-{}_{(aq)} + 2\,H^+{}_{(aq)} \rightarrow Cl^-{}_{(aq)} + I_{2(s)} + H_2O_{(l)}$

8. b. $Cr_{(s)} + H^+_{(aq)} \rightarrow Cr^{3+}_{(aq)} + H_{2(g)}$

$Cr_{(s)} \rightarrow Cr^{3+}_{(aq)}$ (oxidation)

$H^+_{(aq)} \rightarrow H_{2(g)}$ (reduction)

$Cr_{(s)} \rightarrow Cr^{3+}_{(aq)}$ (oxidation)

$2\,H^+_{(aq)} \rightarrow H_{2(g)}$ (reduction)

$Cr_{(s)} \rightarrow Cr^{3+}_{(aq)} + 3\,e\text{-}$ (oxidation)

$2\,H^+_{(aq)} + 2\,e^- \rightarrow H_{2(g)}$ (reduction)

$2\,[Cr_{(s)} \rightarrow Cr^{3+}_{(aq)} + 3\,e\text{-}]$ (oxidation)

$3\,[2\,H^+_{(aq)} + 2\,e^- \rightarrow H_{2(g)}]$ (reduction)

$2\,Cr_{(s)} \rightarrow 2\,Cr^{3+}_{(aq)} + 6\,e\text{-}$ (oxidation)

$6\,H^+_{(aq)} + 6\,e^- \rightarrow 3\,H_{2(g)}$ (reduction)

$2\,Cr_{(s)} + 6\,H^+_{(aq)} \rightarrow 2\,Cr^{3+}_{(aq)} + 3\,H_{2(g)}$

c. $H_2SeO_{3(aq)} + H_2S_{(aq)} \rightarrow Se_{(s)} + HSO_4^-{}_{(aq)}$

$H_2S_{(aq)} \rightarrow HSO_4^-{}_{(aq)}$ (oxidation)

$H_2SeO_{3(aq)} \rightarrow Se_{(s)}$ (reduction)

$H_2S_{(aq)} + 4\,H_2O_{(l)} \rightarrow HSO_4^-{}_{(aq)} + 9\,H^+_{(aq)}$ (oxidation)

$H_2SeO_{3(aq)} + 4\,H^+_{(aq)} \rightarrow Se_{(s)} + 3\,H_2O_{(l)}$ (reduction)

$H_2S_{(aq)} + 4\,H_2O_{(l)} \rightarrow HSO_4^-{}_{(aq)} + 9\,H^+_{(aq)} + 8\,e^-$ (oxidation)

$H_2SeO_{3(aq)} + 4\,H^+_{(aq)} + 4\,e^- \rightarrow Se_{(s)} + 3\,H_2O_{(l)}$ (reduction)

$H_2S_{(aq)} + 4\,H_2O_{(l)} \rightarrow HSO_4^-{}_{(aq)} + 9\,H^+_{(aq)} + 8\,e^-$ (oxidation)

$2\,[H_2SeO_{3(aq)} + 4\,H^+_{(aq)} + 4\,e^- \rightarrow Se_{(s)} + 3\,H_2O_{(l)}]$ (reduction)

$H_2S_{(aq)} + 4\,H_2O_{(l)} \rightarrow HSO_4^-{}_{(aq)} + 9\,H^+_{(aq)} + 8\,e^-$ (oxidation)

$2\,H_2SeO_{3(aq)} + 8\,H^+_{(aq)} + 8\,e^- \rightarrow 2\,Se_{(s)} + 6\,H_2O_{(l)}$ (reduction)

$2\,H_2SeO_{3(aq)} + H_2S_{(aq)} \rightarrow 2\,Se_{(s)} + HSO_4^-{}_{(aq)} + H^+_{(aq)} + 2\,H_2O_{(l)}$

8.   d. $Fe^{2+}_{(aq)} + Cr_2O_7^{2-}_{(aq)} \rightarrow Fe^{3+}_{(aq)} + Cr^{3+}_{(aq)}$

$Fe^{2+}_{(aq)} \rightarrow Fe^{3+}_{(aq)}$ (oxidation)
$Cr_2O_7^{2-}_{(aq)} \rightarrow Cr^{3+}_{(aq)}$ (reduction)

$Fe^{2+}_{(aq)} \rightarrow Fe^{3+}_{(aq)}$ (oxidation)
$Cr_2O_7^{2-}_{(aq)} + 14\,H^+_{(aq)} \rightarrow 2\,Cr^{3+}_{(aq)} + 7\,H_2O_{(l)}$ (reduction)

$Fe^{2+}_{(aq)} \rightarrow Fe^{3+}_{(aq)} + 1\,e^-$ (oxidation)
$Cr_2O_7^{2-}_{(aq)} + 14\,H^+_{(aq)} + 6\,e^- \rightarrow 2\,Cr^{3+}_{(aq)} + 7\,H_2O_{(l)}$ (reduction)

$6\,[Fe^{2+}_{(aq)} \rightarrow Fe^{3+}_{(aq)} + 1\,e^-]$ (oxidation)
$Cr_2O_7^{2-}_{(aq)} + 14\,H^+_{(aq)} + 6\,e^- \rightarrow 2\,Cr^{3+}_{(aq)} + 7\,H_2O_{(l)}$ (reduction)

$6\,Fe^{2+}_{(aq)} \rightarrow 6\,Fe^{3+}_{(aq)} + 6\,e^-$ (oxidation)
$Cr_2O_7^{2-}_{(aq)} + 14\,H^+_{(aq)} + 6\,e^- \rightarrow 2\,Cr^{3+}_{(aq)} + 7\,H_2O_{(l)}$ (reduction)

$6\,Fe^{2+}_{(aq)} + Cr_2O_7^{2-}_{(aq)} + 14\,H^+_{(aq)} \rightarrow 6\,Fe^{3+}_{(aq)} + 2\,Cr^{3+}_{(aq)} + 7\,H_2O_{(l)}$

9.   a. $S^{2-}_{(aq)} + I_{2(s)} \rightarrow SO_4^{2-}_{(aq)} + I^-_{(aq)}$

$S^{2-}_{(aq)} \rightarrow SO_4^{2-}_{(aq)}$ (oxidation)
$I_{2(s)} \rightarrow I^-_{(aq)}$ (reduction)

$S^{2-}_{(aq)} + 8\,OH^-_{(aq)} \rightarrow SO_4^{2-}_{(aq)}$ (oxidation)
$I_{2(s)} \rightarrow 2\,I^-_{(aq)}$ (reduction)

$S^{2-}_{(aq)} + 8\,OH^-_{(aq)} \rightarrow SO_4^{2-}_{(aq)} + 4\,H_2O_{(l)}$ (oxidation)
$I_{2(s)} \rightarrow 2\,I^-_{(aq)}$ (reduction)

$S^{2-}_{(aq)} + 8\,OH^-_{(aq)} \rightarrow SO_4^{2-}_{(aq)} + 4\,H_2O_{(l)} + 8\,e^-$ (oxidation)
$I_{2(s)} + 2\,e^- \rightarrow 2\,I^-_{(aq)}$ (reduction)

$S^{2-}_{(aq)} + 8\,OH^-_{(aq)} \rightarrow SO_4^{2-}_{(aq)} + 4\,H_2O_{(l)} + 8\,e^-$ (oxidation)
$4\,[I_{2(s)} + 2\,e^- \rightarrow 2\,I^-_{(aq)}]$ (reduction)

$S^{2-}_{(aq)} + 8\,OH^-_{(aq)} \rightarrow SO_4^{2-}_{(aq)} + 4\,H_2O_{(l)} + 8\,e^-$ (oxidation)
$4\,I_{2(s)} + 8\,e^- \rightarrow 8\,I^-_{(aq)}$ (reduction)

$S^{2-}_{(aq)} + 4\,I_{2(s)} + 8\,OH^-_{(aq)} \rightarrow SO_4^{2-}_{(aq)} + 8\,I^-_{(aq)} + 4\,H_2O_{(l)}$

9. b. $Si_{(s)} + OH^-_{(aq)} \rightarrow SiO_3^{2-}_{(aq)} + H_{2(g)}$

$Si_{(s)} \rightarrow SiO_3^{2-}_{(aq)}$	(oxidation)
$OH^-_{(aq)} \rightarrow H_{2(g)}$	(reduction)

$Si_{(s)} + 6\,OH^-_{(aq)} \rightarrow SiO_3^{2-}_{(aq)}$	(oxidation)
$OH^-_{(aq)} \rightarrow H_{2(g)} + 2\,OH^-_{(aq)}$	(reduction)

$Si_{(s)} + 6\,OH^-_{(aq)} \rightarrow SiO_3^{2-}_{(aq)} + 3\,H_2O_{(l)}$	(oxidation)
$OH^-_{(aq)} + H_2O_{(l)} \rightarrow H_{2(g)} + 2\,OH^-_{(aq)}$	(reduction)

$Si_{(s)} + 6\,OH^-_{(aq)} \rightarrow SiO_3^{2-}_{(aq)} + 3\,H_2O_{(l)} + 4\,e^-$	(oxidation)
$OH^-_{(aq)} + H_2O_{(l)} + 1\,e^- \rightarrow H_{2(g)} + 2\,OH^-_{(aq)}$	(reduction)

$Si_{(s)} + 6\,OH^-_{(aq)} \rightarrow SiO_3^{2-}_{(aq)} + 3\,H_2O_{(l)} + 4\,e^-$	(oxidation)
$4\,[OH^-_{(aq)} + H_2O_{(l)} + 1\,e^- \rightarrow H_{2(g)} + 2\,OH^-_{(aq)}]$	(reduction)

$Si_{(s)} + 6\,OH^-_{(aq)} \rightarrow SiO_3^{2-}_{(aq)} + 3\,H_2O_{(l)} + 4\,e^-$	(oxidation)
$4\,OH^-_{(aq)} + 4\,H_2O_{(l)} + 4\,e^- \rightarrow 4\,H_{2(g)} + 8\,OH^-_{(aq)}$	(reduction)

$$Si_{(s)} + 2\,OH^-_{(aq)} + H_2O_{(l)} \rightarrow SiO_3^{2-}_{(aq)} + 4\,H_{2(g)}$$

c. $Cr(OH)_{3(s)} + BrO^-_{(aq)} \rightarrow CrO_4^{2-}_{(aq)} + Br^-_{(aq)}$

$Cr(OH)_{3(s)} \rightarrow CrO_4^{2-}_{(aq)}$	(oxidation)
$BrO^-_{(aq)} \rightarrow Br^-_{(aq)}$	(reduction)

$Cr(OH)_{3(s)} + 5\,OH^-_{(aq)} \rightarrow CrO_4^{2-}_{(aq)}$	(oxidation)
$BrO^-_{(aq)} \rightarrow Br^-_{(aq)} + 2\,OH^-_{(aq)}$	(reduction)

$Cr(OH)_{3(s)} + 5\,OH^-_{(aq)} \rightarrow CrO_4^{2-}_{(aq)} + 4\,H_2O_{(l)}$	(oxidation)
$BrO^-_{(aq)} + H_2O_{(l)} \rightarrow Br^-_{(aq)} + 2\,OH^-_{(aq)}$	(reduction)

$Cr(OH)_{3(s)} + 5\,OH^-_{(aq)} \rightarrow CrO_4^{2-}_{(aq)} + 4\,H_2O_{(l)} + 3\,e^-$	(oxidation)
$BrO^-_{(aq)} + H_2O_{(l)} + 2\,e^- \rightarrow Br^-_{(aq)} + 2\,OH^-_{(aq)}$	(reduction)

$2\,[Cr(OH)_{3(s)} + 5\,OH^-_{(aq)} \rightarrow CrO_4^{2-}_{(aq)} + 4\,H_2O_{(l)} + 3\,e^-]$	(oxidation)
$3\,[BrO^-_{(aq)} + H_2O_{(l)} + 2\,e^- \rightarrow Br^-_{(aq)} + 2\,OH^-_{(aq)}]$	(reduction)

9. c. (continued)

$$2 \, Cr(OH)_{3(s)} + 10 \, OH^-_{(aq)} \rightarrow 2 \, CrO_4^{2-}_{(aq)} + 8 \, H_2O_{(l)} + 6 \, e^- \quad \text{(oxidation)}$$
$$3 \, BrO^-_{(aq)} + 3 \, H_2O_{(l)} + 6 \, e^- \rightarrow 3 \, Br^-_{(aq)} + 6 \, OH^-_{(aq)} \qquad \text{(reduction)}$$

$$2 \, Cr(OH)_{3(s)} + 3 \, BrO^-_{(aq)} + 4 \, OH^-_{(aq)} \rightarrow 2 \, CrO_4^{2-}_{(aq)} + 3 \, Br^-_{(aq)} + 5 \, H_2O_{(l)}$$

9. d. $S_2O_3^{2-}_{(aq)} + ClO^-_{(aq)} \rightarrow SO_4^{2-}_{(aq)} + Cl^-_{(aq)}$

$$S_2O_3^{2-}_{(aq)} \rightarrow 2 \, SO_4^{2-}_{(aq)} \qquad\qquad \text{(oxidation)}$$
$$ClO^-_{(aq)} \rightarrow Cl^-_{(aq)} \qquad\qquad \text{(reduction)}$$

$$S_2O_3^{2-}_{(aq)} + 10 \, OH^-_{(aq)} \rightarrow 2 \, SO_4^{2-}_{(aq)} \qquad\qquad \text{(oxidation)}$$
$$ClO^-_{(aq)} \rightarrow Cl^-_{(aq)} + 2 \, OH^-_{(aq)} \qquad\qquad \text{(reduction)}$$

$$S_2O_3^{2-}_{(aq)} + 10 \, OH^-_{(aq)} \rightarrow 2 \, SO_4^{2-}_{(aq)} + 5 \, H_2O_{(l)} \qquad \text{(oxidation)}$$
$$ClO^-_{(aq)} + H_2O_{(l)} \rightarrow Cl^-_{(aq)} + 2 \, OH^-_{(aq)} \qquad\qquad \text{(reduction)}$$

$$S_2O_3^{2-}_{(aq)} + 10 \, OH^-_{(aq)} \rightarrow 2 \, SO_4^{2-}_{(aq)} + 5 \, H_2O_{(l)} + 8 \, e^- \quad \text{(oxidation)}$$
$$ClO^-_{(aq)} + H_2O_{(l)} + 2 \, e^- \rightarrow Cl^-_{(aq)} + 2 \, OH^-_{(aq)} \qquad \text{(reduction)}$$

$$S_2O_3^{2-}_{(aq)} + 10 \, OH^-_{(aq)} \rightarrow 2 \, SO_4^{2-}_{(aq)} + 5 \, H_2O_{(l)} + 8 \, e^- \quad \text{(oxidation)}$$
$$4 \, [ClO^-_{(aq)} + H_2O_{(l)} + 2 \, e^- \rightarrow Cl^-_{(aq)} + 2 \, OH^-_{(aq)}] \qquad \text{(reduction)}$$

$$S_2O_3^{2-}_{(aq)} + 10 \, OH^-_{(aq)} \rightarrow 2 \, SO_4^{2-}_{(aq)} + 5 \, H_2O_{(l)} + 8 \, e^- \quad \text{(oxidation)}$$
$$4 \, ClO^-_{(aq)} + 4 \, H_2O_{(l)} + 8 \, e^- \rightarrow 4 \, Cl^-_{(aq)} + 8 \, OH^-_{(aq)} \qquad \text{(reduction)}$$

$$S_2O_3^{2-}_{(aq)} + 4 \, ClO^-_{(aq)} + 2 \, OH^-_{(aq)} \rightarrow 2 \, SO_4^{2-}_{(aq)} + 4 \, Cl^-_{(aq)} + H_2O_{(l)}$$

10. The activity series of metals lists metals according to their reactivity with hydrogen. Metals are listed from the most likely to react with hydrogen ion to the least likely to react with hydrogen ion. Metals listed above hydrogen will reduce hydrogen ion; metals listed below hydrogen will not reduce hydrogen ion.

11. a. Ba will displace hydrogen from acids.
$$Ba_{(s)} + 2 \, H^+_{(aq)} \rightarrow Ba^{2+}_{(aq)} + H_{2(g)}$$
b. Ag will not displace hydrogen from acids.
c. Cr will displace hydrogen from acids.
$$2 \, Cr_{(s)} + 6 \, H^+_{(aq)} \rightarrow 2 \, Cr^{3+}_{(aq)} + 3 \, H_{2(g)}$$
d. Pb will displace hydrogen from acids.
$$Pb_{(s)} + 2 \, H^+_{(aq)} \rightarrow Pb^{2+}_{(aq)} + H_{2(g)}$$

12. a. This reaction will proceed since Zn lies above Ni in the activity series.
b. This reaction will not proceed since Pb lies below Zn in the activity series.
c. This reaction will proceed since Fe lies above Ag in the activity series.
d. This reaction will not proceed since Hg lies below Pb in the activity series.

13. a. Electrochemical reactions are reactions capable of producing electricity or which require the use of electricity. **b.** An **electrochemical cell** is the equipment in which an electrochemical reaction is performed. **c.** An **electrode** is generally a solid rod, composed of an electrical conductor, which is immersed in the solution in an electrochemical cell. **d.** The **anode** is the electrode where oxidation occurs. **e.** The **cathode** is the electrode where reduction occurs. **f. Voltaic or galvanic cells** are electrochemical cells set up with the two electrodes (anode and cathode) connected to a load device by wire to conduct electricity and with a salt bridge connecting the two solutions to permit ion migration. Voltaic cells spontaneously generate electricity. **g.** A **Daniell cell** uses zinc as the anode and copper as the cathode. It was used to provide electricity in early telegraph equipment.

14. This reaction will not proceed because As is below Al on the activity series.

15. If the two electrodes are not connected by a wire or other electrical conductor, then the electrons produced in the oxidation would have no place to go and that reaction would cease. Also, the reduction needs electrons to continue and, without the source of electrons, that reaction would stop.

16. The salt bridge in a voltaic cell allows ions to move freely between the two solutions to maintain a balance of charges between the solutions. The salt bridge is also useful because it doesn't allow the two solutions to physically mix.

17. A voltaic cell is composed of two solutions. In one solution, oxidation occurs at the anode and electrons are produced. In the other solution, reduction occurs at the cathode and electrons are consumed. Electrons flow through the connecting wire from the anode to the cathode and thus generates electricity. A salt bridge also connects the two solutions and allows ions to flow between the two solutions so as to maintain the overall electrical neutrality of both solutions.

18. In the Daniell cell, the reaction is: $Zn_{(s)} + Cu^{2+}_{(aq)} \rightarrow Zn^{2+}_{(aq)} + Cu_{(s)}$

Oxidation occurs at the anode: $Zn_{(s)} \rightarrow Zn^{2+}_{(aq)} + 2\ e^-$

Reduction occurs at the cathode: $Cu^{2+}_{(aq)} + 2\ e^- \rightarrow Cu_{(s)}$

19. The Daniell cell:

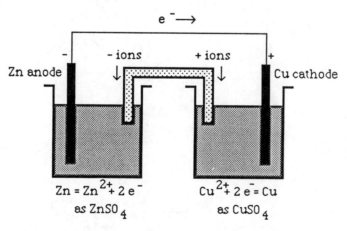

20. Batteries are commercial voltaic cells to store electricity for future use. The three types of batteries are 1) the lead storage battery (such as an automobile battery), 2) the dry cell (such as most of the small batteries used in toys and radios), and 3) the rechargeable nickel-cadmium battery (such as those used in calculators). Lead storage and nickel-cadmium batteries can be recharged but dry cells cannot. All will eventually wear out, though.

21. In the reaction: $Pb_{(s)} + PbO_{2(s)} + H_2SO_{4(aq)} \rightarrow 2\, PbSO_{4(s)} + 2\, H_2O_{(l)}$,

        Pb is oxidized to Pb^{2+} (in $PbSO_4$),

        Pb is then the reducing agent,

        Pb^{4+} (in PbO_2) is reduced to Pb^{2+} (in $PbSO_4$), and

        PbO_2 is then the oxidizing agent.

22. When a lead storage battery is discharged, the Pb and PbO_2 are converted to $PbSO_4$. All three of those species are solids and do not contribute to the density of the acid. However, the conversion consumes H_2SO_4 and produces H_2O. Since H_2SO_4 is more dense than H_2O, the consumption of H_2SO_4 reduces the overall density of the acid solution.

23. If $PbSO_4$ was soluble in water, it would also dissolve in the battery acid. This would reduce the acidity of the H_2SO_4 since the addition of SO_4^{2-} would cause association of the acid.

24. In the reaction: $Zn_{(s)} + 2\, NH_4^+{}_{(aq)} + 2\, MnO_{2(s)} \rightarrow Zn^{2+}{}_{(aq)} + Mn_2O_{3(s)} + 2\, NH_{3(aq)} + H_2O_{(l)}$,

        Zn is oxidized to Zn^{2+},

        Zn is then the reducing agent,

        Mn^{4+} (in MnO_2) is reduced to Mn^{3+} (in Mn_2O_3), and

        MnO_2 is then the oxidizing agent.

25. A salt bridge is not necessary in a dry cell because the paste is viscous enough to prevent mixing of the two component reactants.

26. Electrolysis is the process of forcing nonspontaneous redox reactions to occur by using external electrical energy. The electrochemical cell in which electrolysis occurs is an **electrolytic cell**.

27. The $CuCl_2$ electrolytic cell:

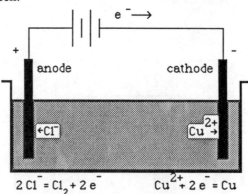

28. In a voltaic cell, the reaction is spontaneous while, in an electrolytic cell, the reaction only goes because of outside electrical energy added. In a voltaic cell, the cathode is positive and the anode is negative while, in an electrolytic cell, the cathode is negative and the anode is positive.

29. The net equation for the electrolysis of water is

$$2\,H_2O_{(l)} \rightarrow 2\,H_{2(g)} + O_{2(g)}$$

30. a. In the reaction: $2\,Fe^{2+}{}_{(aq)} + Br_{2(l)} \rightarrow 2\,Fe^{3+}{}_{(aq)} + 2\,Br^-{}_{(aq)}$
   Fe^{2+} is oxidized to Fe^{3+},
   Fe^{2+} is then the reducing agent,
   Br (in Br_2) is reduced to Br^-, and
   Br_2 is then the oxidizing agent.

b. In the reaction: $3\,Ag_{(s)} + 4\,H^+{}_{(aq)} + NO_3{}^-{}_{(aq)} \rightarrow 3\,Ag^+{}_{(aq)} + NO_{(g)} + 2\,H_2O_{(l)}$
   Ag is oxidized to Ag^+,
   Ag is then the reducing agent,
   N^{5+} (in $NO_3{}^-$) is reduced to N^{2+} (in NO), and
   $NO_3{}^-$ is then the oxidizing agent.

c. In the reaction: $Cu_{(s)} + 2\,Ag^+{}_{(aq)} \rightarrow Cu^{2+}{}_{(aq)} + 2\,Ag_{(s)}$
   Cu is oxidized to Cu^{2+},
   Cu is then the reducing agent,
   Ag^+ is reduced to Ag, and
   Ag^+ is then the oxidizing agent.

d. In the reaction: $2\,MnO_4{}^-{}_{(aq)} + 5\,S^{2-}{}_{(aq)} + 16\,H^+{}_{(aq)} \rightarrow 2\,Mn^{2+}{}_{(aq)} + 5\,S_{(s)} + 8\,H_2O_{(l)}$
   S^{2-} is oxidized to S,
   S^{2-} is then the reducing agent,
   Mn^{7+} (in $MnO_4{}^-$) is reduced to Mn^{2+}, and
   $MnO_4{}^-$ is then the oxidizing agent.

31. a. $NiO_{2(s)} + Fe_{(s)} \rightarrow Ni(OH)_{2(s)} + Fe(OH)_{3(s)}$

$Fe_{(s)} \rightarrow Fe(OH)_{3(s)}$	(oxidation)
$NiO_{2(s)} \rightarrow Ni(OH)_{2(s)}$	(reduction)
$Fe_{(s)} + 3\,OH^-{}_{(aq)} \rightarrow Fe(OH)_{3(s)}$	(oxidation)
$NiO_{2(s)} \rightarrow Ni(OH)_{2(s)} + 2\,OH^-{}_{(aq)}$	(reduction)
$Fe_{(s)} + 3\,OH^-{}_{(aq)} \rightarrow Fe(OH)_{3(s)}$	(oxidation)
$NiO_{2(s)} + 2\,H_2O_{(l)} \rightarrow Ni(OH)_{2(s)} + 2\,OH^-{}_{(aq)}$	(reduction)
$Fe_{(s)} + 3\,OH^-{}_{(aq)} \rightarrow Fe(OH)_{3(s)} + 3\,e^-$	(oxidation)
$NiO_{2(s)} + 2\,H_2O_{(l)} + 2\,e^- \rightarrow Ni(OH)_{2(s)} + 2\,OH^-{}_{(aq)}$	(reduction)
$2\,[Fe_{(s)} + 3\,OH^-{}_{(aq)} \rightarrow Fe(OH)_{3(s)} + 3\,e^-]$	(oxidation)
$3\,[NiO_{2(s)} + 2\,H_2O_{(l)} + 2\,e^- \rightarrow Ni(OH)_{2(s)} + 2\,OH^-{}_{(aq)}]$	(reduction)

31. a. (continued)

$$2\,Fe_{(s)} + 6\,OH^-_{(aq)} \;\rightarrow\; 2\,Fe(OH)_{3(s)} + 6\,e^- \qquad \text{(oxidation)}$$
$$3\,NiO_{2(s)} + 6\,H_2O_{(l)} + 6\,e^- \;\rightarrow\; 3\,Ni(OH)_{2(s)} + 6\,OH^-_{(aq)} \qquad \text{(reduction)}$$

$$\overline{2\,Fe_{(s)} + 3\,NiO_{2(s)} + 6\,H_2O_{(l)} \;\rightarrow\; 2\,Fe(OH)_{3(s)} + 3\,Ni(OH)_{2(s)}}$$

b. $MnO_4^-{}_{(aq)} + I^-_{(aq)} \;\rightarrow\; MnO_4^{2-}{}_{(aq)} + IO_4^-{}_{(aq)}$

$$I^-_{(aq)} \;\rightarrow\; IO_4^-{}_{(aq)} \qquad \text{(oxidation)}$$
$$MnO_4^-{}_{(aq)} \;\rightarrow\; MnO_4^{2-}{}_{(aq)} \qquad \text{(reduction)}$$

$$I^-_{(aq)} + 8\,OH^-_{(aq)} \;\rightarrow\; IO_4^-{}_{(aq)} \qquad \text{(oxidation)}$$
$$MnO_4^-{}_{(aq)} \;\rightarrow\; MnO_4^{2-}{}_{(aq)} \qquad \text{(reduction)}$$

$$I^-_{(aq)} + 8\,OH^-_{(aq)} \;\rightarrow\; IO_4^-{}_{(aq)} + 4\,H_2O_{(l)} \qquad \text{(oxidation)}$$
$$MnO_4^-{}_{(aq)} \;\rightarrow\; MnO_4^{2-}{}_{(aq)} \qquad \text{(reduction)}$$

$$I^-_{(aq)} + 8\,OH^-_{(aq)} \;\rightarrow\; IO_4^-{}_{(aq)} + 4\,H_2O_{(l)} + 8\,e^- \qquad \text{(oxidation)}$$
$$MnO_4^-{}_{(aq)} + 1\,e^- \;\rightarrow\; MnO_4^{2-}{}_{(aq)} \qquad \text{(reduction)}$$

$$I^-_{(aq)} + 8\,OH^-_{(aq)} \;\rightarrow\; IO_4^-{}_{(aq)} + 4\,H_2O_{(l)} + 8\,e^- \qquad \text{(oxidation)}$$
$$8\,[MnO_4^-{}_{(aq)} + 1\,e^- \;\rightarrow\; MnO_4^{2-}{}_{(aq)}] \qquad \text{(reduction)}$$

$$I^-_{(aq)} + 8\,OH^-_{(aq)} \;\rightarrow\; IO_4^-{}_{(aq)} + 4\,H_2O_{(l)} + 8\,e^- \qquad \text{(oxidation)}$$
$$8\,MnO_4^-{}_{(aq)} + 8\,e^- \;\rightarrow\; 8\,MnO_4^{2-}{}_{(aq)} \qquad \text{(reduction)}$$

$$\overline{8\,MnO_4^-{}_{(aq)} + I^-_{(aq)} + 8\,OH^-_{(aq)} \;\rightarrow\; 8\,MnO_4^{2-}{}_{(aq)} + IO_4^-{}_{(aq)} + 4\,H_2O_{(l)}}$$

c. $S_2O_3^{2-}{}_{(aq)} + I_{2(s)} \;\rightarrow\; SO_4^{2-}{}_{(aq)} + I^-_{(aq)}$

$$S_2O_3^{2-}{}_{(aq)} \;\rightarrow\; 2\,SO_4^{2-}{}_{(aq)} \qquad \text{(oxidation)}$$
$$I_{2(s)} \;\rightarrow\; 2\,I^-_{(aq)} \qquad \text{(reduction)}$$

$$S_2O_3^{2-}{}_{(aq)} + 10\,OH^-_{(aq)} \;\rightarrow\; 2\,SO_4^{2-}{}_{(aq)} \qquad \text{(oxidation)}$$
$$I_{2(s)} \;\rightarrow\; 2\,I^-_{(aq)} \qquad \text{(reduction)}$$

$$S_2O_3^{2-}{}_{(aq)} + 10\,OH^-_{(aq)} \;\rightarrow\; 2\,SO_4^{2-}{}_{(aq)} + 5\,H_2O_{(l)} \qquad \text{(oxidation)}$$
$$I_{2(s)} \;\rightarrow\; 2\,I^-_{(aq)} \qquad \text{(reduction)}$$

$$S_2O_3^{2-}{}_{(aq)} + 10\,OH^-_{(aq)} \;\rightarrow\; 2\,SO_4^{2-}{}_{(aq)} + 5\,H_2O_{(l)} + 8\,e^- \qquad \text{(oxidation)}$$
$$I_{2(s)} + 2\,e^- \;\rightarrow\; 2\,I^-_{(aq)} \qquad \text{(reduction)}$$

31. c. (continued)

$$S_2O_3^{2-}{}_{(aq)} + 10\,OH^-{}_{(aq)} \rightarrow 2\,SO_4^{2-}{}_{(aq)} + 5\,H_2O_{(l)} + 8\,e^- \qquad \text{(oxidation)}$$
$$4\,[I_{2(s)} + 2\,e^- \rightarrow 2\,I^-{}_{(aq)}] \qquad \text{(reduction)}$$

$$S_2O_3^{2-}{}_{(aq)} + 10\,OH^-{}_{(aq)} \rightarrow 2\,SO_4^{2-}{}_{(aq)} + 5\,H_2O_{(l)} + 8\,e^- \qquad \text{(oxidation)}$$
$$4\,I_{2(s)} + 8\,e^- \rightarrow 8\,I^-{}_{(aq)} \qquad \text{(reduction)}$$

$$\overline{S_2O_3^{2-}{}_{(aq)} + 4\,I_{2(s)} + 10\,OH^-{}_{(aq)} \rightarrow 2\,SO_4^{2-}{}_{(aq)} + 8\,I^-{}_{(aq)} + 5\,H_2O_{(l)}}$$

d. $As_{(s)} + OH^-{}_{(aq)} \rightarrow AsO_3^{3-}{}_{(aq)} + H_{2(g)}$

$$As_{(s)} \rightarrow AsO_3^{3-}{}_{(aq)} \qquad \text{(oxidation)}$$
$$OH^-{}_{(aq)} \rightarrow H_{2(g)} \qquad \text{(reduction)}$$

$$As_{(s)} + 6\,OH^-{}_{(aq)} \rightarrow AsO_3^{3-}{}_{(aq)} \qquad \text{(oxidation)}$$
$$2\,OH^-{}_{(aq)} \rightarrow H_{2(g)} + 4\,OH^-{}_{(aq)} \qquad \text{(reduction)}$$

$$As_{(s)} + 6\,OH^-{}_{(aq)} \rightarrow AsO_3^{3-}{}_{(aq)} + 3\,H_2O_{(l)} \qquad \text{(oxidation)}$$
$$2\,OH^-{}_{(aq)} + 2\,H_2O_{(l)} \rightarrow H_{2(g)} + 4\,OH^-{}_{(aq)} \qquad \text{(reduction)}$$

$$As_{(s)} + 6\,OH^-{}_{(aq)} \rightarrow AsO_3^{3-}{}_{(aq)} + 3\,H_2O_{(l)} + 3\,e^- \qquad \text{(oxidation)}$$
$$2\,OH^-{}_{(aq)} + 2\,H_2O_{(l)} + 2\,e^- \rightarrow H_{2(g)} + 4\,OH^-{}_{(aq)} \qquad \text{(reduction)}$$

$$2\,[As_{(s)} + 6\,OH^-{}_{(aq)} \rightarrow AsO_3^{3-}{}_{(aq)} + 3\,H_2O_{(l)} + 3\,e^-] \qquad \text{(oxidation)}$$
$$3\,[2\,OH^-{}_{(aq)} + 2\,H_2O_{(l)} + 2\,e^- \rightarrow H_{2(g)} + 4\,OH^-{}_{(aq)}] \qquad \text{(reduction)}$$

$$2\,As_{(s)} + 12\,OH^-{}_{(aq)} \rightarrow 2\,AsO_3^{3-}{}_{(aq)} + 6\,H_2O_{(l)} + 6\,e^- \qquad \text{(oxidation)}$$
$$6\,OH^-{}_{(aq)} + 6\,H_2O_{(l)} + 6\,e^- \rightarrow 3\,H_{2(g)} + 12\,OH^-{}_{(aq)} \qquad \text{(reduction)}$$

$$\overline{2\,As_{(s)} + 6\,OH^-{}_{(aq)} \rightarrow 2\,AsO_3^{3-}{}_{(aq)} + 3\,H_{2(g)}}$$

32. The reaction would be: $Ag_2S_{(s)} + Zn_{(s)} \rightarrow 2\,Ag_{(s)} + ZnS_{(s)}$

The Ag^+ in Ag_2S was reduced to metallic Ag by the zinc coating. The zinc was oxidized to Zn^{2+} in the process.

33. a.
$$Mg_{(s)} \rightarrow Mg^{2+}_{(aq)} + 2\,e^-$$
$$2\,Ag^+_{(aq)} + 2\,e^- \rightarrow 2\,Ag_{(s)}$$

b., c., and d.

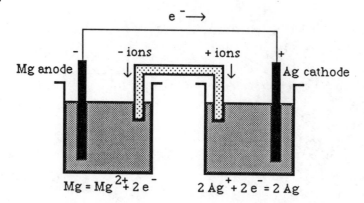

34. The reaction to recharge a lead storage battery is not spontaneous. It spontaneously generates electricity and so it would make sense that it requires applied electricity to reverse the reaction.

35. A salt bridge is not necessary in the lead storage battery since only one of the half-cells is an aqueous solution. The entire lead half-cell is in the solid phase. The $H_2SO_{4(aq)}$ takes care of the necessary ion transport.

36. When the $PbSO_4$ is dislodged from the grids, it is then unavailable for conversion back to $Pb_{(s)}$ and $PbO_{2(s)}$. This problem is typical of half-cells which are entirely solid. The irreversibility of it also ties up SO_4^{2-} ions which cannot be returned to the reaction, although more acid can be added to the battery.

37. When the dry cell battery is allowed to rest, the remaining ions will diffuse through the paste, thus allowing the reaction to occur again. The first episodes of battery "weakness" in dry cells is due to an ion depletion at the junction of the two half-cells; other active ions still exist in the interior of the paste.

38. In the nickel-cadmium battery, the products of both half-reactions are insoluble hydroxides ($Cd(OH)_2$ and $Ni(OH)_2$) which coat their respective electrodes. Since the products remain in contact with the electrodes, applying electricity can reverse the reaction easily.

39. Electroplating consists of putting a thin layer of a metal on the surface of another material. If a stainless steel spoon is used as the cathode in an electrolytic cell containing Ag^+, pure silver will be plated to the surface of the stainless steel.

Sample Quiz Questions

1. Oxidation
   a. occurs at the cathode.
   b. also means a decrease in the oxidation number.
   c. is the addition of electrons to an atom.
   d. is the removal of electrons from an atom.
   e. is the process undergone by the oxidizing agent.

2. Reducing agents
   a. cause another reactant to be oxidized.
   b. are reduced in redox reactions.
   c. cause another reactant to be reduced.
   d. cause a precipitation reaction.
   e. usually have positive oxidation numbers.

3. Which of the following reactions is a redox reaction?
   a. $3 Se_{(s)} + 4 HNO_{3(aq)} \rightarrow 3 SeO_{2(s)} + 4 NO_{(g)} + 2 H_2O_{(l)}$
   b. $CaCl_{2(aq)} + 2 AgNO_{3(aq)} \rightarrow Ca(NO_3)_{2(aq)} + 2 AgCl_{(s)}$
   c. $BaCO_{3(s)} \rightarrow BaO_{(s)} + CO_{2(g)}$
   d. $3 Mg(OH)_{2(s)} + 2 NH_{3(g)} \rightarrow Mg_3N_{2(s)} + 6 H_2O_{(l)}$
   e. $NH_{3(g)} + H_2O_{(l)} \rightarrow NH_4{}^+{}_{(aq)} + OH^-{}_{(aq)}$

4. Consider the reaction

$$ClO_3{}^-{}_{(aq)} + 3 S^{2-}{}_{(aq)} + 3 H_2O_{(l)} \rightarrow Cl^-{}_{(aq)} + 3 S_{(s)} + 6 OH^-{}_{(aq)}$$

   Which substance is the reducing agent?
   a. $S_{(s)}$
   b. $ClO_3{}^-{}_{(aq)}$
   c. $H_2O_{(l)}$
   d. $OH^-{}_{(aq)}$
   e. $S^{2-}{}_{(aq)}$

5. Balance the following redox reaction in acidic solution.

$$Fe^{3+}{}_{(aq)} + I^-{}_{(aq)} \rightarrow Fe^{2+}{}_{(aq)} + I_{2(s)}$$

   a. $Fe^{3+}{}_{(aq)} + 2 I^-{}_{(aq)} \rightarrow 2 Fe^{2+}{}_{(aq)} + I_{2(s)}$
   b. $2 Fe^{3+}{}_{(aq)} + 2 I^-{}_{(aq)} \rightarrow 2 Fe^{2+}{}_{(aq)} + I_{2(s)}$
   c. $2 Fe^{3+}{}_{(aq)} + 2 I^-{}_{(aq)} \rightarrow Fe^{2+}{}_{(aq)} + I_{2(s)}$
   d. $Fe^{3+}{}_{(aq)} + 2 I^-{}_{(aq)} \rightarrow Fe^{2+}{}_{(aq)} + I_{2(s)}$
   e. $2 Fe^{3+}{}_{(aq)} + 2 I^-{}_{(aq)} \rightarrow 2 Fe^{2+}{}_{(aq)} + I_{2(s)} + 2 H^+{}_{(aq)}$

6.　Balance the following redox reaction in acidic solution.

$$NO_3^-{}_{(aq)} + H^+{}_{(aq)} + I_{2(s)} \rightarrow NO_{2(g)} + H_2O_{(l)} + IO_3^-{}_{(aq)}$$

a. $10\ NO_3^-{}_{(aq)} + 8\ H^+{}_{(aq)} + I_{2(s)} \rightarrow 10\ NO_{2(g)} + 2\ H_2O_{(l)} + 2\ IO_3^-{}_{(aq)}$

b. $5\ NO_3^-{}_{(aq)} + 8\ H^+{}_{(aq)} + I_{2(s)} \rightarrow 5\ NO_{2(g)} + 4\ H_2O_{(l)} + 2\ IO_3^-{}_{(aq)}$

c. $10\ NO_3^-{}_{(aq)} + 4\ H^+{}_{(aq)} + I_{2(s)} \rightarrow 10\ NO_{2(g)} + 2\ H_2O_{(l)} + 2\ IO_3^-{}_{(aq)}$

d. $10\ NO_3^-{}_{(aq)} + 8\ H^+{}_{(aq)} + I_{2(s)} \rightarrow 10\ NO_{2(g)} + 4\ H_2O_{(l)} + 2\ IO_3^-{}_{(aq)}$

e. $10\ NO_3^-{}_{(aq)} + 8\ H^+{}_{(aq)} + I_{2(s)} \rightarrow 10\ NO_{2(g)} + 4\ H_2O_{(l)} + IO_3^-{}_{(aq)}$

7.　Balance the following redox reaction in acidic solution.

$$H_2O_{2(aq)} + Cr_2O_7^{2-}{}_{(aq)} \rightarrow Cr^{3+}{}_{(aq)} + O_{2(g)}$$

a. $3\ H_2O_{2(aq)} + Cr_2O_7^{2-}{}_{(aq)} + 8\ H^+{}_{(aq)} \rightarrow 2\ Cr^{3+}{}_{(aq)} + 3\ O_{2(g)} + 7\ H_2O_{(l)}$

b. $H_2O_{2(aq)} + Cr_2O_7^{2-}{}_{(aq)} \rightarrow 2\ Cr^{3+}{}_{(aq)} + O_{2(g)}$

c. $H_2O_{2(aq)} + Cr_2O_7^{2-}{}_{(aq)} \rightarrow 2\ Cr^{3+}{}_{(aq)} + 9\ O_{2(g)}$

d. $3\ H_2O_{2(aq)} + Cr_2O_7^{2-}{}_{(aq)} \rightarrow 2\ Cr^{3+}{}_{(aq)} + 3\ O_{2(g)} + 3\ H_{2(g)}$

e. $3\ H_2O_{2(aq)} + Cr_2O_7^{2-}{}_{(aq)} \rightarrow 2\ Cr^{3+}{}_{(aq)} + 3\ O_{2(g)}$

8.　Balance the following redox reaction in acidic solution.

$$Zn_{(s)} + NO_3^-{}_{(aq)} \rightarrow Zn^{2+}{}_{(aq)} + NH_4^+{}_{(aq)}$$

a. $4\ Zn_{(s)} + NO_3^-{}_{(aq)} \rightarrow 4\ Zn^{2+}{}_{(aq)} + NH_4^+{}_{(aq)} + 3\ H_2O_{(l)}$

b. $4\ Zn_{(s)} + NO_3^-{}_{(aq)} + 10\ H^+{}_{(aq)} \rightarrow 4\ Zn^{2+}{}_{(aq)} + NH_4^+{}_{(aq)}$

c. $4\ Zn_{(s)} + NO_3^-{}_{(aq)} \rightarrow 4\ Zn^{2+}{}_{(aq)} + NH_4^+{}_{(aq)}$

d. $4\ Zn_{(s)} + NO_3^-{}_{(aq)} + 6\ H^+{}_{(aq)} \rightarrow 4\ Zn^{2+}{}_{(aq)} + NH_4^+{}_{(aq)} + 3\ H_2O_{(l)}$

e. $4\ Zn_{(s)} + NO_3^-{}_{(aq)} + 10\ H^+{}_{(aq)} \rightarrow 4\ Zn^{2+}{}_{(aq)} + NH_4^+{}_{(aq)} + 3\ H_2O_{(l)}$

9.　Balance the following redox reaction in basic solution.

$$CrO_4^{2-}{}_{(aq)} + NO_2^-{}_{(aq)} \rightarrow Cr(OH)_{3(s)} + NO_3^-{}_{(aq)}$$

a. $CrO_4^{2-}{}_{(aq)} + 3\ NO_2^-{}_{(aq)} + H_2O_{(l)} \rightarrow Cr(OH)_{3(s)} + 3\ NO_3^-{}_{(aq)} + 3\ OH^-{}_{(aq)}$

b. $2\ CrO_4^{2-}{}_{(aq)} + 3\ NO_2^-{}_{(aq)} + 5\ H_2O_{(l)} \rightarrow 2\ Cr(OH)_{3(s)} + 3\ NO_3^-{}_{(aq)} + 4\ OH^-{}_{(aq)}$

c. $2\ CrO_4^{2-}{}_{(aq)} + NO_2^-{}_{(aq)} + 7\ H_2O_{(l)} \rightarrow 2\ Cr(OH)_{3(s)} + NO_3^-{}_{(aq)} + 8\ OH^-{}_{(aq)}$

d. $2\ CrO_4^{2-}{}_{(aq)} + 3\ NO_2^-{}_{(aq)} \rightarrow 2\ Cr(OH)_{3(s)} + 3\ NO_3^-{}_{(aq)}$

e. $2\ CrO_4^{2-}{}_{(aq)} + NO_2^-{}_{(aq)} + 5\ H_2O_{(l)} \rightarrow 2\ Cr(OH)_{3(s)} + NO_3^-{}_{(aq)} + 4\ OH^-{}_{(aq)}$

10. Balance the following redox reaction in basic solution.

$$Cl_{2(g)} \rightarrow Cl^-_{(aq)} + ClO^-_{(aq)}$$

a. $2\,Cl_{2(g)} + 2\,OH^-_{(aq)} \rightarrow 2\,Cl^-_{(aq)} + 2\,ClO^-_{(aq)} + H_2O_{(l)}$

b. $Cl_{2(g)} + 4\,OH^-_{(aq)} \rightarrow Cl^-_{(aq)} + ClO^-_{(aq)} + 2\,H_2O_{(l)}$

c. $2\,Cl_{2(g)} + OH^-_{(aq)} \rightarrow 2\,Cl^-_{(aq)} + 2\,ClO^-_{(aq)}$

d. $2\,Cl_{2(g)} + 4\,OH^-_{(aq)} \rightarrow 2\,Cl^-_{(aq)} + 2\,ClO^-_{(aq)} + 2\,H_2O_{(l)}$

e. $Cl_{2(g)} + 4\,OH^-_{(aq)} \rightarrow Cl^-_{(aq)} + ClO^-_{(aq)} + 2\,H_2O_{(l)}$

11. Balance the following redox reaction in basic solution.

$$Fe(OH)_{2(s)} + NO_3^-_{(aq)} \rightarrow Fe(OH)_{3(s)} + NO_2^-_{(aq)}$$

a. $2\,Fe(OH)_{2(s)} + NO_3^-_{(aq)} + H_2O_{(l)} \rightarrow 2\,Fe(OH)_{3(s)} + NO_2^-_{(aq)}$

b. $Fe(OH)_{2(s)} + NO_3^-_{(aq)} + H_2O_{(l)} \rightarrow Fe(OH)_{3(s)} + NO_2^-_{(aq)} + OH^-_{(aq)}$

c. $2\,Fe(OH)_{2(s)} + 2\,NO_3^-_{(aq)} + H_2O_{(l)} \rightarrow 2\,Fe(OH)_{3(s)} + 2\,NO_2^-_{(aq)}$

d. $Fe(OH)_{2(s)} + NO_3^-_{(aq)} + H_2O_{(l)} \rightarrow Fe(OH)_{3(s)} + NO_2^-_{(aq)}$

e. $2\,Fe(OH)_{2(s)} + NO_3^-_{(aq)} \rightarrow 2\,Fe(OH)_{3(s)} + NO_2^-_{(aq)} + H_2O_{(l)}$

12. Balance the following redox reaction in basic solution.

$$CN^-_{(aq)} + MnO_4^-_{(aq)} \rightarrow MnO_{2(s)} + CNO^-_{(aq)}$$

a. $CN^-_{(aq)} + MnO_4^-_{(aq)} + H_2O_{(l)} \rightarrow MnO_{2(s)} + CNO^-_{(aq)} + 2\,OH^-_{(aq)}$

b. $CN^-_{(aq)} + 2\,MnO_4^-_{(aq)} + 3\,H_2O_{(l)} \rightarrow 2\,MnO_{2(s)} + CNO^-_{(aq)} + 6\,OH^-_{(aq)}$

c. $3\,CN^-_{(aq)} + 2\,MnO_4^-_{(aq)} + H_2O_{(l)} \rightarrow 2\,MnO_{2(s)} + 3\,CNO^-_{(aq)} + 2\,OH^-_{(aq)}$

d. $3\,CN^-_{(aq)} + MnO_4^-_{(aq)} + 2\,OH^-_{(aq)} \rightarrow MnO_{2(s)} + 3\,CNO^-_{(aq)} + H_2O_{(l)}$

e. $3\,CN^-_{(aq)} + 2\,MnO_4^-_{(aq)} \rightarrow 2\,MnO_{2(s)} + 3\,CNO^-_{(aq)} + OH^-_{(aq)}$

13. Which of the following displacement reactions is spontaneous?

a. $2\,Au + 3\,Sn^{2+} \rightarrow 2\,Au^{3+} + 3\,Sn$

b. $Ca + Cu^{2+} \rightarrow Ca^{2+} + Cu$

c. $As + Al^{3+} \rightarrow As^{3+} + Al$

d. $Pb + Mg^{2+} \rightarrow Pb^{2+} + Mg$

e. $Zn + 2\,K^+ \rightarrow Zn^{2+} + 2\,K$

14. Which of the following displacement reactions is spontaneous?

a. $Pb + Zn^{2+} \rightarrow Pb^{2+} + Zn$

b. $2 Cr + 3 Ba^{2+} \rightarrow 2 Cr^{3+} + 3 Ba$

c. $Ni + Fe^{2+} \rightarrow Ni^{2+} + Fe$

d. $H_2 + Mg^{2+} \rightarrow 2 H^+ + Mg$

e. $3 Ag + Au^{3+} \rightarrow 3 Ag^+ + Au$

15. Which of the following displacement reactions is nonspontaneous?

a. $Zn + Ni^{2+} \rightarrow Zn^{2+} + Ni$

b. $Cr + As^{3+} \rightarrow Cr^{3+} + As$

c. $H_2 + Pb^{2+} \rightarrow 2 H^+ + Pb$

d. $Ni + 2 Ag^+ \rightarrow Ni^{2+} + 2 Ag$

e. $3 Na + Au^{3+} \rightarrow 3 Na^+ + Au$

16. Which of the following displacement reactions is nonspontaneous?

a. $Ba + Ca^{2+} \rightarrow Ba^{2+} + Ca$

b. $3 Cu + 2 Al^{3+} \rightarrow 3 Cu^{2+} + 2 Al$

c. $Fe + Hg^{2+} \rightarrow Fe^{2+} + Hg$

d. $Pb + Hg^{2+} \rightarrow Pb^{2+} + Hg$

e. $3 H_2 + 2 Au^{3+} \rightarrow 6 H^+ + 2 Au$

17. A voltaic cell

a. is usually housed in a single vessel.

b. cannot be reversed.

c. requires the application of external electricity.

d. must prevent the half-cells from physically mixing.

e. is comprised of a nonspontaneous reaction.

18. Voltaic cells

a. are of little commercial value.

b. are generally large, bulky devices.

c. generate electricity.

d. are reversible.

e. require only an oxidation half-cell.

19. A battery

a. produces the same amount of electricity, regardless of composition.

b. is rechargeable.

c. generally has no liquid components.

d. produces a constant amount of electricity for the duration of its lifetime.

e. spontaneously produces electricity.

20. Batteries are

a. generally transportable.

b. always based on metal redox reactions.

c. all rechargeable.

d. only used to operate small devices.

e. generally expensive.

21. Electrolytic cells
    a. generally are composed of two vessels.
    b. generate electricity.
    c. are spontaneous cells.
    d. can be used for electroplating.
    e. have little commercial value.

22. Silver can be plated onto nickel
    a. by applying electricity to a nickel anode in a solution of silver ions.
    b. by applying electricity to a silver anode in a solution of nickel ions.
    c. by applying electricity to a nickel cathode in a solution of silver ions.
    d. by allowing a solution of nickel ions to react with a piece of silver.
    e. by dipping the nickel object into a solution of silver ions.

Answers to the Sample Quiz Questions

1. (d), 2. (c), 3. (a), 4. (e), 5. (b), 6. (d), 7. (a), 8. (e), 9. (b), 10. (d), 11. (a), 12. (c), 13. (b), 14. (e), 15. (c), 16. (b), 17. (d), 18. (c), 19. (e), 20. (a), 21. (d), 22. (c)

RADIOACTIVITY AND NUCLEAR PROCESSES

CHAPTER
17

Chapter Overview

Chapter 17 focuses on nuclear processes. As such, the material is clearly different from that in any other chapter. In all the other chapters, the properties of atoms and their behaviors have been studied and those properties and behaviors are invariably related to their electronic structure. Here, the discussion centers on the nucleus of the atom and the changes that nuclei can undergo.

With the newness of the topic, the chapter begins with several definitions and basic information. Concepts such as radioisotopes, decay, and several modes of nuclear transformation are discussed. Balancing nuclear reactions, the differentiation between natural and artificial radioactivity, and characteristic reaction pathways are covered.

The detection of radioactivity is covered next, including Geiger counters and scintillation counters. The concept of the half-lives of nuclear reactions is also described.

Following a short section on radiation safety, applications of nuclear reactions are discussed, including medical X-rays, radioisotopic dating, the use of tracers, radiation therapy, and medical diagnostic tools.

Finally, the chapter concludes with a discussion of nuclear power. Included in this section are fission power plants, nuclear weapons, and the possibility of the development of fusion power plants.

Solutions to the Study Questions and Problems

1. **Radioactivity** is the process of transforming an unstable atom into a stable atom. **Radioactive decay** is the mechanism used, such as the emission of a particular particle, in the transmutation of an unstable atom into a new, stable one.

2. Radioisotopes attempt to achieve stability by alpha (α), beta (β), or gamma (γ) decay.

3. Transmutation is the process of changing an atom of one element into an atom of another element. Radioactivity results in transmutation as nuclear stability is sought.

4. If the neutron-to-proton ratio is close to 1, then no radioactive decay should occur.

5. An alpha particle is a helium nucleus, composed of two protons and 2 neutrons. Emission of an alpha particle reduces the atomic number of the nucleus by two, thereby transmuting the atom into an atom of the element with the atomic number two less than the reacting atom, and reducing the mass number by four.

6. The sum of the mass numbers on the reactant side of the equation must be the same as the sum of the mass numbers on the product side. Also, the sum of the atomic numbers on the reactant side of the equation must be the same as the sum of the atomic numbers on the product side. Thus, neither mass nor charge can be created or destroyed in a nuclear reaction.

7. Alpha decay lowers the atomic number by two and lowers the mass number by four since an alpha particle is $_2^4He$.

8. A beta particle is an emitted electron. Beta emission will increase the atomic number of an unstable nucleus while leaving the mass number unchanged. Therefore, beta emission can stabilize a nucleus by decreasing the n/p ratio.

9. Beta particles are created at the instant of emission by splitting a neutron into a proton and an electron.

10. A positron is created when a proton splits into a neutron and a small particle of negligible mass and a positive charge, the positron. Positron emission will decrease the atomic number of the nucleus but not affect the mass number. This can stabilize a nucleus by increasing the n/p ratio.

11. Electron capture is when a nucleus absorbs or captures an *outside* electron. This converts a proton into a neutron, decreasing the atomic number but leaving the mass number unchanged. This can stabilize a nucleus by increasing the n/p ratio.

12. The types and effects of beta decay are:

Change	Reaction	Atomic Number	Mass Number
$_{-1}^{0}\beta$ emission	$_0^1n \rightarrow {_{-1}^0}\beta + {_1^1}p$	increases by 1	is unchanged
$_1^0\beta$ emission	$_1^1p \rightarrow {_1^0}\beta + {_0^1}n$	decreases by 1	is unchanged
$_{-1}^0e$ capture	$_1^1p + {_{-1}^0}e \rightarrow {_0^1}n$	decreases by 1	is unchanged

13. Gamma rays (γ) are high energy radiation released by some unstable nuclei. With the very high energy, the wavelengths of gamma rays are very short. Gamma rays are usually given off with other forms of decay.

14. Since gamma rays are not particles and have no charge, gamma emission does not affect the atomic number or the mass number of the nucleus.

15. The types of decay are:

1) Alpha (α) decay - emission of alpha particles. Alpha decay lowers the atomic number by two and lowers the mass number by four.

2) Beta (β) decay - emission of electrons or positrons or capture of outside electrons. All three forms of beta decay involve the interconversion of neutrons and protons. None of them affect the mass number but all do alter the atomic number by one.

15. (continued)

3) Gamma (γ) decay - usually accompanies one of the other two types of decay. It does not change either the mass number or the atomic number of the nucleus. γ-rays are high energy radiation, not particles.

16. a. $_{84}^{198}Po \rightarrow {}_2^4\alpha + {}_{82}^{194}Pb$

 b. $_{82}^{210}Pb \rightarrow {}_{-1}^0\beta + {}_{83}^{210}Bi$

 c. $_{78}^{192}Pt \rightarrow {}_2^4\alpha + {}_{76}^{188}Os$

 d. $_{84}^{205}Po \rightarrow {}_2^4\alpha + {}_{82}^{201}Pb$

17. a. $_{93}^{238}Np \rightarrow {}_{-1}^0\beta + {}_{94}^{238}Pu$

 b. $_{94}^{237}Pu + {}_{-1}^0e \rightarrow {}_{93}^{237}Np$

 c. $_2^6He \rightarrow {}_3^6Li + {}_{-1}^0\beta$

 d. $_3^8Li \rightarrow {}_4^8Be + {}_{-1}^0\beta$

18. a. Cosmic rays are particles (alpha, beta, protons, and some larger nuclei) entering the earth's atmosphere from the sun and other sources in outer space. **b. Primary cosmic rays** are those cosmic rays which actually enter the atmosphere *from* space. **c. Secondary cosmic rays** are rays *produced in the atmosphere* when primary cosmic rays collide with atoms or molecules of the atmosphere. They are composed of all of the fundamental atomic particles. **d.** When a radioactive atom decays, the product may not be stable. This new nucleus will then decay and so on until a stable isotope is formed. This sequence of decay processes is known as a **radioactive disintegration series. e. Artificial radioactivity** is induced by bombarding a stable isotope with subatomic particles and producing an unstable isotope. **f.** The elements beyond uranium on the periodic table are known as the **transuranium elements.** The transuranium elements can be synthesized by bombardment of other nuclei. **g. Transmutation** is the process of changing one element into another. The ancient alchemists worked hard trying to transmute various elements into gold.

19. a. $_{94}^{239}Pu + {}_0^1n \rightarrow {}_{95}^{240}Am + {}_{-1}^0\beta$

 b. $_{94}^{239}Pu + {}_2^4\alpha \rightarrow {}_{96}^{242}Cm + {}_0^1n$

 c. $_{95}^{241}Am + {}_2^4\alpha \rightarrow {}_{97}^{243}Bk + 2\,{}_0^1n$

 d. $_{96}^{242}Cm + {}_2^4\alpha \rightarrow {}_{98}^{245}Cf + {}_0^1n$

20. The sequence is:

$$_{13}^{27}Al + {}_2^4\alpha \rightarrow {}_{15}^{30}P + {}_0^1n$$
$$_{15}^{30}P \rightarrow {}_{14}^{30}Si + {}_1^0\beta$$

21. a. Radiation is energy emitted by matter and includes γ-rays, X-rays, α particles, β particles, etc. **b. Ionizing radiation** can cause ionization of atoms in the substance it strikes. **c. X-rays** are a form of light radiation of slightly higher energy than ultraviolet light that can cause ionization in the substances they strike. **d.** A **Geiger counter** is a device that measures the amount of ionizing radiation being emitted from a source. **e.** A **scintillation counter** detects low-energy nuclear radiation such as alpha and beta emissions. **f.** A **film badge** is worn by people who work around radiation. Nuclear radiation will expose the film so the film badge can be used to determine the amount of radiation the person has been exposed to.

21. g. A **half-life** is the amount of time required for one-half of the atoms of a radioisotope sample to decay. h. The **activity of a radioactive sample** is the number of radioactive disintegrations in a given period of time. i. The **dosage of nuclear radiation** is the amount of radiation which can be delivered by a radioactive material. j. The **energy level of radiation** is the amount of energy emitted by a radioactive material.

22. X-rays are generated using high speed electrons to bombard a metal target. The bombarding electrons knock inner-shell electrons out of the metal and as electrons drop into the "holes", X-rays are emitted.

23. A Geiger counter contains unionized gas (usually argon) in a closed chamber. When ionizing radiation enters the chamber through a window which is transparent to it, the gas is ionized and the charged particles move to electrodes, completing the electrical circuit. The intensity of the radiation is registered on a meter and by a clicking sound. The higher the meter reading and the more frequent the clicks, the higher the intensity of the radiation.

24. A scintillation counter contains special compounds that emit light (scintillate) when exposed to nuclear radiation. The emitted light is measured with sensitive detectors and the amount of light produced is converted to an electrical signal and read on a meter.

25. a. A **Curie** is a measurement of activity of nuclear disintegrations. One Curie (1 Ci) is 3.7×10^7 disintegrations per second. b. A **roentgen** is a measurement of dosage of ionizing radiation. One roentgen (1 R) produces 2.1×10^{-9} coulombs of charge in 1 cm^3 of dry air at 0 °C and 1 atmosphere of pressure. c. A **rad** is a measurement of dosage of energy absorbed. One rad is 100 ergs of energy absorbed per gram of tissue. d. A **rem** is a measurement of dosage of biological damage. One rem is the biological damage caused by the absorption of one roentgen of radiation. e. An **electron-volt** is the energy absorbed by an electron while accelerating through a voltage change of one volt.

26. **Free radicals** are highly reactive molecular fragments formed when nuclear radiation breaks apart molecules. When free radicals are formed, particularly those from water molecules, they change other biological molecules and their structures. The most serious changes occur in DNA and cause the cells to die or be irreversibly altered.

27. One large single dose of radiation is more harmful than small doses spread out over time because one large exposure will destroy enough DNA and cells to cause serious illness or death. Small short term exposures can be recovered from as the cell's DNA is not entirely destroyed.

28. Nuclear radiation alters DNA. This altered DNA may be unable to reproduce normally or may lack the ability to control normal cellular processes. This can easily lead to uncontrolled growth of cancerous cells.

29. To minimize radiation exposure:

1) A shield can be placed between the radiating object and the worker. This will protect since radiation travels in a straight line.
2) Avoid the source of radiation as much as possible and stay away from it as far as possible.
3) Use lower intensity sources of radiation whenever possible.
4) Avoid eating, drinking, smoking, and any form of hand-to-mouth activity in the vicinity of radioactive sources.

30. Throughout their lives, organisms exchange ^{14}C with the environment, establishing an equilibrium concentration of it in their cells. After their deaths, the ^{14}C continues to decay but no more is being incorporated from the environment and so the concentration of ^{14}C in the cells decreases with time. By knowing the half-life of ^{14}C (5730 years) and measuring the amount of ^{14}C in a sample, archeologists can estimate the age of the sample.

31. Melvin Calvin shined light on algae in a CO_2 atmosphere enriched with ^{14}C and analyzed the cells for the presence of ^{14}C. He was then able to theorize the chemical pathway by which cells convert CO_2 to glucose and other compounds.

32. Radiation sickness often accompanies radiation therapy because normal cells are destroyed along with the cancerous cells. Radiation sickness is the set of symptoms which is observed in the radiation damage to normal cell function.

33. Radioisotopes are introduced into the body through ingestion or injection. The body is scanned with a scintillation camera and the areas where the radiation is concentrated show up as light areas on photographic film. Correct choice of the radioisotope will concentrate the isotope in the organ you want to scan.

34. a. The **mass defect** is the deficiency of mass when the calculated mass of a nucleus is compared to the actual mass. This difference in mass is equivalent to the energy holding the nucleus together. b. The **nuclear binding energy** is the energy equivalent of the mass defect and is the amount of energy released in the combination of nucleons to form the nucleus. It is, therefore, the amount of energy holding the nucleus together. c. The **average binding energy** is the nuclear binding energy divided by the mass number of the nucleus. It is the average binding energy per proton and neutron. d. **Nuclear fusion** is the process of combining two light nuclei into a heavier nucleus of intermediate mass number. This results in a release of energy and a mass decrease and leads to increased stability. e. **Nuclear fission** is the process of splitting a heavy nucleus into lighter nuclei of intermediate mass numbers. This results in a release of energy and a mass decrease and leads to increased stability.

35. The greater the mass defect in a nucleus, Δm, the higher the nuclear binding energy following from the equation $E = \Delta m c^2$. Therefore, the greater the mass defect, the greater amount of energy is being used to hold the nucleus together and the greater the amount of energy available for release when the nucleus is altered.

36. Nuclear fission is the process of splitting a heavy nucleus into lighter nuclei. Nuclear fusion is the process of combining lighter nuclei into a heavier one. In many ways, the two processes are the reverse of each other.

37. The binding energies of the parent nucleus and the smaller fragments produced by fission are sufficiently different that large amounts of energy are released by the fission process.

38. Some of the advantages of nuclear power are the relative safety of plant operations and the low fuel costs as compared to fossil fuel power plants. Some of the disadvantages are the disposal of the radioactive wastes and the fairly low abundance of fissionable materials. It must be noted that this is a controversial social and political issue and many other advantages and disadvantages can be thought of from those points of view.

39. The nuclear reaction in the reactor of a power plant is a controlled reaction while the reaction in an atomic bomb is, by design, uncontrolled. The other difference is that the fissionable material in the fuel of power plants accounts for only about 3% of the fuel's mass while about 97% of the fuel material in an atomic bomb is fissionable.

40. The **critical mass** is the smallest amount of fissionable isotope required to self-sustain a nuclear chain reaction. If the critical mass is not present, many of the neutrons produced escape into the environment and the chain reaction ceases.

41. The two methods of atomic bomb assembly are the **implosion method** and the **gun method**. In the gun method, two pieces of fuel of subcritical mass are at opposite ends of a tube. When pushed together by the detonation of a conventional explosive, the combined mass exceeds the critical mass and the bomb will explode as the neutrons cannot escape and the chain reaction escalates. In the implosion method, pieces of subcritical material are spherically arranged and are combined in the center of the sphere by the detonation of conventional explosives which are also spherically arranged. The combined fissionable mass is supercritical and its detonation then follows. The two devices really only differ in how the subcritical masses are arranged and how they are combined.

42. Many reactions occur in the sun. However, the simplest and the most abundant reaction is

$$_1^1H + {}_1^2H \rightarrow {}_2^3He + energy$$

43. The main difference between an atomic bomb and a hydrogen bomb is that the atomic bomb uses a fission reaction to generate its explosive force while the hydrogen bomb uses a fusion reaction to generate its force. Note that the hydrogen bomb is triggered by an atomic bomb. Nonetheless, the vast majority of the explosive force of the hydrogen bomb comes from the fusion reaction.

44. The two major problems in developing fusion power plants are the containment of the reaction and the maintenance of the high temperatures required. Engineers and physicists have achieved the necessary confinement and temperature (about 60,000,000 °) but maintaining these conditions has been a problem. Progress continues, however.

45. Neutrons are thought to act as "spacers", at least partially keeping the protons apart and reducing repulsions. This would account for the relative stability of light nuclei and the relative reactivity of heavy nuclei.

46. Positrons are created when a proton splits into a neutron and a positron by the reaction:

$$_1^1p \rightarrow {}_0^1n + {}_1^0\beta$$

47. a. $_{27}^{56}Co \rightarrow {}_{26}^{56}Fe + {}_1^0\beta + \gamma$

   b. $_{88}^{223}Ra \rightarrow {}_{86}^{219}Rn + {}_2^4\alpha$

   c. $_6^{10}C \rightarrow {}_5^{10}B + {}_1^0\beta$

   d. $_7^{18}N \rightarrow {}_8^{18}O + {}_{-1}^0\beta$

   e. $_{77}^{190}Ir + {}_{-1}^0e \rightarrow {}_{76}^{190}Os$

48. Since cosmic rays are composed of such a variety of particles, there are many ways in which tritium could be formed by cosmic ray bombardment. Some of the more easily performed reactions might be:

$$_1^1H + 2\,_0^1n \rightarrow {}_1^3H$$
$$_2^4He \rightarrow {}_1^3H + {}_1^1H$$
$$3\,_1^1H \rightarrow {}_1^3H + 2\,_1^0\beta$$

49. The amount remaining would be:

after 1 half-life:	50%
after 2 half-lives:	25%
after 3 half-lives:	12.5%
after 4 half-lives:	6.25%

50. The alpha particles invaded the lips and mouths of the women. As alpha particles don't travel very far, they did most of their damage in the mouth area. The alpha particles did a great deal of damage in a small area of tissue leading to cancer as the cells couldn't recover.

51. Nuclear radiation can destroy DNA and, therefore, cells. If used constructively, cancerous cells can be preferentially destroyed by focusing the radiation and shielding normal tissues as well as possible. If the exposure to radiation is indiscriminate and large areas of healthy cells are exposed, then the destruction of normal cells will be common and damage to normal biological functions will result.

52. A nuclear reaction becomes a chain reaction when at least the critical mass of a material is present. At that mass, when neutrons are produced, enough of them are absorbed by other fissionable nuclei to sustain the reaction.

Sample Quiz Questions

1. Transmutation
   a. is a fusion process.
   b. results in changing an atom of one element to an atom of another element.
   c. occurs only in the upper atmosphere where cosmic rays are abundant.
   d. is a fission process.
   e. may result in changing an atom of one element to an atom of another element.

2. Radioactivity
   a. requires the emission of one or more particles.
   b. is initiated by bombardment.
   c. is only detectable for fission processes.
   d. is the spontaneous alteration of nuclei to achieve stability.
   e. is a process which reduces the n/p ratio in a nucleus.

3. Write the balanced nuclear equation for beta emission by ^{24}Mg.
   a. $^{24}Mg \rightarrow {}^{24}Na + {}_{-1}^{0}\beta$
   b. $^{24}Mg \rightarrow {}^{24}Al + {}_{-1}^{0}\beta$
   c. $^{24}Mg \rightarrow {}^{24}Na + {}_{1}^{0}\beta$
   d. $^{24}Mg \rightarrow {}^{24}Al + {}_{1}^{0}\beta$
   e. $^{24}Mg \rightarrow {}^{24}Na + {}_{0}^{0}\beta$

216 Introduction to Chemistry

4. Write the balanced nuclear equation for alpha emission by ^{255}Lr.
    a. $^{255}Lr \rightarrow \; ^{255}No + \; _1^0\alpha$
    b. $^{255}Lr \rightarrow \; ^{259}Md + \; _2^4\alpha$
    c. $^{255}Lr \rightarrow \; ^{254}No + \; _1^1\alpha$
    d. $^{255}Lr \rightarrow \; ^{254}Lr + \; _0^1\alpha$
    e. $^{255}Lr \rightarrow \; ^{251}Md + \; _2^4\alpha$

5. Write the balanced nuclear equation for proton emission by ^{32}S.
    a. $^{32}S \rightarrow \; ^{31}Cl + \; _1^1H$
    b. $^{32}S \rightarrow \; ^{31}P + \; _1^1H$
    c. $^{32}S \rightarrow \; ^{32}P + \; _1^1H$
    d. $^{32}S \rightarrow \; ^{32}Cl + \; _1^1H$
    e. $^{32}S \rightarrow \; ^{31}S + \; _0^1H$

6. Fill in the blank with the missing item in the reaction

$$_{13}^{27}Al + \; _2^4\alpha \rightarrow \underline{\qquad} + \; _0^1n$$

    a. $_{13}^{30}Al$
    b. $_{15}^{27}P$
    c. $_{16}^{30}S$
    d. $_{15}^{31}P$
    e. $_{15}^{30}P$

7. Complete the nuclear equation

$$_5^{10}B + \; _1^1H \rightarrow \; _2^4\alpha + \underline{\qquad}$$

    a. $_6^{11}C$
    b. $_8^{15}O$
    c. $_4^7Be$
    d. $_7^{14}N$
    e. $_3^7Li$

8. What nucleus is formed when $_{82}^{196}$Pb undergoes two successive electron captures?
    a. $_{81}^{196}Tl$
    b. $_{83}^{196}Bi$
    c. $_{84}^{196}Po$
    d. $_{80}^{196}Hg$
    e. $_{82}^{194}Pb$

9.   What nucleus is formed when $_{33}^{69}$As undergoes positron emission?

   a. $_{33}^{68}$As

   b. $_{31}^{69}$Ga

   c. $_{34}^{69}$Se

   d. $_{35}^{70}$Br

   e. $_{32}^{69}$Ge

10. Complete the reaction

$$_{92}^{238}U + {_0^1}n \rightarrow {_{92}^{235}}U + \underline{\hspace{2cm}}$$

   a. $_0^1 n$

   b. $4\,_0^1 n$

   c. $3\,_0^1 n$

   d. $_{-1}^0\beta + {_1^0}\beta$

   e. $_2^4\alpha$

11. Artificial radioactivity
   a. is initiated by bombarding an unstable nucleus.
   b. is not a common occurrence.
   c. uses bombardment to change a stable nucleus into an unstable one.
   d. requires the use of neutrons to initiate the reaction.
   e. is limited to bombardment by one kind of particle.

12. A radioactive disintegration series
   a. is a characteristic, fixed series of nuclear reactions.
   b. is a series of ten disintegrations.
   c. is the only way most radioisotopes can achieve stability.
   d. is a variable pathway of reaction used by many unstable nuclei.
   e. is a set of simultaneous reactions of an unstable nucleus.

13. The Curie is a measurement of
   a. the amount of energy absorbed per gram of tissue.
   b. the biological damage of 1 roentgen of radiation.
   c. the amount of radiation which produces 2.1×10^{-9} coulombs of charge.
   d. the number of nuclear disintegrations per second.
   e. the amount of energy absorbed per kilogram of tissue.

14. The roentgen is a measurement of
   a. the amount of energy absorbed per gram of tissue.
   b. the biological damage of 1 roentgen of radiation.
   c. the amount of radiation which produces 2.1×10^{-9} coulombs of charge.
   d. the number of nuclear disintegrations per second.
   e. the amount of energy absorbed per kilogram of tissue.

15. For a nuclear reaction, what percentage of the sample will remain after six half-lives?
    a. 12.5 %
    b. 6.25%
    c. 3.125%
    d. 1.5625%
    e. 0.78125%

16. In medical diagnostics, radioisotopes
    a. are injected and an X-ray photo is taken.
    b. are limited to the study of blood disorders.
    c. produced by the body are photographed with a scintillation camera.
    d. are given in doses high enough to concentrate in all areas of the body.
    e. are chosen by whether they selectively concentrate in the area of the body being studied.

17. Mass defect
    a. is a phenomenon which is related to the amount of energy holding the nucleus together.
    b. is the mass missing from an atom which cannot be accounted for.
    c. is found to be independent of the energy of a nuclear reaction.
    d. occurs in some radioactive isotopes.
    e. does not occur in stable nuclei.

18. Nuclear fission
    a. is characterized by gamma emission.
    b. is characterized by absorbing neutrons.
    c. generates fewer nuclei than it started with.
    d. has yet to be used outside the laboratory.
    e. generates more nuclei than it began with.

19. Nuclear fusion
    a. is characterized by gamma emission.
    b. is characterized by absorbing neutrons.
    c. generates fewer nuclei than it started with.
    d. has yet to be used outside the laboratory.
    e. generates more nuclei than it began with.

20. A nuclear power plant
    a. is inexpensive to build, compared to fossil fuel power plants.
    b. cannot explode.
    c. contains a critical mass of fissionable material.
    d. has no serious pollution problems.
    e. is not a potential hazard to those who work in them.

21. The atomic bomb
    a. produces a more destructive blast than any other weapon in the history of mankind.
    b. is a fusion device.
    c. cannot be assembled very safely.
    d. is an out-of-date device.
    e. has not yet been used in war.

22. The hydrogen bomb
    a. produces a more destructive blast than the atomic bomb.
    b. produces only low-level radiation after its initial blast.
    c. has little in common with the atomic bomb.
    d. is a fission device.
    e. has been used in war.

Answers to the Sample Quiz Questions

1. (b), 2. (d), 3. (a), 4. (e), 5. (b), 6. (e), 7. (c), 8. (d), 9. (e), 10. (b), 11. (c), 12. (a), 13. (d), 14. (c), 15. (d), 16. (e), 17. (a), 18. (e), 19. (c), 20. (b), 21. (d), 22. (a)

INTRODUCTION TO ORGANIC CHEMISTRY

CHAPTER 18

Chapter Overview

Chapter 18 introduces the basic features of organic chemistry. The coverage is heavily structural in emphasis. Given the extensive chemistry of organic compounds, this choice of emphasis is appropriate. The chapter begins with a definition of the scope of organic chemistry and the differentiation between "organic carbon" and "inorganic carbon". Included is a brief summary of carbon's preferences in bonding.

Hydrocarbons are covered extensively, grouped by alkanes, alkenes, and alkynes. IUPAC nomenclature and structural isomerization are emphasized. Cyclic hydrocarbons, including aromatic compounds, are also covered, more from the aspect of their differences from non-cyclic compounds.

Following the basic concepts of hydrocarbons is a description of the major organic functional groups, such as halides, ethers, esters, amines, and carboxylic acids, and their distinguishing characteristics.

The chapter concludes with an optional section dealing with orbital hybridization and molecular orbitals. This section concentrates qualitatively on how these more advanced bonding models can be used to satisfactorily account for the observed properties of organic molecules.

Solutions to the Study Questions and Problems

1. Organic chemistry is the study of most covalent carbon compounds. Inorganic chemistry is the study of the compounds of the other elements and those compounds of carbon which don't fall under organic chemistry. For carbon compounds, the differentiation is often arbitrary.

2. **a.** C can form single, double, and triple bonds with carbon. **b.** H can form single bonds with carbon. **c.** P can form single bonds with carbon. **d.** S can form single (and occasionally double) bonds with carbon. **e.** Cl can form single bonds with carbon. **f.** N can form single and double (and occasionally triple) bonds with carbon. **g.** O can form single and double bonds with carbon.

3. **a. Hydrocarbons** are compounds composed only of carbon and hydrogen.

3. **b. Aliphatic hydrocarbons** are all hydrocarbons which are not aromatic. They usually are straight or branched chain hydrocarbons although there are some cyclic ones. **c.** An **aromatic hydrocarbon** contains special ring structures and multiple covalent bonds.

4. In hydrocarbons, carbon can exist in straight chains, branched chains, or rings. Between carbon atoms, there can be single, double, or triple bonds.

5. Most hydrocarbons occur in petroleum, natural gas, and in trees and other plants. Petroleum and natural gas provide the vast majority of hydrocarbons used.

6. The general physical properties of hydrocarbons include:

    1) Hydrocarbons are colorless.
    2) Hydrocarbons tend to be nonpolar.
    3) Hydrocarbons are insoluble in water but soluble in nonpolar solvents, including other hydrocarbons.
    4) Hydrocarbons with fewer than five carbons are gases at room temperature. Those with six through eighteen carbon atoms are liquids. The liquid hydrocarbons are less dense than water. Those with more than eighteen carbon atoms are solids. n-pentane, the straight-chain five carbon hydrocarbon is a gas on a hot day and a liquid on cooler days (B.P. = 36.1 °C or 97 °F).

7. **a. Alkanes** are hydrocarbons which contain only single bonds. **b. Saturated hydrocarbons** contain each carbon atom bonded to four other atoms. Since four is the total number of bonds carbon is capable of making, the term "saturated" is fitting. **c.** A **homologous series** is a set of compounds in which each member differs from the preceding one only by the addition of a single constant group of atoms. The succeeding member also differs only by the addition of the same group of atoms. **d.** A **molecular formula** shows the number and kind of each atom present in a molecule. **e.** The **condensed structural formula** shows the major structural features of a molecule. **f.** The **structural formula** shows as many of the structural features of a molecule as possible. **g. Isomers** are compounds with the same molecular formula but different structural formulas.

8. The general molecular formula for open-chain alkanes is C_nH_{2n+2}, where n is the number of carbon atoms in the molecule. Of the list of formulas given, only **b.** (C_4H_{10}) and **e.** (C_7H_{16}) are open-chain alkanes.

9. **a.** C_5H_{12}:

$$
\begin{array}{ccccccccc}
 & H & H & H & H & H & & & \\
 & | & | & | & | & | & & & \\
H- & C- & C- & C- & C- & C & -H & & \\
 & | & | & | & | & | & & & \\
 & H & H & H & H & H & & & \\
\end{array}
$$

    b. C_8H_{18}:

$$
\begin{array}{ccccccccc}
H & H & H & H & H & H & H & H \\
| & | & | & | & | & | & | & | \\
H-C- & C- & C- & C- & C- & C- & C- & C-H \\
| & | & | & | & | & | & | & | \\
H & H & H & H & H & H & H & H \\
\end{array}
$$

9. **c.** C_3H_8:

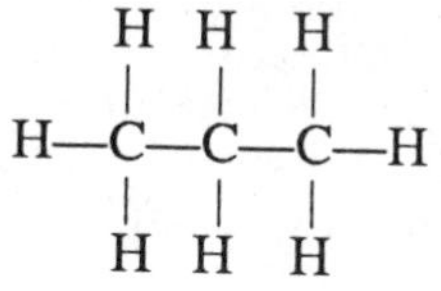

$$
\begin{array}{c}
\overset{\displaystyle H}{|}\;\overset{\displaystyle H}{|}\;\overset{\displaystyle H}{|} \\
H{-}C{-}C{-}C{-}H \\
\underset{\displaystyle H}{|}\;\underset{\displaystyle H}{|}\;\underset{\displaystyle H}{|}
\end{array}
$$

10. The structural isomers of C_6H_{14} are:

$CH_3{-}CH_2{-}CH_2{-}CH_2{-}CH_2{-}CH_3$

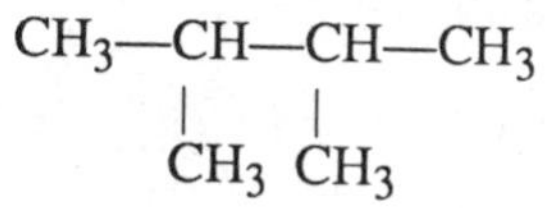

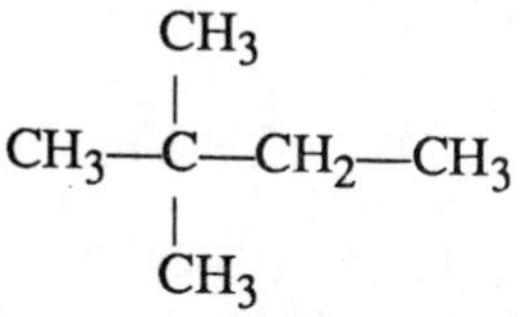

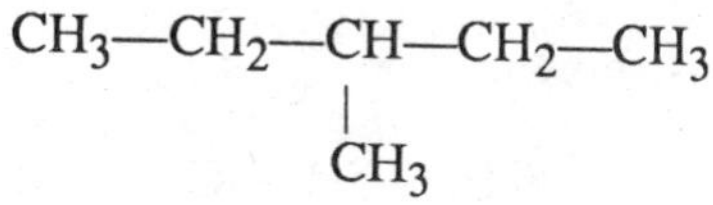

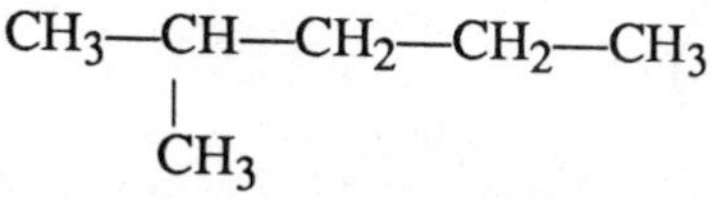

$CH_3{-}CH{-}CH{-}CH_3$
       $|$ $|$
     CH_3 CH_3

    CH_3
     $|$
$CH_3{-}C{-}CH_2{-}CH_3$
     $|$
    CH_3

$CH_3{-}CH_2{-}CH{-}CH_2{-}CH_3$
            $|$
          CH_3

$CH_3{-}CH{-}CH_2{-}CH_2{-}CH_3$
     $|$
    CH_3

11. Most alkanes are obtained from petroleum. Methane (CH_4) is the primary constituent of natural gas. Propane (C_3H_8) is used as a liquid fuel. Butane (C_4H_{10}) is also a liquid fuel, most visibly in disposable cigarrette lighters.

12. **a.** methylpropane
b. 2,4,4,6-tetramethyloctane
c. 2-methylpentane
d. 3-methyl-5-propyloctane
e. 2,2,4-trimethylpentane

13. pentane or *n*-pentane (the *n*- denotes the linear chain): $CH_3{-}CH_2{-}CH_2{-}CH_2{-}CH_3$

2-methylbutane: $CH_3{-}CH{-}CH_2{-}CH_3$
                 $|$
               CH_3

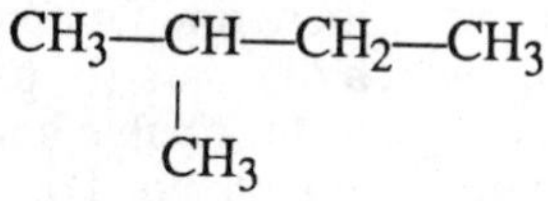

dimethylpropane (numbering is not required since propane only has one carbon to branch from):

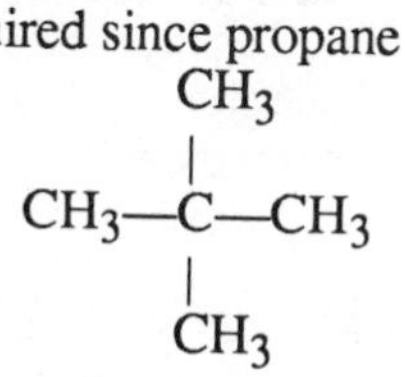

          CH_3
           $|$
    $CH_3{-}C{-}CH_3$
           $|$
          CH_3

14. **a.** 2-methylpentane:

         CH_3
          $|$
$CH_3{-}CH{-}CH_2{-}CH_2{-}CH_3$

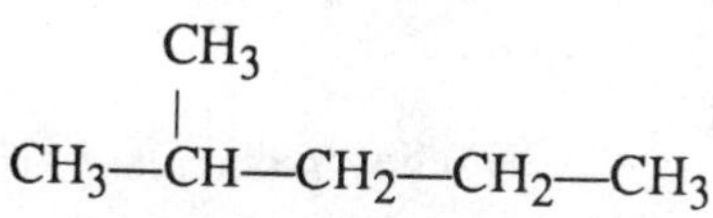

14. b. 2,2-dimethylbutane:

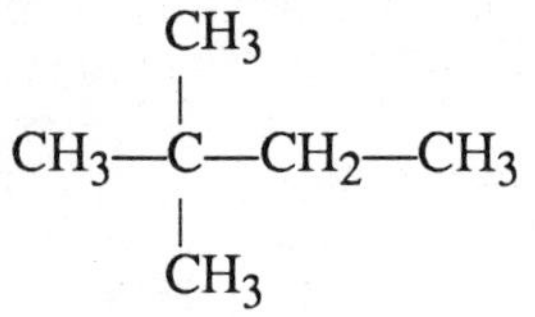

$$CH_3$$
$$|$$
$$CH_3-C-CH_2-CH_3$$
$$|$$
$$CH_3$$

c. 3,3-dimethyl-5-ethyldecane:

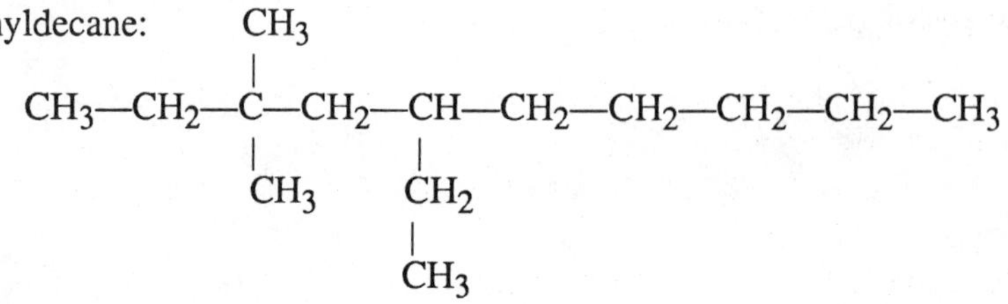

$$CH_3$$
$$|$$
$$CH_3-CH_2-C-CH_2-CH-CH_2-CH_2-CH_2-CH_2-CH_3$$
$$|\qquad\qquad |$$
$$CH_3\qquad CH_2$$
$$|$$
$$CH_3$$

d. 3,4-diethyl-5-methylnonane:

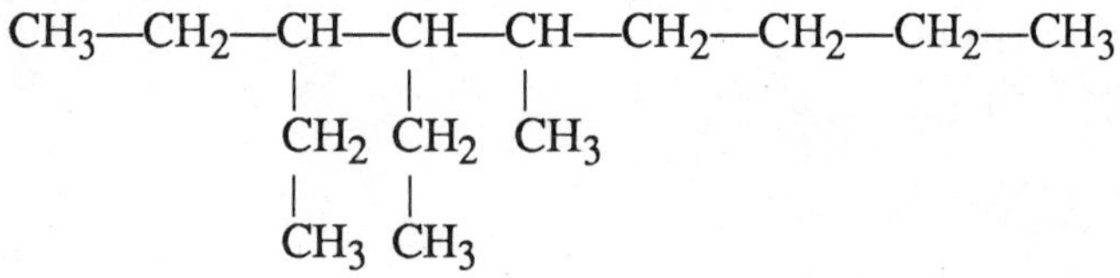

$$CH_3-CH_2-CH-CH-CH-CH_2-CH_2-CH_2-CH_3$$
$$|\quad\ |\quad\ |$$
$$CH_2\ CH_2\ CH_3$$
$$|\quad\ |$$
$$CH_3\ CH_3$$

e. 4-methyl-6-propyldecane:

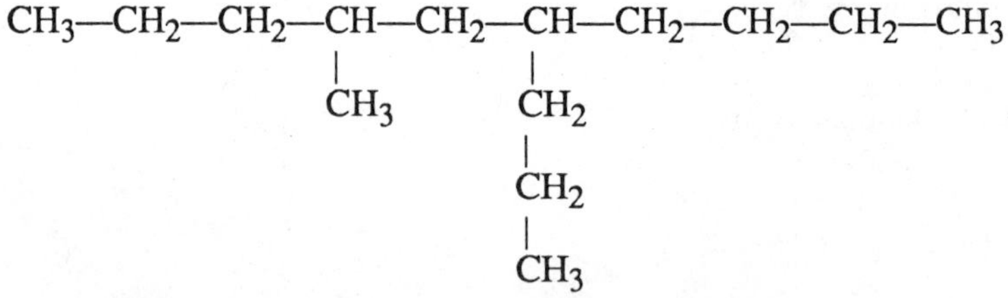

$$CH_3-CH_2-CH_2-CH-CH_2-CH-CH_2-CH_2-CH_2-CH_3$$
$$|\qquad\qquad |$$
$$CH_3\qquad CH_2$$
$$|$$
$$CH_2$$
$$|$$
$$CH_3$$

15. a. An **unsaturated hydrocarbon** contains one or more multiple covalent bonds between carbon atoms. **b.** An **alkene** is an aliphatic hydrocarbon with one or more double bonds between carbon atoms. **c. Geometric isomers** are isomers of alkenes in which the main (or parent) carbon chain of the molecule includes the double bond. If the main chain exits the double bond on the same side as it enters, the isomer is called *cis*. If the main chain exits the double bond on the side opposite to which it enters, the isomer is called *trans*. **d. Alkynes** are aliphatic hydrocarbons with one or more triple bonds between carbon atoms.

16. Saturated hydrocarbons have **no** multiple bonds while unsaturated hydrocarbons have one or more multiple bonds.

17. The general formula for open-chain alkenes with one double bond is C_nH_{2n}, where n is the number of carbon atoms in the molecule. Of the list of formulas given in Question #8, only **a.** $(C_{12}H_{24})$ and **d.** (C_5H_{10}) are open-chain alkenes.

18. The ethene molecule $(C_2H_4$ or $H_2C=CH_2)$ lies in one plane. The bond angles around each carbon atom are 120°.

19. a. *cis* - the main chain enters and exits the double bond on the same side. **b.** neither - the main chain ends at the double bond. Since both groups attached to one carbon are identical, there is only one possible arrangement. **c.** *trans* - the main chain enters and exits the double bond on opposite sides. **d.** *cis* - the main chain enters and exits the double bond on the same side.

20. Some alkenes are produced by removing hydrogen from alkanes. Others can be made by adding hydrogen to alkynes. Ethene is used as a starting material in the production of ethyl alcohol, ethylene glycol, polyethylene, and polystyrene.

21. The general formula for open-chain alkynes with one triple bond is C_nH_{2n-2}, where n is the number of carbon atoms in the molecule. Of the list of formulas given in Question #8, only **c.** (C_6H_{10}) and **f.** $(C_{10}H_{18})$ are open-chain alkynes.

22. The ethyne molecule (C_2H_2 or $HC{\equiv}CH$) is linear with a triple bond between the carbon atoms. Being linear, all bond angles are 180°.

23. The common name for ethyne is acetylene. Ethyne is used as the fuel in oxyacetylene welding torches and in the synthesis of other organic compounds. Ethyne is produced from coal followed by the high temperature conversion of methane to ethyne.

24. a. propene
   b. 4-methyl-1-hexyne
   c. 4-methyl-1-pentene
   d. 3-methyl-2-pentene
   e. 5-ethyl-3-methyl-1-heptyne
   f. 3-heptene
   g. 6-methyl-3-heptene

25. Cyclic aliphatic hydrocarbons are aliphatic chains joined to form a ring of carbon atoms.

26. a. cyclopentene:

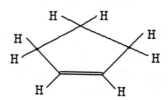

   b. cyclopropane:

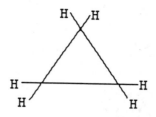

26. c. cycloheptane:

27. a. Aromatic hydrocarbons are compounds which are structurally related to benzene (C_6H_6).

In the benzene ring, the six π electrons of the three formal double bonds are spread out or delocalized over all six of the carbon-carbon bonds. **b. Resonance structures** show the alternative placement of the multiple bonds in an organic compound. They are, in essence, the set of "legal" electron dot formulas for the compound. **c. A derivative** is a compound made or derived from another compound. **d. Polycyclic aromatic hydrocarbons** consist of two or more aromatic rings fused together (sharing an edge). (See the answers to Question #31 for examples)

28. Originally, aromatic compounds were called that because many of their derivatives have pleasant odors. We now know that a pleasant odor is not necessarily a property of these compounds so we no longer associate a nice odor with the historical term.

29. Kekulé proposed that benzene had two distinct but equivalent structures which could not be isolated from each other. Benzene's behavior indicated only one structure, though. He resolved the apparent conflict by hypothesizing that the electrons of the double bonds are spread out evenly throughout the carbon ring, a concept called delocalization.

30. The chemical characteristics of aromatic hydrocarbons include:

1) They usually have a distinctive odor.
2) They are planer; all the atoms of the compound lie in a plane.
3) They are insoluble in water.
4) They are soluble in nonpolar solvents, including other aromatic liquids.
5) They are unusually stable toward chemical reaction.

31. naphthalene:

phenanthrene:

32. A **functional group** is a group of atoms found in many different compounds but which reacts in the same way in each compound. Organic compounds are often categorized by functional groups as the functional groups often dictate the chemical behavior of compounds and are more likely to react than the hydrocarbon parts of the compounds.

33. Alkyl groups are not usually considered functional groups as they are generally inert and do not react as readily as most functional groups.

34. a. vitamin A:

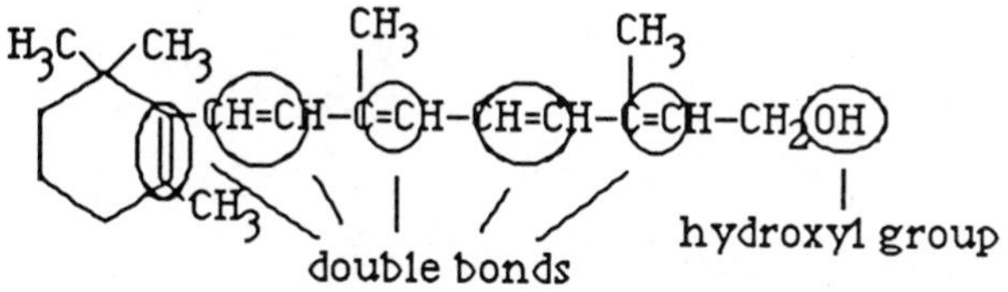

double bonds

hydroxyl group

b. niacin:

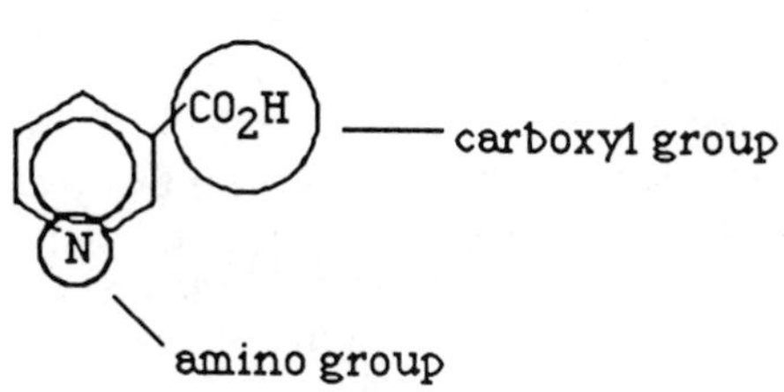

carboxyl group

amino group

c. thyroxine:

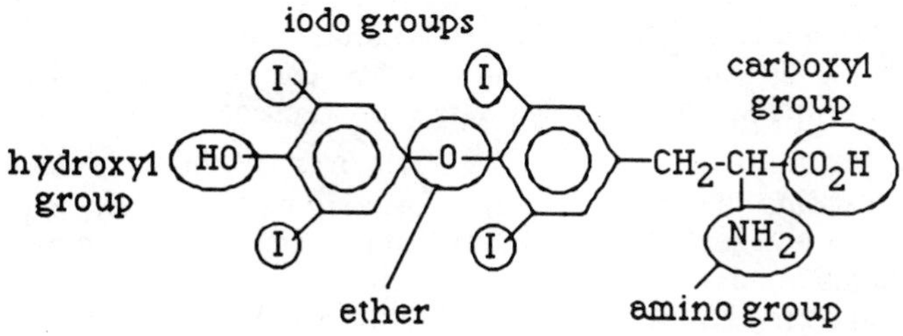

iodo groups

hydroxyl group

carboxyl group

ether

amino group

d. testosterone:

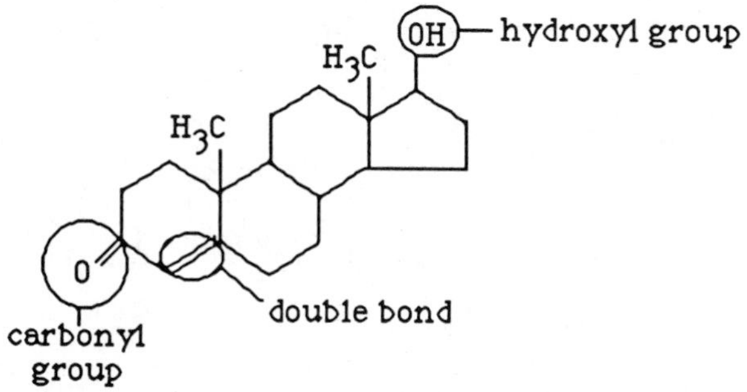

hydroxyl group

carbonyl group

double bond

34. e. epinephrine:

hydroxyl groups

f. butyl acetate:

ester group

35. a. A **molecular orbital** is the electron cloud formed by the overlap and merger of two atomic orbitals. **b.** A **sigma molecular orbital** (σ) is formed from two *s* atomic orbitals, two *p* atomic orbitals (oriented so the orbitals point toward each other), or an *s* and a *p* atomic orbital (with the *p* orbital pointing toward the *s* orbital). In each case, the sigma molecular orbital is symmetrical around the internuclear axis. **c. Hybrid orbitals** are mixtures of *s* and *p* atomic orbitals of one atom which result in new "blended" atomic orbitals. These hybrid orbital sets have their own characteristic shapes and energy levels. **d.** An *sp*³ **orbital** is a hybrid orbital formed from the mixing of one *s* and three *p* atomic orbitals. The mixing actually results in a set of four equivalent hybrid orbitals, each with one large lobe and one small lobe. **e.** An *sp*² **orbital** is a hybrid orbital formed from the mixing of one *s* and two *p* atomic orbitals. The mixing actually results in a set of three equivalent hybrid orbitals, each with one large lobe and one small lobe. **f. Pi molecular orbitals** (π) are formed using the *p* atomic orbitals left over from the formation of *sp*² and *sp* hybrid orbital sets. In bonding, the hybrid orbitals form sigma bonds between atoms while the unhybridized *p* orbitals on adjacent atoms (assuming they exist on both atoms) can overlap and merge to form an additional bond, the clouds of which do not lie on the internuclear axis. **g.** An *sp* **orbital** is a hybrid orbital formed from the mixing of one *s* and one *p* atomic orbitals. The mixing actually results in a set of two equivalent hybrid orbitals, each with one large lobe and one small lobe.

36. Molecular orbitals are formed when two atomic orbitals, including hybridized ones, overlap and merge to form a bond.

37. For the formation of *sp*³ hybridized orbitals:

38. methane, CH_4:

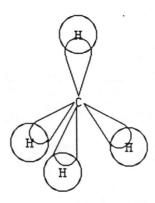

39. For the formation of sp^2 hybridized orbitals:

$$\underline{\uparrow}\ \underline{\uparrow}\ \underline{\quad}$$
$$2p$$
$$\underline{\uparrow\downarrow}$$
$$2s$$
$$\underline{\uparrow\downarrow}$$
$$1s$$

$$\Rightarrow$$

$$\underline{\uparrow}$$
$$2p$$
$$\underline{\uparrow}\ \underline{\uparrow}\ \underline{\uparrow}$$
$$2sp^2$$
$$\underline{\uparrow\downarrow}$$
$$1s$$

40. In benzene, all of the carbon atoms in the ring are sp^2 hybridized. All of the carbons also have one unhybridized p orbital extending above and below the plane of the molecule. All of these p orbitals can overlap and merge, forming pi molecular orbitals, and share electrons. Through delocalization, there is then an electron cloud above the ring and one below the ring and the electrons are equally shared.

41. For the formation of sp hybridized orbitals:

$$\underline{\uparrow}\ \underline{\uparrow}\ \underline{\quad}$$
$$2p$$
$$\underline{\uparrow\downarrow}$$
$$2s$$
$$\underline{\uparrow\downarrow}$$
$$1s$$

$$\Rightarrow$$

$$\underline{\uparrow}\ \underline{\uparrow}$$
$$2p$$
$$\underline{\uparrow}\ \underline{\uparrow}$$
$$2sp$$
$$\underline{\uparrow\downarrow}$$
$$1s$$

42. ethyne, C_2H_2:

43. **a.** In a single bond, the molecular orbital is a sigma orbital, symmetrical around the internuclear axis, and formed by hybrid orbitals (only hydrogen doesn't make hybrid orbitals). **b.** In a double bond, one molecular orbital is a sigma orbital, symmetrical around the internuclear axis, and formed by hybrid orbitals while the second bond is formed by the overlap and merger of two unhybridized p orbitals, one on each atom. The sigma component of a double bond is formed by sp^2 hybrid orbitals. **c.** In a triple bond, one molecular orbital is a sigma orbital, symmetrical around the internuclear axis, and formed by hybrid orbitals while the second and third bonds are formed, for each of them, by the overlap and merger of two unhybridized p orbitals, one on each atom. The sigma component of a triple bond is formed by sp hybrid orbitals.

44. Carbon has neither a strong desire to gain electrons nor to give up electrons. It is, therefore, quite happy to share electrons. Since carbon has four valence electrons, it has the capacity to share four more electrons, donated by other atoms.

45. In CH_4, the bond angles are 109.5°. The molecule is tetrahedral and the carbon uses the four sp^3 hybrid orbitals to form the bonds.

46. There is only one isomer of propane, C_3H_8, because there is only one way to string three carbon atoms together. All attempts to draw structural isomers lead to pictures which, although they may look different, are all connected the same way.

47. 2,2,4-trimethylpentane: CH_3

$$CH_3-\overset{\displaystyle |}{\underset{\displaystyle \underset{\displaystyle CH_3}{|}}{C}}-CH_2-\overset{\displaystyle \underset{\displaystyle \underset{\displaystyle CH_3}{|}}{}}{CH}-CH_3$$

heptane: $CH_3-CH_2-CH_2-CH_2-CH_2-CH_2-CH_3$

48. 2-Butene can have geometric isomers because it can have the main chain enter and exit the double bond either on the same side (*cis*) or on opposite sides (*trans*). The only possible location of the double bond in propene is at an end carbon. Both substituents of the end carbon are then hydrogens and so there is no difference between going through the double bond to the opposite side or to the same side.

49. **a.** 3-heptene: $CH_3-CH_2-CH=CH-CH_2-CH_2-CH_3$

b. 2-methyl-3-octyne: $CH_3-\overset{\displaystyle \underset{\displaystyle \underset{\displaystyle CH_3}{|}}{}}{CH}-C\equiv C-CH_2-CH_2-CH_2-CH_2-CH_3$

c. 2-methyl-2-hexene: $CH_3-\overset{\displaystyle \underset{\displaystyle \underset{\displaystyle CH_3}{|}}{}}{C}=CH-CH_2-CH_2-CH_3$

d. 3-propyl-2-octene: $CH_3-CH=\overset{\displaystyle \underset{\displaystyle \underset{\displaystyle CH_2-CH_2-CH_3}{|}}{}}{C}-CH_2-CH_2-CH_2-CH_2-CH_3$

$$CH_3$$
$$|$$

49. e. 5-ethyl-3,5-dimethyl-1-heptene: $CH_2=CH-CH-CH_2-C-CH_2-CH_3$

$$|\qquad\qquad |$$
$$CH_3\qquad CH_2-CH_3$$

f. 2,4-dimethyl-3-nonene: $CH_3-CH-CH=C-CH_2-CH_2-CH_2-CH_2-CH_3$

$$|\qquad\quad |$$
$$CH_3\qquad CH_3$$

g. 2,4,6-decatriene: $CH_3-CH=CH-CH=CH-CH=CH-CH_2-CH_2-CH_3$

50. The carbon atoms in benzene are sp^2 hybridized. All the carbons are connected in the ring by sigma bonds. The left over unhybridized p orbitals, one on each carbon, extend above and below the plane of the ring. These p orbitals overlap and merge into pi molecular orbitals with the six electrons (from the three formal double bonds) shared equally around the ring. You end up with a ring-shaped electron cloud above the ring of atoms and one below the atoms. The hydrogen atoms are bonded to the carbons using the third sp^2 hybrid orbital of each carbon.

51. ethene, C_2H_4:

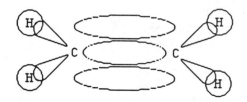

Sample Quiz Questions

1. Which of the following statements is correct?
    a. Carbon can form single and double bonds with halogens.
    b. Carbon can form single, double, and triple bonds with sulfur.
    c. Carbon can form only single bonds with nitrogen.
    d. Carbon can form single and double bonds with oxygen.
    e. Carbon can form single and double bonds with hydrogen.

2. Organic chemistry
    a. is the study of most covalent compounds of carbon.
    b. is the study of compounds containing carbon, oxygen, nitrogen, and hydrogen.
    c. includes the chemistry of CO and CO_2.
    d. is the study of the chemistry between carbon and chlorine.
    e. is a limited field of study since it deals primarily with one element.

3. Aliphatic hydrocarbons
    a. are carbon compounds derived from fats.
    b. always have open-chain structures.
    c. are compounds of hydrogen and carbon which do not resemble benzene.
    d. include esters.
    e. are carbon and hydrogen compounds, regardless of whether atoms of other elements are present in the molecule.

4. Hydrocarbons
    a. of fewer than 6 carbon atoms are liquids at room temperature.
    b. tend to be colored materials.
    c. tend to be fairly polar molecules.
    d. tend to dissolve easily in water.
    e. of more than 18 carbon atoms are solids at room temperature.

5. The general formula for open-chain alkanes is
    a. C_nH_{2n+4}
    b. C_nH_{2n+2}
    c. C_nH_{2n}
    d. C_nH_{2n-2}
    e. C_nH_{2n-4}

6. Which of the following is an open-chain alkane?
    a. C_5H_{10}
    b. C_7H_{12}
    c. C_9H_{22}
    d. C_3H_6
    e. C_6H_{14}

7. Name the alkane,

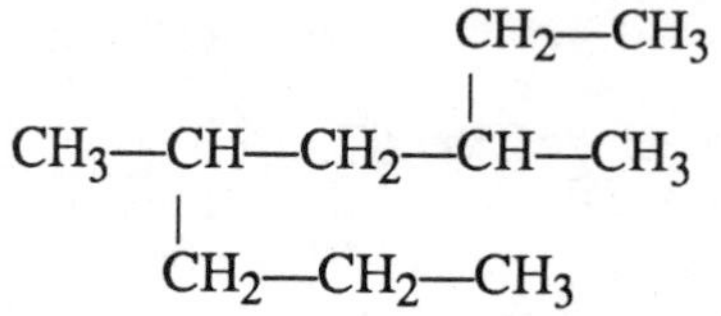

$$
\begin{array}{c}
CH_2\text{---}CH_3 \\
| \\
CH_3\text{---}CH\text{---}CH_2\text{---}CH\text{---}CH_3 \\
| \\
CH_2\text{---}CH_2\text{---}CH_3
\end{array}
$$

    a. 4-ethyl-2-propylpentane
    b. 4-methyl-2-propylhexane
    c. 3,5-dimethyloctane
    d. 2-ethyl-4-methylheptane
    e. 3,4-dimethyldecane

8. Name the alkane,

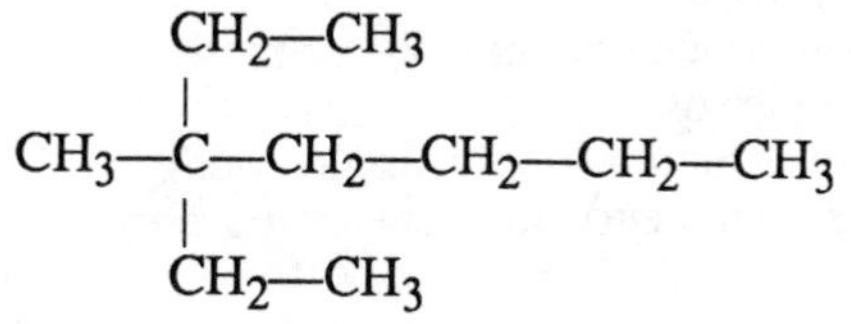

$$CH_2—CH_3$$
$$|$$
$$CH_3—C—CH_2—CH_2—CH_2—CH_3$$
$$|$$
$$CH_2—CH_3$$

    a. 2,2-diethylhexane
    b. 3-ethyl-3-methylheptane
    c. 3-butyl-3-methylpentane
    d. 3-ethyl-3-propylheptane
    e. 5-ethyl-5-methylheptane

9. Name the alkane,

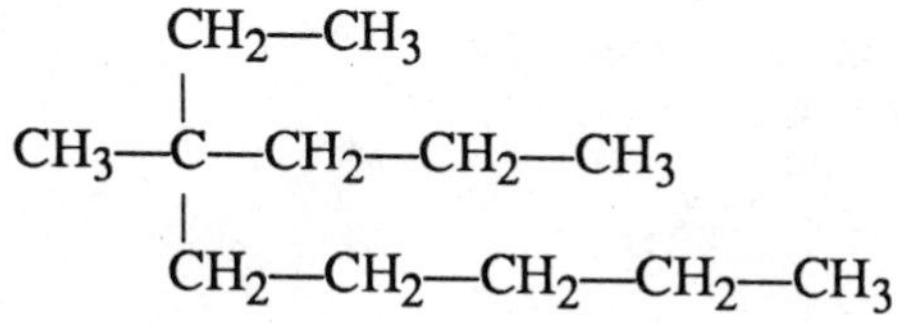

$$CH_2—CH_3$$
$$|$$
$$CH_3—C—CH_2—CH_2—CH_3$$
$$|$$
$$CH_2—CH_2—CH_2—CH_2—CH_3$$

    a. 3-methyl-3-pentylhexane
    b. 3-methyl-3-propyloctane
    c. 6-ethyl-7-methylnonane
    d. 4-ethyl-4-methylnonane
    e. 2-pentyl-2-ethylpentane

10. Name the alkane,

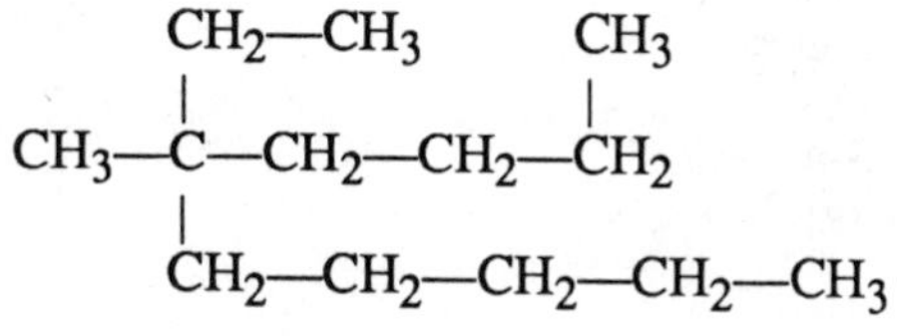

$$CH_2—CH_3 \qquad CH_3$$
$$| \qquad\qquad\quad |$$
$$CH_3—C—CH_2—CH_2—CH_2$$
$$|$$
$$CH_2—CH_2—CH_2—CH_2—CH_3$$

    a. 5-ethyl-5-methyldecane
    b. 2-butyl-2-ethylheptane
    c. 5-methyl-6-ethyldecane
    d. 6-ethyl-6-methyldecane
    e. 3-butyl-3-methyloctane

11. What is the general molecular formula for open-chain alkenes with one double bond?
    a. C_nH_{2n+4}
    b. C_nH_{2n+2}
    c. C_nH_{2n+1}
    d. C_nH_{2n}
    e. C_nH_{2n-2}

12. An alkene
       a. is a saturated hydrocarbon.
       b. is a hydrocarbon which contains one or more double bonds.
       c. is a cyclic hydrocarbon.
       d. is a hydrocarbon which has only single bonds.
       e. is a hydrocarbon which contains one or more triple bonds.

13. Name the alkene,

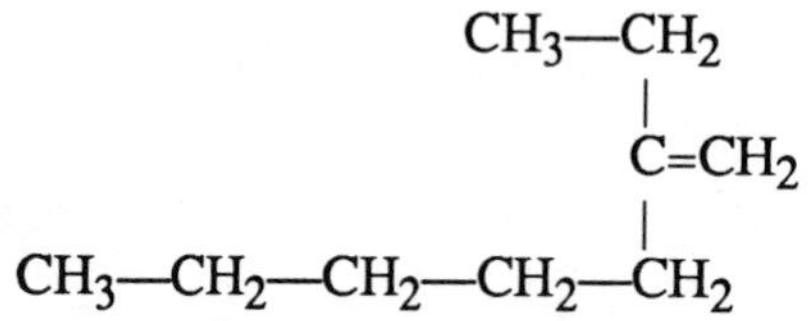

$$
\begin{array}{c}
CH_3\!-\!CH_2 \\
| \\
C\!=\!CH_2 \\
| \\
CH_3\!-\!CH_2\!-\!CH_2\!-\!CH_2\!-\!CH_2
\end{array}
$$

       a. 2-ethyl-1-heptene
       b. 3-methyl-4-pentylpropane
       c. 3-methyl-3-octene
       d. 2-pentyl-1-butene
       e. 6-ethyl-6-heptene

14. Name the alkene,

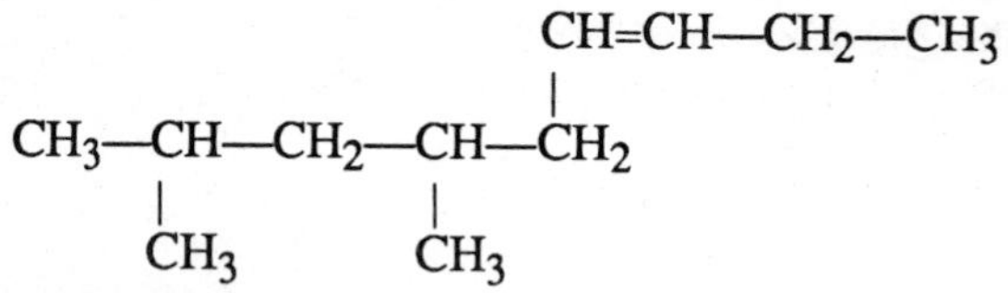

$$
\begin{array}{c}
CH\!=\!CH\!-\!CH_2\!-\!CH_3 \\
| \\
CH_3\!-\!CH\!-\!CH_2\!-\!CH\!-\!CH_2 \\
|\qquad\qquad\quad | \\
CH_3\qquad\quad CH_3
\end{array}
$$

       a. 2,4-dimethyl-6-nonene
       b. 1-ethyl-4,6-dimethyl-1-heptene
       c. 6-methyl-7-propyl-3-heptene
       d. 6,8-dimethyl-3-nonene
       e. 6-methyl-6-butyl-3-hexene

15. Name the alkyne,

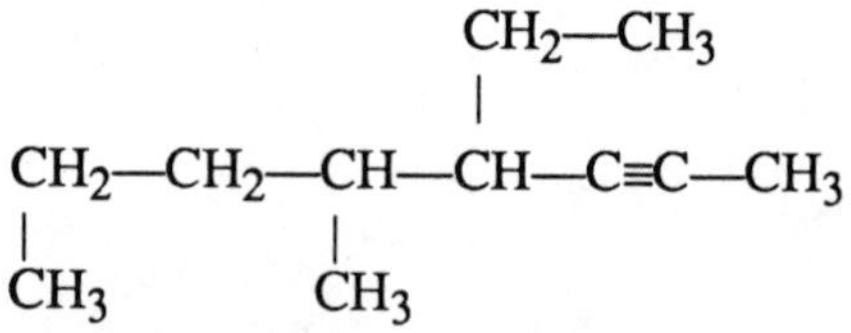

$$
\begin{array}{c}
CH_2\!-\!CH_3 \\
| \\
CH_2\!-\!CH_2\!-\!CH\!-\!CH\!-\!C\!\equiv\!C\!-\!CH_3 \\
|\qquad\qquad\quad | \\
CH_3\qquad\quad CH_3
\end{array}
$$

       a. 4-ethyl-5-methyl-2-octyne
       b. 4-ethyl-5-methyl-2-octene
       c. 4-ethyl-5,7-dimethyl-2-heptyne
       d. 4-ethyl-1,5-dimethyl-1-heptyne
       e. 5-ethyl-4-methyl-6-octyne

16. Name the alkyne,

$$CH_2\text{---}CH\text{---}CH_2\text{---}CH\text{---}CH\text{---}C\equiv C\text{---}CH_2$$

$$\quad\quad\; CH_3 \quad\quad\quad CH_3 \;\; CH_2\text{---}CH_3 \;\; CH_3$$

    a. 5-ethyl-6,8-dimethyl-3-nonane
    b. 5-ethyl-2,4-dimethyl-6-nonyne
    c. 5-hexyl-3-heptyne
    d. 1,3-diethyl-4,6-dimethyl-1-heptyne
    e. 5-ethyl-6,8-dimethyl-3-nonyne

17. Aromatic hydrocarbons
    a. all have pleasant odors.
    b. are structurally related to benzene.
    c. are cyclic aliphatic hydrocarbons.
    d. contain the ester functional group.
    e. are ring compounds with more than one double bond.

18. Kekulé structures
    a. are now considered totally incorrect.
    b. account for all of the properties of benzene.
    c. explain delocalization of electrons.
    d. show that benzene should have two forms.
    e. show that benzene and naphthalene are the same compound.

19. The functional group R—O—R is characteristic of
    a. esters.
    b. carboxylic acids.
    c. ethers.
    d. alcohols.
    e. ketones.

20. The functional group R—C=O is characteristic of

$$\quad\quad\quad\quad\quad\quad\quad\quad\quad | $$

$$\quad\quad\quad\quad\quad\quad\quad\quad\quad H$$

    a. alcohols.
    b. ketones.
    c. ethers.
    d. esters.
    e. aldehydes.

21. An sp^2 hybrid orbital
    a. is one of three equivalent orbitals in a set.
    b. results from mixing an s atomic orbital and a p atomic orbital.
    c. gives bond angles of 109.5°.
    d. is one of four equivalent orbitals in a set.
    e. results from mixing an s atomic orbital and three p atomic orbitals.

22. A triple bond
        a. gives bond angles of 120°.
        b. consists of two sigma bonds and one pi bond.
        c. contains four electrons.
        d. is characteristic of alkenes.
        e. consists of one sigma bond and two pi bonds.

Answers to the Sample Quiz Questions

1. (d), 2. (a), 3. (c), 4. (e), 5. (b), 6. (e), 7. (c), 8. (b), 9. (d), 10. (a), 11. (d), 12. (b), 13. (a), 14. (d), 15. (a), 16. (e), 17. (b), 18. (d), 19. (c), 20. (e), 21. (a), 22. (e)

ADDITIONAL RESOURCE MATERIALS

The following is a list of books, papers, and audio-visual aids which have been found to be useful resources in the course.

Chapter 1 Chemistry: Origins and Scope

Bronowski, J., The Ascent of Man, Boston/Toronto: Little, Brown, and Co., 1973, Chapter 4 and the corresponding videotape ("The Hidden Structure").

Bunker, D.L., "Why Should Anyone Study Chemistry?" Chemistry, September 1970, p. 16.

Ihde, A.J., The Development of Modern Chemistry, New York: Harper and Row, 1964, Chapter 1.

Kauffman, G., and Payne, Z.A., "Contributions of Ancients and Alchemists," Chemistry, April 1973, p. 6.

Partington, J.R., A Short History of Chemistry, London: Macmillan, 1965, Chapters 1-4.

Chapter 2 Scientific Measurements

"Determining Significant Figures," Prentice-Hall Media, Tarrytown, New York. An audio-cassette/filmstrip program.

"The Factor Unit Method," Prentice-Hall Media, Tarrytown, New York. An audio-cassette/filmstrip program.

Goldish, D.M., Basic Mathematics for Beginning Chemistry, 3rd Ed., New York: Macmillan, 1983, Chapters 1 and 7.

"Metrics for Measure," BFA Educational Media, Santa Monica, California, 1975. A 13-minute animated film in color.

"Powers of Ten," Pyramid Films, Santa Monica, California, 1978. A 9-minute color film that dramatically demonstrates distance in terms of powers of ten.

"Precision and Accuracy," Prentice-Hall Media, Tarrytown, New York. An audio-cassette/filmstrip program.

Ritchie, C., "Conversion to the Metric System," Scientific American, July 1970, p. 17.

Chapter 3 Elements, Atoms, and Compounds

Bronowski, J., The Ascent of Man, Boston/Toronto: Little, Brown, and Co., 1973, Chapter 10 and the corresponding videotape ("World Within World").

Dinga, G.P., "The Elements and the Derivation of Their Names and Symbols," Chemistry, February 1968, p. 20.

Frieden, E., "The Chemical Elements of Life," Scientific American, July 1972, p. 52.

Chapter 3 Elements, Atoms, and Compounds
    Ihde, A.J., The Development of Modern Chemistry, New York: Harper and Row, 1964, Chapter 9.
    Jaffe, B., Crucibles: The Lives and Achievements of the Great Chemists, New York: Tudor, 1934.
    "The Elements," Audio Learning, Inc., Mt. Vernon, New York. A 30-minute audio-cassette/filmstrip program.

Chapter 4 Electron Arrangements in Atoms
    "Electron Configurations and Orbital Diagrams," Prentice-Hall Media, Tarrytown, New York. An audio-cassette/filmstrip program.
    Ludor, W.F., "Atomic Structure Without Quantum Theory," Chemistry, June 1975, p. 6.

Chapter 5 Chemical Periodicity

    "Atomic Structure and the Periodic Chart: An Introduction," Prentice-Hall Media, Tarrytown, New York. An audio-cassette/filmstrip program.
    "Classification of the Elements: Metals; Nonmetals; Metalloids," Prentice-Hall Media, Tarrytown, New York. An audio-cassette/filmstrip program.
    "The Group Relationship," Prentice-Hall Media, Tarrytown, New York. An audio-cassette/filmstrip program.
    Seaborg, G.T., "The Periodic Table: Tortuous Path to Man-Made Elements," Chemical and Engineering News, 16 April 1979, p. 46
    "The Periodic Table," Audio Learning, Inc., Mt. Vernon, New York. A 30-minute audio-cassette/filmstrip program.

Chapter 6 Chemical Bonds
    "Atomic Structure and Bonding," Audio Learning, Inc., Mt. Vernon, New York. A 30-minute audio-cassette/filmstrip program.
    "Bonding Between Atoms of Different Elements: Metals and Nonmetals - The Ionic Bond," Prentice-Hall Media, Tarrytown, New York. An audio-cassette/filmstrip program.
    "Bonding Between Atoms of Different Elements: Nonmetals and Covalent Compounds," Prentice-Hall Media, Tarrytown, New York. An audio-cassette/filmstrip program.
    Companion, A., Chemical Bonding, New York: McGraw-Hill, 1964.
    Gray, H.B., Chemical Bonds, Menlo Park, California: W.A. Benjamin, 1973.
    Pauling, L., The Nature of the Chemical Bond, 3rd Ed., Ithaca, New York: Cornell University Press, 1960.
    Sanderson, R.T., "What Is Bond Polarity and What Difference Does It Make?" Chemistry, September 1973, p. 12.

Chapter 7 Naming Inorganic Compounds
    "Naming Chemical Substances," Prentice-Hall Media, Tarrytown, New York. A two-part audio-cassette/filmstrip program.

Chapter 8 Calculations Based on Chemical Formulas
    "Atomic Weights, Molecular Weights, and the Mole Concept," Prentice-Hall Media, Tarrytown, New York. An audio-cassette/filmstrip program.
    "Formulas From Analysis of Composition of Compounds," Prentice-Hall Media, Tarrytown, New York. An audio-cassette/filmstrip program.

Chapter 9 Chemical Equations
    "Balancing Chemical Equations by Inspection," Prentice-Hall Media, Tarrytown, New York. An audio-cassette/filmstrip program.
    "Calculations Involving Equations," Prentice-Hall Media, Tarrytown, New York. An audio-cassette/filmstrip program.

Chapter 9 Chemical Equations

Greene, G.S.D., "An Algebraic Method for Balancing Chemical Equations," <u>Chemistry</u>, March 1975, p. 19.

"Limiting Reagent Concept," Prentice-Hall Media, Tarrytown, New York. An audio-cassette/filmstrip program.

"Stoichiometric Concepts," Prentice-Hall Media, Tarrytown, New York. An audio-cassette/filmstrip program.

Chapter 10 Gases

"Boyle's Law, Charles' Law, and Gay-Lussac's Law," Prentice-Hall Media, Tarrytown, New York. An audio-cassette/filmstrip program.

"Chemistry: Gaseous Volume and the Mole," Bergwall Productions, Garden City, New York. A three-part audio-cassette/filmstrip program.

"General Gas Law and Dalton's Law of Partial Pressures," Prentice-Hall Media, Tarrytown, New York. An audio-cassette/filmstrip program.

"Generalized Gas Equation: $PV = nRT$," Prentice-Hall Media, Tarrytown, New York. An audio-cassette/filmstrip program.

"Pressure, Volume, and Boyle's Law," Kalmia Co., Concord, Massachusetts, 1974. A 4-minute silent film in color.

Chapter 11 Liquids and Solids

"Chemistry: The Forces in Solids, Liquids, and Gases," Bergwall Productions, Garden City, New York. A five-part audio-cassette/filmstrip program.

"Crystallization," Churchill Films, Los Angeles, California, 1975. An 11-minute color film showing crystals growing and melting, as photographed on the stage of a polarizing microscope.

Thomsen, D.E., "The Tie That Binds Molecules," <u>Science News</u>, 1 December 1973, p. 344.

Chapter 12 Water and Aqueous Solutions

Boyd, T.A., "The Wonder of Water," <u>Chemistry</u>, June 1974, p. 6.

"Chemistry: Looking at the Solution," Bergwall Productions, Garden City, New York. A series of five audio-cassette/filmstrip programs.

"Chemistry: Molarity of Solutions," Bergwall Productions, Garden City, New York. A series of three audio-cassette/filmstrip programs.

"Dilution and Titration Problems," Prentice-Hall Media, Tarrytown, New York. An audio-cassette/filmstrip program.

"Introduction to Preparing Percent, Molar, and Normal Solutions," Prentice-Hall Media, Tarrytown, New York. An audio-cassette/filmstrip program.

Chapter 13 Chemical Equilibria and Rates of Reactions

Bent, H.A., "Haste Makes Waste - Pollution and Entropy," <u>Chemistry</u>, October 1971, p. 6.

"Catalysis," Wards Natural Science Establishment, Inc., Rochester, New York, 1961. A 17-minute black-and-white film.

"Energy and Entropy in Chemical Reactions," Prentice-Hall Media, Tarrytown, New York. A two-part audio-cassette/filmstrip program.

"Equilibrium Constant: Gaseous Systems," Prentice-Hall Media, Tarrytown, New York. An audio-cassette/filmstrip program.

"How Fast? How Far?" Audio Learning, Inc., Mt. Vernon, New York. A 30-minute audio-cassette/filmstrip program on reaction rates and chemical equilibria.

Morris, D.L., "The Carbonates: An Entertainment in Chemical Equilibrium," <u>Chemistry</u>, July 1974, p. 6.

Yohe, G.R., "Dominoes and Activation Energy," <u>Chemistry</u>, October 1976, p. 8.

_____ , "The Catalyst," <u>Chemistry</u>, September 1973, p. 8.

Chapter 14 Acids, Bases, and Salts
"Acid Rain: The Choice Is Ours," Nova Scientific Corp., Burlington, North Carolina. An audio-cassette/filmstrip program.
"Acids and Bases," Audio Learning, Inc., Mt. Vernon, New York. A 30-minute audio-cassette/filmstrip program.
Drago, R.S., "A Modern Approach to Acid-Base Chemistry," Journal of Chemical Education 51, 300 (1974).
Ember, L.R., "Acid Pollutants: Hitchhikers Ride the Wind," Chemical and Engineering News, 14 September 1981, p. 20.
Kohn, H.W., "The Rolaids Caper, or Titration in the Classroom," Chemistry, March 1973, p. 27.
Stokes, J.C., and Lockhart, W.L., "Where Has All the Sulfuric Acid Gone?" Chemistry, October 1978, p. 10.
"Unworthy Salt," Sciquest, September 1981, p. 25. More on the controversy between salt in foods and its role in contributing to high blood pressure.

Chapter 15 Electrolytes, pH, and Buffers
"Buffers," Biology Media, Berkeley, California. A slide/tape program.
"Hydrolysis of Salts," Prentice-Hall Media, Tarrytown, New York. An audio-cassette/filmstrip program.
"Investigators Focus on Intracellular pH," Science 14 August 1981, p. 745.
Joyce, R.J., "pH Simplified," Science Supply News. Free reprints are available from Markson Science, Inc., 220C Oak Street, Del Mar, California 92014.
"pH, pOH, and Buffers," Prentice-Hall Media, Tarrytown, New York. An audio-cassette/filmstrip program.

Chapter 16 Oxidation and Reduction
"Balancing Redox Equations: Change in Oxidation Number Method," Prentice-Hall Media, Tarrytown, New York. An audio-cassette/filmstrip program.
"Balancing Redox Equations: Ion-Electron Method," Prentice-Hall Media, Tarrytown, New York. An audio-cassette/filmstrip program.
"Burning, Breathing, and Redox," Audio Learning, Inc., Mt. Vernon, New York. A 30-minute audio-cassette/filmstrip program.
"Oxidation and Reduction Equations," Prentice-Hall Media, Tarrytown, New York. An audio-cassette/filmstrip program.

Chapter 17 Radioactivity and Nuclear Processes
"Fission and Fusion Reactions," Prentice-Hall Media, Tarrytown, New York. An audio-cassette/filmstrip program.
"Energy: The Nuclear Alternative," Churchill Films, Los Angeles, California. A 22-minute color film on fission power.
"The Nucleus: Composition, Stability, and Decay," Prentice-Hall Media, Tarrytown, New York. An audio-cassette/filmstrip program.

Chapter 18 Introduction to Organic Chemistry
Blumer, M., "Polycyclic Aromatic Hydrocarbons in Nature," Scientific American, March 1976, p. 34.
Breslow, R., "The Nature of Aromatic Compounds," Scientific American, August 1972, p. 32.
"Chemicals From Petroleum," Audio Learning, Inc., Mt. Vernon, New York. A 30-minute audio-cassette/filmstrip program.